# Bertha

murder and intrigue in the post World War II South

*I Hope you enjoy*
*"Bertha"*

## Mike Ragland

*Mike Ragland*
*12/3/2016*

Wheredepony Press
Rome GA
USA

# Bertha
## murder and intrigue in the post-WW II South

This book is based on actual events that occurred in Floyd County, Georgia during the time mentioned.

copyright © 2011 Mike Ragland
PO Box 58
Cave Spring, GA  30124
www.mikeragland.com
mikeragland.wordpress.com

ISBN
978-0-9818252-6-7
978-0-9833643-1-3 kindle

edited by Dekie Hicks
interior design by Dekie Hicks

cover photography and design: SchroederVision
www.schroedervision.com

Wheredepony Press
Rome, GA
www.wheredeponypress.com

manufactured in the United States of America

THIS MAY BE THE SOUTH'S MOST SPECTACULAR COURT
TRIAL IN THE RECENT ANNALS OF CRIME.

Henderson Lanham, Solicitor General
Rome/Floyd County Circuit
State of Georgia
1946

From **Leigh E. Patterson**, District Attorney, Rome Judicial Circuit 2010:

I have known Mike Ragland since I came to work in the Floyd County District Attorney's Office as a Governor's intern way back in the summer of 1988. He was a Captain at the Rome Police Department back then and was later promoted to Major. When he told me he was writing a book about a local murder case from back in the day, I was interested to see which one he would choose. I never dreamed he meant a murder case from the 1940's. Or one involving a female defendant. Sometimes juries don't like to believe women are capable of the most terrible crimes like murder, so reading about the police investigation and prosecution was interesting to me since I am now the elected District Attorney for the Rome Judicial Circuit. The autopsies, evidence collection, and testing for poison in the Hill case may have been primitive by today's standards, but those men still got the job done.

For all local history buffs, the book is full of local color with descriptions of old downtown Rome, the courthouse and jail. Mike also takes us on a ride around Floyd County to all the local communities—like Armuchee, Cave Spring, Lindale, Silver Creek, Coosa, and Shannon. Like many Romans, I have been in or know of most of the places mentioned in the book. The bootleggers from Armuchee, the baseball leagues of Celenese, Shannon, and Lindale, and the mentions of the Berry College campus will bring a smile to your face when reading *Bertha*.

I loved the accounts of all the local eateries and the folks who frequented them. BBQ, biscuits, grits, cornbread, teacakes, and apple cobbler are but a few of the southern cooking mentions in the book. Mike's description of the "Breakfast Club" of local businessmen who met at The Partridge to discuss politics in and around Rome is the absolute truth. When I first ran for District Attorney in 2002, I was invited by the Honorable John Frazier (who had represented Bertha Hill) to meet with the Breakfast Club for coffee one morning at The Partridge to see what they thought about me. I had known Judge Frazier since I came to Rome, attended church with him, and worked on some of my first criminal cases with him presiding. I really appreciated the opportunity to be "cross-examined" by them and trust me when I tell you that they grilled me. If I could get their stamp of approval, I felt like I would have a fighting chance to be District Attorney. I felt like a pup being watched over by a pack of old wise hounds!

So grab a cup of coffee or some sweet tea, pull up a chair, and sit a spell, as my Granny used to say. This here's some good readin'!

# Acknowledgements

This book would never have come to fruition had J.T. Bishop, a retired school teacher, not brought to our Volunteer Coffee Club at the Rome Area History Museum a pulp detective magazine. He knew that I was a retired Rome Police Officer. He handed me the magazine, pointed out a specific article and asked if I remembered the woman the article was about. I scanned the story briefly and handed back the magazine and said that I did not know that story. It had happened way before my time on the force, and I doubted that it was true.

But it was.

Well not really. The gist was basically true, but I would find out later the story had been greatly embellished. I have since obtained six or seven more detective magazines that were written from 1946 to the mid 1950's. Her story differs in each one to a certain extent. However there are some consistencies.

After the meeting I took a copy of the story home with me and read it several times. The following week, while at the Rome/Floyd Library, I asked Pat Millican if she had any record of such a story. She immediately went to the newspaper archives and typed in Bertha Gossett Hill. The news stories just kept popping up. So without question, Pat and the staff at the library made a very viable contribution to this project. Some of those are listed below. I hope I didn't miss anyone. If I did, I sincerely apologize.

To Pat Millican, and the staff at the Rome/Floyd County Library including Chelsea Callahan, Jacqueline Siniard, Kristin Pearson, Daryl Jean Gould, and Patty Berry Hackett Moseley (PeeBee) who were instrumental in doing the bulk of the research and documentation of the information that was used from the library. Thank you so much.

And to Margaret Hollingsworth who did most of the original editing, built the social media platform for this author and was a first class motivator and cheerleader. Many thanks. She is also the daughter of Hillis Hollingsworth. He was one of the breakfast club members from '59 and '60. Margaret is the granddaughter of Clayton Hollingsworth, who was the Superintendent of the Georgia School for the Deaf in Cave Spring in 1946.

Russell McClanahan, the chief archivist at the Rome Area History Museum was also very instrumental in assisting with interviews and research.

Teri LaDantec, author, editor, and publisher, has ties to Rome and was instrumental in editing, and offering positive suggestions on how to improve the text.

Dr. Edward Blackwelder, noted Criminologist, who has interviewed Ted Bundy, Wayne Williams, Susan Atkins and Judith Neeley, along with many other convicted and suspected murderers, gave me some of his insight into the personality of a sociopath during lunch one Sunday afternoon at the Partridge Café.

Christine Russell, wife of Chief Deputy Frank Russell, explained to Russell McClanahan and me about life in the Floyd County Jail. She shared an apartment with her husband and family at the jail during the War years, and was living there the year that Bertha was confined in the jail between trials. She also donated to the History Museum the quilt top that Bertha made for her brother Danny Garrett. It's still brand new and will be on exhibit at the museum.

Leigh Patterson, the local District Attorney was instrumental and helpful in explaining legal terms that I didn't know.

Eric Haney, noted author who listened to my story and then offered some advice that tweaked the story into the direction that it took.

Dianna Edwards Haney, noted author and wife of Eric, also was instrumental in offering advice on how to proceed with the story.

Floyd County Superior Court Judge Larry Salmon, Max Thompson, Lindy Dew, Marie Evans, Ronald Lynch, Ron Cescutti, and Betty Mize for their help on answering questions and sharing information about the Armuchee area during the forties.

Thank you also to Dorothy Black Headrick (daughter of John and Pauline Black), Rovine Black, Elizabeth Gossett Roach, Nellie Gilmore Lowery, Billy Godfrey, Debbie Smith, Danielle Niedermeier, Perron Lewis Davis, James "Dunk" Lastinger, Mary Ruth Early, and Peggy Couch Hale for their help in gathering information on the Alexis, Lawrence, and Farrill communities of Cherokee County, Alabama in the thirties and forties.

John Terry (Bertha's cousin ), Betty Dutton Redd (Bertha's cousin who shared a room with her in Americus, Georgia for a month after the baby died), J. T. Bishop and Travis Hardin, who are also relatives of Bertha.

Phil Hill of Pittsboro, North Carolina gave me some valuable information about his Dad, Leroy. He also sent me a photo taken from the marker at Leroy's burial site.

Ben Lucas, Clarence "Snooky" Salmon, Charles Graves and Nelle Reagan, are media personalities who helped in various ways.

Linda White, who was present when Bertha was brought by sheriff's deputies to the beauty shop where her mother worked (Lu Hannon's) to get her hair fixed before some of her last court appearances in '58 and '59.

Charles Rainwater, Charlie Keys, Gary Reeves, John Davis (Chief Deputy Sheriff under Joe Adams), Leigh Brock Barbra (executive director of The Rome History Museum) Rome Police Chief Elaine Snow, Dr. Greg Sumner, Wiley Hughes, Cathy Sims and Parnick Jennings.

My friend John Schulz, author and past president of the Rome Area Writers, who has helped guide me through the business end of the writing trade. Without him I would have been as lost as a ball in high weeds.

## Special Acknowledgements

Elizabeth Gossett Roach, a first cousin of Neal's who contributed greatly to the information covered in the book.

Marie Tippins Hulsey, who worked with Bertha at McClellan's 5 & 10 cent store also made invaluable contributions.

Both of these fine ladies passed away during 2010 before I could finish this book. They contributed greatly to the story. And I thank them from the bottom of my heart.

And a very special thank you to the ones that kept me at the keyboard. That would include my wife Martha, my daughter Bekki, and my grandchildren, Caleb and Mattie Parris. Without your encouragement and company on cemetery walks and information-seeking trips, I would have never finished.

And another special thanks to Dekie Hicks, owner of Wheredepony Press. I'm sure she had trouble finding a pony in my idea of a manuscript. I trust her explicitly. Do you think an Alabama (Roll Tide) fan would let an Auburn grad touch his book if he didn't know for a fact that she did a great job?

Bill and Vicki Schroeder of Schroeder Vision took some old photos of the trial that had never been developed and enhanced them significantly. They were able to use a couple of those and complete the graphics for the front cover. Then, after traveling to Howell cemetery, they were able to use photos taken there to design the back cover. All the cover graphics were in 1946 black and white.

And a final thanks to "Goldie," my big yeller cat that lay on my desk and watched me closely on so many long nights. She was instrumental in the making of this book for she let me bounce thoughts and sentences off of her and never gave me any bad info.

I have to list this book as historical fiction. The reason is that I put words in the mouths of historical figures. I have researched this story for almost two years. I know pretty much every move that Frank Russell made. I know where he went, whom he talked too, and basically what he said. But I don't know exactly. Therein was my problem. It doesn't take a rocket scientist to link two events. You pretty much know what was said at one event in order for the next event to take place. But you can't be sure of the exact phraseology.

Most of the characters in this story are real, although there are some that are not. Those that are fictitious were to help the story move along and they for the most part represent real characters, although I don't know who they were. Let me explain.

Frank, like most good investigators, had informers, and like most good police officers he didn't name them. I know pretty much what they told him. But I don't know who they were. So I gave them the names of Jack Highfield and Caleb Hayden.

The explosion in Armuchee was just to illustrate that there was a wild and woolly element in that community during the thirties, forties and fifties. Most of the Armuchee residents were good, hard-working, God-fearing Americans. But not all were. The criminal element was there, alive and well.

Jake Wade and kin in "Booger Holler" are fictitious, but there have been many outlaws and bootleggers around that part of the county. The Holler is a real place.

The twins at the Georgia School for the Deaf are fictitious. One report states that Frank did get some info from a Seer, true or not. There were a lot of them around North Georgia and the edge of Alabama in the forties.

Bertha's childhood girl friends visited her on a regular basis. I chose not to use real names and invented the two that I did use. I'm not sure of all they discussed.

This was also true with the Gypsies. They came through the city every year, and I had people who visited the camps tell me they saw Bertha and Leroy there.

Mattie Weaver was not a real character. Bertha was jailed at times with as many as four other women. But through her influence she was able to change that. I had to have a Mattie to be able to know what Bertha was thinking and saying while incarcerated. It's pretty much in news clippings, interviews and trial records. However, I don't think it was all listed.

Back in the 60s while serving aboard the *USS Chopper* SS-342, one of my shipmates was Lonnie Franklin, who now serves as one of South Carolina's premier archaeologists The following quote highlights his thoughts on archaeology and historical facts.

₪   ₪

"The simple project of restoring missing pieces to a monument is going to the heart of archaeology. The investigation of an artifact and the infusion of a historical story remind us of the Drama, Romance and Tragedy that once was—that really happened—not just a scene from a movie, or an old tale. They really lived and died. And when we hold that artifact that was left behind, coupled with our story—it brings it all back to life."

—Dr. Lonnie Franklin

# Prologue

Leroy Hill was dead! Ollie Watkins looked at the still figure and thought to herself, What's happened here? He wasn't but twenty-eight years old. Nobody should die like this. Even in death his vacant eyes seemed to have a confused look. Ollie had watched her parents die, peacefully, nothing like this.

My Lord, she thought, Leroy was a mess. The bed was filthy, but they couldn't change it while he was alive. Ollie let her mind wander back over the past three days as she relived them once again.

Leroy had vomited almost continuously, and screamed in pain if you touched him. For awhile he said that his legs were paralyzed. But they weren't. He couldn't keep them still and was rolling all over the bed. He kept complaining about stuff around his heart and how he needed to vomit to get it out. His wife Bertha had given him salt and soda water to make him throw up.

Mrs. Watkins thought, "Lordy it's been a long time since Monday." That was the night she sent for her daughter Missy to help tend to the sick man. Missy had stayed for a couple of hours Monday night. Both of them returned Tuesday and spent the night trying to give Bertha a little rest. They comforted Leroy as best they could by placing wet towels on his forehead and talking to him.

Missy had asked Bertha if she wanted her to go and get a doctor, but Bertha said no, Leroy had been in the hospital several times in the last two months and the doctors said there was nothing else they could do for him. She had given him a capsule, which he threw up. Then she gave him some liquid medicine in a glass and he had asked what it was. Bertha had replied that she didn't know, but it was one of his prescriptions. Leroy had said not to give him anymore because it burned him too bad.

On Wednesday night he told Ollie and Missy to take him to the hospital at daylight and get Doctor McCall to open him up and see what was around his heart and get it out. He hadn't lived till morning. Ollie glanced at the mantle clock when he died. It was two a.m. Thursday, February 14th.

Ollie looked at Bertha, who was sitting quietly in a chair with a strange look on her face.

"He's gone, Bertha," she said with a lump in her throat.

"I know, Mrs. Watkins," she said almost in a whisper. "He's not suffering anymore. I hope he's at peace."

Missy gave Bertha a big hug and was choking back tears when she said, "Honey, we got to call a funeral home and get an ambulance up here."

Bertha answered by saying, "I want Jordan Funeral home over in Centre. They're the ones done Mama and Papa."

Missy turned to her mother and said, "Mama, I'll help Bertha dress Leroy if you'll walk up to Lynch's grocery and get Mrs. Lynch to call for the ambulance."

Ollie Watkins left Bertha's and began the walk up the road to the Lynch household. The Lynchs were actually Bertha's next door neighbors but their house was still a couple hundred yards away.

Even though it was after two in the morning, several cars came by. Ollie couldn't help but wonder where they were going so early in the morning. Traffic was always heavy on this road. She'd been told Highway 27 runs from somewhere up north to Florida. The war had been over for a mere six months, and now there seemed to be plenty of gas. Once rationing had been lifted, the traffic flow seemed to increase daily.

As she neared the Lynch home, she quit wondering about cars and began banging on the door. After a very short time a man's voice rang out. "Who is it?"

Ollie could hear the excitement in his voice. Out in the country like this, if somebody came to your door at this time of the morning, something was wrong.

"It's me, Mr. Lynch," Ollie replied, "and I need Jessie."

Mr. Lynch opened the door and said "Come in, Ollie. What's wrong?"

"Lord, Mr. Lynch, Leroy died and I need y'all to call the Jordan Funeral home over in Alabama and get them to send an ambulance to come and get him," she said and then continued, "Reckon they know the way by now.

"I guess they do, Ollie," he said. They had been to Bertha's house twice in the last year when her Mama and Papa had passed away.

Jessie Lynch came out of the bedroom and said to Ollie, "Just give me a minute and I'll go with you back to Bertha's. Cyril," she said to her husband, "you go on up to the store and call for that ambulance. I'll be up there helping with Leroy."

"I'm already on the way," he stated as he tied his last shoe.

The two women started walking back down the narrow highway when Jessie Lynch asked. "What happened, Ollie? We knew that Leroy was sick but this is a surprise. We didn't expect him to die."

"I know," Ollie replied. "Bertha came for me on Monday and I stayed most of the day. She came back again Tuesday evening and said that he was worse. Me and Missy have been there ever since. He died a while ago, kind of sudden like."

"Didn't Bertha call a doctor?" Jessie asked.

"Leroy wouldn't let her," Ollie replied, shaking her head as if she didn't believe her own words. "He told me and Missy on Monday and Tuesday that he would be all right. Bertha said that the doctors had told her there was nothing else they could do for him."

As the two women neared the house, Jessie asked, "Ollie, does Carrie know about this yet?"

"I don't think so," Ollie said. "If you will go in and see if Bertha and Missy need any help, I'll go and get Carrie."

Jessie turned into the front door path as Ollie walked on to get Carrie Poole. The Pooles were also neighbors who lived on the other side of Bertha and were just a little further on than the Lynchs.

When Jessie entered the house, the two women were well on their way to having Leroy laid out. Jessie pitched in and by the time Ollie came back with Carrie Poole and her daughter Louise, the body was nearly ready. The Poole women took Bertha to her bedroom and had her lie down. They told her to just lie still and they would take care of everything.

"Mrs. Poole, I'm so grateful," Bertha said, "Now that I'm all alone in this world, I don't know what I'd do without y'all."

"Like I said Bertha, you just lay back and rest. We're gonna get you through this just fine," Carrie replied, taking Bertha's hand in hers and giving it a healthy pat.

Right before daylight, Paul Jordan pulled up with the funeral home ambulance. The ladies had cleaned the house, given Bertha a bath and put her back to bed. One had made coffee and was now cooking breakfast.

Mr. Jordan spoke briefly with Bertha while he drank a cup of hot black coffee. Bertha told Mr. Jordan that she wanted Leroy brought back home. They would have a small funeral service at the house and then bury Leroy next to her Mama and Papa in Howell Cemetery. Paul said that he would have Leroy back before dark and then he slowly drove away.

Ollie Watkins stood at the door watching the ambulance drive away with Leroy and thinking about what the preacher said just the other Sunday about how the Lord wouldn't put more of a burden on us than we can handle, but my goodness, it's got to be getting close with this poor child. One thing's for certain, she's certainly going to need all her friends around her for awhile.

# Chapter 1

Doctor B.V. Elmore was disgusted as he walked down Broad Street. It was barely eight o'clock in the morning and already he felt that it was going to be a lousy day.

He had just left his breakfast club meeting at the Partridge Restaurant. He had been attending the early morning breakfast session for over ten years. Normally he had a good time and enjoyed himself. He always got caught up on the latest news and the comings and goings of the business community. There were several newsmen who attended, at least part of the time, and they kept their finger on the pulse of the city.

What had made him so mad today was that for the third time in two weeks he had lost the flip and had to buy everyone's breakfast. And then Happy Quarles had laughed at him. Happy was one of the radio news broadcasters who was always there. He could not remember Happy ever buying breakfast. They matched coins every morning after breakfast and the loser had to pay. Some seemed to never lose, but B.V. thought, I'm not one of them.

The walk was over when he reached his home on East 3rd Avenue. From there he would drive to his office next to Floyd Hospital. He had gotten in the habit of walking to the restaurant every morning and then returning home for his car. He recalled that during the war there was a saying that *walking wasn't crowded*, and that every step you took helped get our soldiers back home a little quicker.

He had hardly gotten to the office and hung up his coat when the phone rang. Dr. Elmore answered it as always "Health Commissioners

Office." The voice on the other end began to tell him of a death.

B.V. interrupted with, "wait a minute, let me go sit down and find a pad and pencil." After locating the items, he said, "Now who did you say was dead? No, I don't believe I know a Leroy Hill." And then he said, "No, I don't believe I know her either." Then he asked the anonymous caller, "When did he die, and where?" Dr. Elmore was writing as fast as he could. "I need to know if there was an attending physician present when he died, and if a funeral home removed the body." After a moment he said, "I see." The conversation ended with Dr. Elmore assuring the caller that he could find the residence.

B.V. sat in his office an extra moment pondering what he had just been told. He found it strange that the caller had sounded so concerned, but wouldn't give his name.

Dr. Elmore headed north as he left the city. As he drove up U.S. 27, he could reflect on the beauty of the place. He had come from Florida back in '21 to take the Health Commissioner's job. That had been twenty-five years ago. When he arrived, he had no intention of spending his life in Georgia. But Rome was everything that he and his wife Velma had dreamed of.

Nestled in the northwest corner of the state amidst the rolling hills of Dixie, he had fallen in love. Yes, he thought, in love with a city, her people, his church, and the medical community itself which was top notch. It was unbelievable that a small southern city of 28,000 would have such a medical presence. And the old folks, that is, the *real* old folks had told him that it had always been that way.

He noticed as he proceeded north that the flood waters were beginning to recede. Rome had received an inordinate amount of rain the past week and the rivers and creeks were all in flood stage. It had also been rather warm for February, he thought. That was probably why we got rain rather than snow.

Off to the left he could see the beautiful spires and buildings of Berry College. Crafted by Italian stonemasons and artisans, it looked like something from medieval Europe. The college itself was founded by Miss Martha Berry. B.V. had known the founder well. They had served on many a committee together over the years, and her death in 1942 during the War was a sad affair in Rome. This was a lady who had dedicated her life to teaching the children of parents who couldn't afford to pay for an education. She had built a fine college of some 25,000 acres and it was still growing.

As he passed the college he began to enter the little farming community of Pleasant Valley. He caught himself talking out loud. Now what did the caller say? He said to go by the Baptist church on his left and then go past the intersection of the CCC road. This was the road that was built by the Civilian Conservation Corp during the Depression. The next house past the intersection, the caller had said, and B.V. could see several men milling around in the front yard, and one woman going into the house as he parked the car in the yard and got out.

"Gentleman, I'm Dr. B.V. Elmore, Health Commissioner," he said as he introduced himself. "Could you tell me if I got the right place? Is this the home of Leroy Hill?" asked the Doc.

"Yes sir, it sure is," one of the men answered. "I'm Cyril Lynch," he said. "And this is Henry Poole and Marvin Watkins," he added as the men shook hands with the doctor.

B.V. made a little small talk with the men about all the rain and warm weather and then said, "Heard you fellows had a long night. I'm awfully sorry for your loss."

Mr. Watkins spoke up. "It's been a long night for everybody, you're right, but a long three days for the women folk."

"I'm sure it has," B.V. answered, and then said, "Will one of you show me where the deceased's wife is?"

"Just go on in the house, Doc, one of the womenfolk will show you where she's at," Mr. Watkins replied.

As Dr. Elmore entered the house, he saw several ladies in the front room of the small house, and he asked. "Which one of you ladies is Mrs. Hill?"

"Oh, she's in the back bedroom," Missy Holloway said, "Come on and I'll take you to her."

Dr. Elmore entered the room and saw a lady lying on the bed covered up with a quilt. "Mrs. Hill, I'm Dr. Elmore, Health Commissioner, and I'm truly sorry about Leroy," he said as he introduced himself to Bertha. B. V. couldn't get over the fact that the lady in the bed looked awful familiar. He then asked, "Mrs. Hill, do I know you? Have we ever met?"

"Please have a seat Dr. Elmore." Bertha gestured to a chair by the bed, and then continued, "Well, you've seen me for sure. I work in McClellan's ten cent store and you used to have an office above us before you moved to the new one. You were right next door to Dr. McCall."

"Yes, I was, I surely was. I thought you looked familiar. And I love those fresh hot peanuts that y'all have in the candy counter," said B.V., and then added, "How are you feeling Mrs. Hill?"

"Not real well, I'm afraid. I haven't slept much in the past three days, and I feel all jittery inside" she answered.

Dr. Elmore reached for the medical bag that he carried with him everywhere he went. Medicine first, he thought to himself, always medicine first. After a brief examination, he turned to one of the women who had followed him into the room and said, "When I leave, I'll give you something that will help Mrs. Hill get some rest, if you'd be so kind as to see that she gets it."

"Yes sir, I'll be glad to, anything I can do to help Bertha," said Jessie Lynch. All the other women in the room were nodding their approval and willingness to help also.

"Now, Mrs. Hill, tell me what happened to Leroy? Dr. Elmore asked.

"Please call me Bertha," she said, reaching and taking the doctor's hand. "Everybody does."

"Ok, Bertha, what happened to Leroy?" he asked again.

"Well," she said in a voice low and vulnerable, "I don't rightly know. He'd been sick for several weeks with stomach trouble, but he didn't think it was serious, and I didn't either. I certainly didn't think he was gonna die."

"Had he seen a doctor about the stomach problem?" asked Dr. Elmore

"Yes he had, but not this time. He wouldn't go. Said that they hadn't done anything for him yet, why bother?" Bertha's eyes were fastened on Dr. Elmore, and he noticed that they were as soft as her voice. They weren't red, like he would expect from crying, but appeared to be damp, or maybe glistening was a better word. I've seen a lot of death in my sixty-one year,s he thought, but she's really going to have a hard time. He genuinely felt sorry for this young woman. She seemed so fragile.

"Did you get a doctor to fill out a death certificate? I'll need to see it for my records?" he asked.

"No I didn't. Don't the funeral home take care of all that?" she asked.

"Not necessarily," he said. "Which funeral home did you call?"

"I called Paul Jordan over in Cherokee County, Alabama. That's where I'm from Dr. Elmore. I want Leroy buried next to my Mama and Papa over there in Howell cemetery. Mr. Jordan said that he would have Leroy back here by dark. And we're going to have a short funeral here at the house. That's all Leroy wanted."

"Bertha did you get a permit to move the body across the state line?" he asked.

"No I did not. Don't the funeral home take care of that too?" asked Bertha looking deep into his eyes, and squeezing his hand ever so softly. "I don't have much education and don't know about those things. Can you handle those things for me Dr. Elmore?"

The doctor removed his hand and began making notes. After several minutes of writing he asked, "Tell me about the last three days when he refused to see a doctor." He noticed that several of the neighbor ladies had eased into the room and were listening to everything he and Bertha said.

Bertha described the last three days in detail as the health commissioner made even more notes. She then stated, "It was like something he ate or took that poisoned him. His death was kind of weird. You can ask Mrs. Watkins and Missy," she said, as she looked over in the direction where the ladies were standing. "They were here all night."

Dr. Elmore finished with his questioning and placed his notes in his bag. As he stood to leave he turned once again to the young woman in the bed and said, "All right Bertha, you get some rest. We'll get all these permits taken care of. Don't worry about anything else."

"Doctor, thank you for coming and checking on me. I really appreciate it," Bertha said.

"No problem ma'am. That's my job. You ladies look after her, and follow my orders on the medicine I left," he said, addressing no one lady in particular.

Dr. Elmore bade his farewells to the group of men gathered outside. He noticed that the group had almost doubled since his arrival and that there were several more women waiting to go in the house.

As he turned his car into the main road, he took the watch from his pocket to check the time so that he could later add to his notes. It was just now 10:00 a.m. He thought about the situation all the way to town. Something didn't seem right. Twenty-eight year old men don't die from stomach aches. Well, at least not frequently. He stopped at his office, still deep in thought. He wrote and then re-wrote his notes, adding every detail. As he finished reading them for the second time he made a decision. He had to talk to the Sheriff.

ﭏ　　ﭏ

Dr. Elmore parked his car in front of the courthouse, climbed the steps, and walked down the corridor to the sheriff's office. The outer office was open and he could see that no one was there. He knocked on the door of the inner office and heard a familiar voice telling him to come in. As he walked into the room he took his handkerchief from his pocket and wiped the little trickle of sweat that was just beginning to form on his forehead.

"Hot ain't it?" said the man sitting behind the desk. He motioned with his hand to a waiting chair, and said," To what do I owe the pleasure of this visit from the Health Commissioner? I certainly hope that it's a social visit, and not a business one. We don't have a major epidemic breaking out, do we?" asked Sheriff Mark Horton with a big smile on his face.

"Not that I know of Sheriff, but things have a way of sneaking up on you," answered Dr. Elmore.

"Ain't that the truth," Mark replied. "Well, what's on your mind, doc? Anything I can help you with today."

"Sheriff, do you know Leroy Hill?" asked the Commissioner.

Mark dropped his head, furrowing his head in thought, "I know the name, but for the life of me I can't place him," said the Sheriff who then asked, "Do I need to?"

"He's dead, Mark," said Dr. Elmore. "He died about two o'clock this morning. I've just left his place up in Pleasant Valley. I spoke to his widow and a few of the neighbors that had already gathered at the house. Based on statements made by them, well, here I am."

"I don't like where you're taking this, Doc, do I need to start making notes?" asked Sheriff Horton.

That's what Dr. Elmore liked most about Sheriff Horton. He had picked up right away that this was going to be a little more than an office visit to discuss a recent death. Yes, he thought, Floyd County was fortunate to have such a concerned and thoughtful lawman at the top of the ladder. "I think you should, Sheriff," said the Doctor.

"First things first," said the Sheriff. "Are you saying that Leroy Hill didn't die a natural death?"

"I'm not saying that at all. Let me explain," answered the Doctor. He quickly went over ever thing that had transpired that morning, ending with his visit to the Sheriff's office.

Mark started feeling a little better. "So you're saying that your biggest concern is that of not having a Removal from the State Permit," he said.

"That's certainly one of them," the doc answered.

"Well doc, just ask the attending physician. Maybe he can spread a little light on it." Mark replied.

"That's another thing," Elmore said. "There was no attending physician and no death certificate either."

"I see what you're saying, Dr. Elmore, but these country folks don't always follow the rules. That's mostly because they don't know the rules. I wouldn't worry too much about permits. We'll call Paul Jordan over in Cherokee County and I'm sure he'll help straighten this out," answered the Sheriff.

"You're right Sheriff. Paul's a good man and the law's a little bit different across the state line. But one of my main concerns was something that Bertha said herself. And there were two other women in the room who had been present at the time of death. None of them tried to correct her. Not in the least bit. I find that strange." Dr. Elmore stated.

"What was that?" Mark asked.

"She said that there was something weird about the way Leroy died. He just kept getting sicker and sicker for three days and wouldn't tell anybody where he'd been or what he had eaten or drunk. He refused to see a doctor. That's not normal," said the Doc. "Twenty-eight year old men rarely die from a belly ache. There's the anonymous caller that informed me of the death in the first place. The way the neighbors acted while I was there. They didn't say or do anything out of the ordinary. It's just that I thought they wanted to."

"Look Mark, you know that I don't spook easy," Elmore said. "There probably ain't nothing to any of this, but I just want to be sure. Does any of this make sense?" asked Dr. Elmore, leaning back in his chair and grabbing a fresh breath of air.

"Yeah, it makes sense Doc. You're a heck of an investigator. When something's out of line you have to find out why," said the sheriff. "You want me to check this out?" asked Mark.

"Would you Mark?" asked the commissioner as he stood to leave.

"You'll hear from us later today or tomorrow," Mark told the doctor as he walked him to the office door.

Sheriff Horton returned to his desk. He slowly re-read his notes. He leaned back in his chair, folded his hands in his lap, and stared at the ceiling for a long moment. He then re-lit his pipe, inhaled deeply and slowly let the smoke escape from his lungs.

Mark began to rationalize with himself. That old boy's been around for awhile. There isn't a lot he ain't seen or done. He's doctored through two wars and a depression; saw all kinds of sadness and misery.

For him to come and report this and be genuinely concerned disturbed the Sheriff. It really does sound weird, he thought, and if nothing else I respect Dr. Elmore enough to find out if there is anything unnatural about Leroy's death.

# Chapter 2

Sheriff Horton summoned one of his deputies and told him to go to the jail and notify Deputy Frank Russell to grab an early dinner and come to the office as soon as he finished. Mark hated to load Frank down with this case. He already ran the jail, but he was the best investigator that he had.

Frank and his wife actually lived in the jail. They had a four room apartment that was designated for the Chief Deputy or Jail administrator, and in Frank's case he was both. That way there was always somebody on duty at the jail if needed. Frank was reading and studying new police tactics all the time. Mark was sure that Frank was way ahead of his time.

Before coming to the Sheriff's Department, Frank had been the self-appointed training officer for the Rome Police Department. In 1933, he had established the Rome P.D.'s fingerprint and photography lab in the basement of City Hall. He had been promoted to sergeant a few years later and had been commended by no less than J. Edgar Hoover, the head of the F.B.I., for his work in criminal science.

Mark thought, It's easier to get daylight by a rooster than it is to have Frank Russell miss a piece of evidence in a criminal case. If there's anything to this death, Frank will find it. If not, Dr. Elmore will be satisfied, because he knows how thorough Frank is in anything he does.

ּ    ּ

After the dinner break Sheriff Horton sat down with Frank Russell and briefed him on the meeting that he had earlier in the day with the Health Commissioner. He went over his notes in detail until he was certain that Frank had as much knowledge about the death of Leroy Hill as he did.

He gave Frank just a moment to digest everything and then he said,

"We ain't got no real cause to worry that poor woman on top of all she's been through, but we need to clear this up. Heck, Leroy could have got hold of some bad liquor. That could have been what killed him. Just check and see if she can add anything to what she told Dr. Elmore."

Frank pulled out his plug of Bloodhound chewing tobacco from his jacket. From his pants pocket he retrieved a little three bladed Case pocket knife. Opening the smallest blade, which was used for nothing but cutting tobacco, he cut himself a generous chew. Without looking up he offered the plug to the Sheriff who shook his head indicating no thanks.

Frank worked on his chew for a minute or two then said, "Sheriff, I know Leroy Hill and Bertha. Not real well, but I know who they are. They've been hitting the bars and clubs pretty regularly for the last six months or so. Leroy has been partying hard since he came here. And Bertha's with him most of the time. Now I ain't heard of no poison whiskey in quite a spell. However, there is a lot of whiskey out there that ain't real good stuff."

Frank stood up and got a paper coffee cup, stuffed a napkin in it, took a healthy spit and then continued.

"They're still cooking a lot of pop skull up in that Pleasant Valley country and Leroy sure drank his fill. But he didn't drink any more than a lot of other men around here. You said that the Doc told you that young men don't die of stomach problems. I also like to add that they don't die of alcoholism at that age either.

Leroy came down here from the Carolinas with that construction company that built the airport for the Navy. Those guys are real hard workers. You would think that he would be in tip top shape. I got to agree with the Doc, something ain't exactly right."

"Frank," Sheriff Horton said, looking squarely into the eyes of his Deputy. "Find out if there is anything to this death and let me know."

"We may never know, Sheriff," Frank said, "But I'll do my best."

"I know you will Frank. That's why I want you to handle this investigation," said the sheriff, picking up a handful of papers and beginning to read.

Frank knew that he was being excused and that this discussion was over by the change of direction the sheriff was taking. He excused himself, accepting a wave from the boss as he exited the office.

Frank walked back to the jail to pick up his car. While there he told his wife that the Sheriff wanted him to clear up a few questions about a recent death in the Pleasant Valley community, and he would probably be late getting back. He told her that he would grab a bite to eat in a local restaurant, and for her not to hold supper, because he didn't know exactly when he would be back in the jail.

Frank headed his car north toward Pleasant Valley. He was glad to be out of the jail even if it was just for the afternoon. *I love police work. But it gets to be awful mundane at times, in fact most of the time. It's so predictable that you can almost plan your schedule for weeks at a time.* He grinned. *It's good that I added 'almost.' That's what keeps us doing it year after year. You think you know what tomorrow's going to bring, but you can't be absolutely sure.*

Frank liked working cases where he had to use his brain a little bit. There were altogether too many smoking gun cases, where the bad guy was waiting to surrender when the police arrived. They were usually blubbering and remorseful and saying how sorry they were and how they didn't mean to. No real police work to do there, just complete the paperwork and get it ready to go to court.

That's what he expected to do with Leroy's death--find out what he died from and why. Frank saw his job as finding out if his death was from natural causes that up to this point had been overlooked. But right now that was all speculation. Frank had yet to begin his investigation and he absolutely did not want a preconceived notion. As he walked up on the porch he was met by one of the neighborhood women coming out the front door.

"Ma'am, I'm Deputy Russell from the sheriff's office," Frank said. "May I please speak to Mrs. Hill?"

"Please do come in, Deputy Russell. I'm Louise Poole, one of the neighbors. Bertha's in the back room lying down. If you'll just wait here for a minute, I'll go and check if she's awake and be right back."

Frank looked around the front room while he waited for Louise to return. He thought to himself, this room has been scrubbed. These neighborhood ladies have cleaned this place from top to bottom. If it ever was a crime scene, it sure isn't now. There were several ladies present in the front room where Frank had been told to wait. While there, he asked, "Were any of you ladies here last night at the time of death?"

One of them spoke up and said, "I was here. Bertha sent for me, saying that Leroy was mighty sick and that he wouldn't let her do nothing for him. She said that she was plumb worn out and that she really needed some help."

Frank had already begun taking notes. "Could I get your name ma'am, and your address?"

"I'm Mrs. Marvin Watkins, and we're neighbors to Bertha. We live right down the road only a couple of houses," she said.

"Mrs. Watkins, do you have a phone?" Frank asked.

"Lord no, Deputy," she replied. "The nearest phone in this community is up the road a piece at Lynch's Grocery. If we need to use the phone, the Lynchs are mighty obliging to the community by letting all the folks hereabouts use it."

"I see," said Frank, as he continued to write. "You said that when Bertha came and got you, she said that Leroy was feeling mighty poorly. Did she give you any idea what the trouble was?"

"She did, said that he had a tremendous stomach ache. He was acting like he had gotten hold of something that had poisoned him."

"Why didn't she call a doctor if the stomach trouble was that bad?" Frank asked.

"You'd have to know Leroy, Deputy," Mrs. Watkins said. "He could be a mighty stubborn man. And Bertha did want him to go to a doctor. In fact, she asked him to go to the hospital while I was there."

"What did he say?" asked Deputy Russell.

"He laughed at her, said that he would be all right, asked Bertha to fix him a cup of coffee and later some soda water. That had been on Monday afternoon, but on Tuesday and Wednesday, he just kept getting sicker and sicker. If you ask me, Mr. Sheriff, Leroy was a lot sicker than he let on."

"Have you ever seen him that way before?" Frank asked.

"Never, not even when he was drinking hard. Leroy was a hard worker. He worked construction, drove them big trucks, did some mechanic work when he could get it and recently he had been working in the mill over at Shannon. That boy never spent a minute in a bed during daylight, no sir, not him," Mrs. Watkins replied, watching to make sure that Frank had written everything down that she said.

At that moment Louise Poole came back into the room and motioned for Frank to follow her into the room where Bertha was lying in bed. There were still several women in the room comforting her, and attempting to help her with her grief. One of those ladies told Frank that the pastor from the Pleasant Valley Baptist Church had just left and he seemed to offer her some relief.

Frank thought that the woman lying on the top of the covers still looked exhausted and very pale. He, like Dr. Elmore, expressed his sympathy and then came right to the point.

"Mrs. Hill, I'm Deputy Frank Russell from the sheriff's office, and the last thing we want to do is bother you at a time like this, but we received a report from the Health Commissioner stating that you said it was weird the way Leroy died. And now I'm told by one of the neighbor ladies that you mentioned that he was acting like he was poisoned."

"I didn't mean anything definite, Mr. Russell. I could just tell that he had gotten hold of something somewhere."

"You mean accidental, Mrs. Hill. You're not saying that somebody intentionally poisoned Leroy, are you?"

"I'm not saying that at all. How could I? Leroy wouldn't tell me where he'd been, or what he'd had to eat or drink. I asked him over and over. I don't know how many times. Mrs. Watkins and Missy heard me ask him several times, but he just shrugged it off and said that he would be alright. But he wasn't; he just kept getting sicker and sicker."

"Mrs. Watkins said that you tried to call a doctor, is that right?" Frank asked.

"Several times," Bertha replied, "and I tried to get him to go to the hospital but he refused."

Frank was beginning to have many questions about this whole incident. But right now he kept telling himself to keep focused and don't start running rabbits all over the place. There'll be enough time for that later.

"Do you suspect anybody, Mrs. Hill?" Frank asked.

Frank noticed that seemed to startle her just a little. She hesitated for a few moments before replying.

"Deputy Russell, I don't think I have to tell you about Pleasant Valley, Floyd Springs, Everett Springs or all of the Armuchee communities. Mostly they're God-fearing, hard working family people. Lord knows that everybody around here watched after each other during the whole war. Nobody went without something to eat, wood to cook with and coal to stay warm with.

"But also there are those that made sure that plenty of whiskey was available. If your car broke down and you needed a part, well you could get it if you knew where to go. All manner of black market sugar, cigarettes and meat was also available. Leroy knew all of them folks. I don't know what all he was involved in, or even if he was. He was mighty quiet when it came to his business. Leroy partied hard almost every night. He drank a lot and loved the clubs. So no, I don't suspect anybody, but with Leroy anything's possible."

"Did Leroy ever haul whiskey for any of the local bootleggers?" asked the deputy. "Reason I asked is that about three or four months ago some of our deputies were chasing a whiskey car that wrecked. The driver bailed out and ran, and was never caught. We were told that Leroy owned that car. He was asked about it, and said that he had sold it a month earlier. Do you know anything about that?"

"That's the last thing Leroy would tell me," said Bertha. "But we did own a car that Leroy told me he sold at the end of the summer."

"Mrs. Hill, do you mind if I look around in the house before I leave?" Frank asked. "I'll be back to speak to you in a few minutes. I just want to get a feel for the place."

"Oh, you go ahead, Mr. Russell," replied Bertha. "If you need anything just ask Missy or Louise, and they'll get it for you."

Frank already knew that the house was being prepared for a funeral and was very clean. But he wanted to satisfy himself by looking into the medicine cabinet and the kitchen pantry. He found a bottle of turpentine, one of iodine and a big bottle of castor oil. These were standard items in anyone's medicine cabinet.

In the pantry, he found a fruit jar with about a third of its contents still in it. He took a whiff and knew at once that this was some foul smelling stuff. It was no doubt local brewed white whiskey, but he doubted that it would be poisonous. Still he brought it along as he said his farewells to Bertha and the other ladies in the house.

Sheriff Mark E. Horton

Deputy Sheriff Frank L. Russell

# Chapter 3

Frank thought about the death of Leroy Hill all the way back to the sheriff's office. After parking at the jail, he crossed the street to the courthouse and went straight in to see the boss.

"Might be something to this death, Sheriff," Frank said. "Bertha had told some of the neighbor ladies that he was acting like he was poisoned. So our Doc ain't the only one that got that from her. I picked up this leftover jar of hooch up at the house. I think we need to get it analyzed. Don't think we'll find anything. But it needs to be eliminated."

Frank went over the conversation that he and Bertha had in detail. He especially covered the part of Leroy being on the friendly side of all the known outlaws living in the community.

"Frank, from what you've told me, we still ain't got much," said the Sheriff. "What are you planning to do next?"

"Think I'll walk downtown, ask a few questions and maybe grab a bite to eat," Frank replied. "Tomorrow I want to visit those hospitals that Leroy was in recently and find out just what he was treated for and see if we can get a line on what was wrong with him."

"That sounds good, Frank," replied the sheriff. "Just keep me informed. And I'll take care of getting the whiskey analyzed. And Frank, I'm going to be here pretty late tonight. If you get anything just stop back by and let me know."

Frank left the office and wandered down Rome, Georgia's main thoroughfare, which was known as Broad Street simply because it was six lanes wide with enough room left over for parking on each side. Frank had once heard that it was the widest main street in the state.

Whether it was or not didn't really matter to Deputy Russell. What did matter was that it was the commercial hub of the entire county. There were a number of joints and restaurants that sold beer and wine along the main Street. He was sure that they were going to know Leroy if what he had been told at Bertha's house was true.

Frank recalled that Bertha had said that she worked on Broad, and there should be a number of local businessmen and store clerks who could familiarize him with her habits also.

Frank walked several blocks from the courthouse to the last block of Broad Street where it ended at the bridge that crossed the Etowah River. He knew this as the Cotton Block. This is where the county's cotton farmers used to pull their wagons loaded with cotton and sell it to the brokers who waited anxiously for the year's crop. Frank had seen pictures of days gone by when the Cotton Block would be so full of wagons and teams that the farmers often had to sleep on their rigs because there wasn't any way to move.

Those old pictures fascinated Frank. Well, to tell the truth, all pictures did. Photography was one of Frank's hobbies. He felt that there was definitely a place for it in police work, and he practiced the craft whenever he had the opportunity.

Frank's walk had taken him to Joe's Quick Lunch. He slipped inside and found an empty stool toward the back. He ordered the Blue Plate special of the day, and slowly sipped on a cup of black coffee while waiting for his supper. He was so deep in thought that he almost didn't hear the familiar voice of the restaurant owner as he slid onto the next stool.

"Where you been, pard?" he asked. "We ain't seen you in here for at least a couple of weeks."

"Has it been that long, Joe?" Frank replied. He was slowly coming out of his trance, when he recognized that Joe Adams had sat down next to him."

Frank liked Joe. He, like Frank, had been a City Police Officer for awhile. But Joe loved to cook and he loved to talk. He had told Frank back before the war that he thought he could put all of that together if he owned his own restaurant. Not long after that conversation, Frank had heard that Joe had bought the Quick Lunch. He had been open for over six years, and seemed to be as happy as a fat dog in the sunshine.

"Frank, you got a good case going, huh?" Joe asked with a big smile on his face.

"Why do you think that?" Frank asked. He couldn't hide the fact that

Joe had surprised him.

"Frank, when you come in here and eat, it's usually lunch. The only time we see you this late is when you're working on something and don't know when you're going to get home." Joe replied as he looked straight into Frank's eyes. "Am I right or not?"

"Joe, you ought to get back into police work. Even as good a cook as you are, you could be of more service to the people of the county if you were back with us."

"You know, I might consider it, if I could figure out how I could talk to everybody that I wanted to, for as long as I wanted to, and still do as much cooking as I wanted. But you know Frank, ain't no Chief or Sheriff gonna allow that."

"Guess you're right, Joe," Frank said. "But since you brought it up, let me ask you a question."

"Been waiting on you, pard. I knew something was on your mind when you walked in the door. So let her rip."

"Joe, did you know Leroy Hill?" asked Frank.

"I heard about that this morning. They said ole Leroy died last night. But I didn't hear all the details. Guess they'll be in the *Rome News* today or tomorrow." Joe replied.

"Then you did know him?" asked Frank once again. He knew Joe Adams well enough not to interrupt or to try to hurry him if he wanted to get any kind of information at all.

"Everybody that's got a joint or a restaurant that sells any kind of alcohol is going to know Leroy," said Joe. "He was a dang good customer too, always livened the place up when he arrived. Seemed like he drew a crowd everywhere he went. You've seen those kind of people Frank, I know. He's always glad to see you, big smile on his face, big handshake or pat on the back. He just made most folks feel good and forget about any troubles that they might have. Yeah, every tavern owner in Rome and Floyd County's gonna miss ole Leroy."

"Did he drink a lot, and can you tell me who some of those followers were? Was any of the whiskey-running crowd from up in Pleasant Valley ever with him?" asked the deputy.

"Slow down, pard," Joe said. "Yeah, Leroy drank a lot. But he didn't get falling down drunk like some of my customers do.

"I really run a restaurant, and sell beer. I don't actually run a tavern like some of the other folks do. There is still a good bit of drinking that goes on, but most of them old boys were familiar with my police background and they don't drink too much here.

"I guess that I failed to mentioned that most of the crowd that Leroy drew was either women, or guys looking for women. Leroy was one good looking man, at least that's what the women seemed to think. And it must be true, because he always had one with him who usually picked up his tab. If Leroy had a problem, it was money and women. He always had too little of one and too much of the other."

"What about Bertha?" Frank asked. "Did you know her too?"

"She came in with him quite often. After she would get off work they sometimes met here for supper. She had been with him for almost a year, I guess. But the last few times Leroy was in here, Bertha wasn't with him. She seemed like good people to me Frank. Don't think you're gonna find anything bad on her at all."

Frank finished his plate and stood up to leave. After he paid the cashier he turned and said, "You still got the best barbecue in town."

"Hurry back, pard," Joe said, "I still like to play police now and then."

Frank found out that Joe was right. He checked with several other establishments that sold beer and wine as he worked his way back up Broad toward the courthouse. He got the same information on each stop.

Finally he reached McClellan's Five and Ten. As he entered the store, the smell of hot roasted peanuts coming from the candy counter almost made him wish he'd left room for something else to eat.

He asked the first sales lady who approached him if she would be so kind to tell the store manager that he would like to speak to him. She was gone for less than a minute. When she came back there was a man following her who Frank knew as Charles Cantrell. He'd been the store manager since before the war. He was kind of heavy, with thinning hair and he seemed to be a jolly sort. Charles shook Frank's hand with a firm grip that he didn't expect.

This guy's a lot stronger than he looks. I sure am glad he's the friendly type.

"What can I do for the Sheriff's department today?" Cantrell asked.

"I need to talk to you about Bertha Hill," Frank said, and then added, "I guess you heard about her husband."

"Yes we did," he said, "Wasn't that awful? What do you need to know about Bertha? I don't really know when she'll return to work."

"Can we go to your office Mr. Cantrell?" Frank asked, noticing that all the sales girls had closed into hearing distance.

"We sure can, Deputy," he said, "and just call me Charles."

As they entered the small cluttered office, Charles moved a stack of papers from a chair and motioned for Frank to take a seat. As soon as they both were seated Charles asked, "Now what is it you want to know? I'm afraid that I don't know very much about Bertha outside of the store."

"Well, that's part of why I'm here," said Frank. "We're just trying to clear up a few discrepancies that were noted in the Health Commissioner's report. The questions that I have are all work related."

"How long has Bertha worked for the company, what kind of employee she has been, and whether she is trustworthy and honest. Those are the things I'm interested in at the moment."

"I don't see how that has any affect on her husband's death, but I don't mind answering them, not about Bertha I don't," replied the store manager. "Bertha was with this store for about six years. When she came to work for us she had never worked for anybody and had no work record of any kind that we could get a reference from.

"She stated that her first husband's father over in Cherokee County, Alabama owned and operated a small country store and that she frequently worked for him. We needed help so we gave her a job. She was a tireless worker. Deputy Russell, that woman could work circles around anybody in this store. She was promoted several times and at present is the floor manager. I can't say anything but good things about her work record. She has increased business since she has been on the floor."

"How's that?" inquired the deputy.

"There are ladies who will walk past Allen's and Kress's to come here just to let Bertha wait on them. If we've got it, Bertha either knows where it is, or she will find it. The Broad Street ladies love the service and she is so polite. She just does that little extra that seems to come natural. A quality that's not trainable, it's just something that you have or you don't."

"Mr. Russell, we have competition from Allen's and Kress's that I've already named. And there's also Silver's and Redford's. We ask our employee's to go that extra mile in service to set us apart. Bertha does that and more. And I must add that she has also increased the volume of sales from our male patrons."

Frank had been scribbling in his note pad since he sat in the chair. With everything he had noted from Joe, and now Mr. Cantrell, he was figuring on spending a late night in the office re-writing his notes. And he still had more questions.

"How did she increase the volume of sales with your men customers?" asked Frank. He really wanted to hear this answer. He was expecting some newfangled sales technique.

"If Bertha had a flaw Mr. Russell, it was the fact that she was the biggest flirt in the store. She used a lot of 'honeys,' 'sweeties' and 'babies' to the male customers. The men for the most part loved it. And she built up quite a clientele that returned day after day, especially if they worked on Broad. The thing about it was that her flirting was real. This woman genuinely loves men.

"She had a rough time with her first husband when she came to work here. There were days when she came to work with a bruise or a fat lip and was obviously hiding it. After her divorce, she slowly came out of her shell and became very independent. That's when she began to go out of her way to please the male customers."

"Was it all harmless flirting, Mr. Cantrell?" asked Frank, "Or do you know?"

"She had a girlfriend with an apartment somewhere on Second Avenue. A school teacher, I believe. Sometimes she took longer dinner breaks than normal. I know that the teacher worked days, of course, and that Bertha had a key. And I know that she some time used the apartment.

"That ain't much Deputy Russell, but it's like I said when you arrived. I don't know much about her life out of this store, nor do I want to."

Frank thanked Mr. Cantrell for his help and left the store with more questions than he had when he got there. He made several more stops at various restaurants and stores on the way back to the courthouse but picked up nothing more than he already had.

When he got back to the courthouse, Sheriff Horton was waiting for him. "Frank," he said, "Just got a call from B.V. Elmore. He wanted to know if you got anymore from Bertha, or from anybody else. Said that he would be in the office for a while tonight working late and to call him as soon as you came back."

"Sheriff, first thing I want to know is what do the initials B.V. stand for? That's all I've ever heard the man called."

Mark laughed out loud, and then said, "I'll tell you Frank, but please don't repeat it. I'm telling you now that he does not like it"

"And?" Frank asked.

"Buena Vista," said Mark, "Buena Vista Elmore."

"Good grief," Frank said, "Who would name a helpless baby something like that?"

"I don't know, Frank," Mark replied. "Maybe somebody who's daddy or grandpa fought in that battle back in the Mexican War."

"Back to business. What have you found out?" Mark asked.

Frank spent the next ten minutes or so bringing the Sheriff up to date on what he had found out so far. Mark listened intently until Frank finished his report and then asked, "What about the hospitals, Frank? Were you able to get anything from them at all?"

"I ain't got around to asking them yet Sheriff." Frank said. "It's like I said earlier, they're on tomorrow's to do list."

"I know that you got to have some ideas Frank," said Mark. "You just want to call it a night and start back tomorrow morning early?"

"That may be a good idea," Frank said. "But let me run a couple of things by you first."

"I'm listening," said Sheriff Horton.

"Mark, we haven't seen the body. When B.V. got there Leroy was already on his way to Alabama in the back of a hearse. Bertha told him and me that he refused to see a doctor. The neighborhood women also stated that to both of us. She then told the doctor that his death was kind of weird, and told one of the women and myself that he acted like he was poisoned.

"Joe Adams said that he ran with a crowd from all walks of life. I think that we ought to take a look at that body before it goes back to Alabama for burial. Once Leroy's in the ground in another state it will be almost impossible to get him back. A .22 caliber bullet makes a tiny hole that is sometimes almost invisible. So does a puncture wound, from say an ice pick or from a knife with a slim blade. That might explain why he didn't want to see a doctor. Remember, he wouldn't even tell Bertha where he'd been, much less what he ate or drank."

"Are you talking about an autopsy?" Sheriff Horton asked.

"I am. And get this. Bertha told me that Jordan Funeral home was supposed to have Leroy back at the house tonight before dark. She was going to have a short funeral and send him back to Alabama for burial. She didn't say anything about sitting up with the dead tonight.

"Heck, they done set up with Leroy for three long nights. I'm afraid she'll do the funeral tonight and Leroy will be gone. I suggest that we intercept the body on the way to her house, get it to a local funeral home tonight and ask for a coroner's inquest tomorrow. Then after the autopsy we will have a better idea on where we stand and what we got. What do you think?"

Mark just sat and stared at his chief investigator for a long time. A million thoughts were racing through his head, and most of them were not good. After what seemed like an hour he looked at Frank and said, "Frank, I'm agreeable to that. But if we're going to do it, let's do it right. We're going to have to move fast, but take the time to make sure that we're covering all the bases at the same time.

"Moving fast and slow at the same time sounds like a pretty good trick," Frank said.

"Here's what I mean," said Mark. "First, let's back up and go over what you just said a little slower. We've got a body that's due back tonight to the home place. Like you said, they may do the funeral as soon as it arrives and send the body right back for burial tomorrow.

"Hopefully, Bertha won't object to an autopsy, but you never can tell. I've dealt with grieving family members who didn't want their loved ones cut up for any reason. We can get a permit to seize the body, but it may be tomorrow before it's issued.

"Plus we've got at least two politicians to convince in order to get this done, and right now they have no idea that any of this is going on. And to top it all off, I've still not convinced myself that there is anything out of line here. But I do think you're right about the autopsy. That should answer a lot of questions."

"Well Chief, have you got a plan to handle all of this in record time?" Frank wanted to know.

"You've already hit on part of it Frank," Mark said. "I want you to go over to the jail and pick up Davis. Then go up on the highway somewhere past the college and wait on that hearse. There's only one way that they can get here, so that shouldn't be too hard."

"As soon as you make the interception, let Davis ride with them up to Jennings Funeral Home on North Broad. Then you go on up to Bertha's and tell her that we've decided to autopsy Leroy based on what she told you and the Health Commissioner. That's when we'll find out if she's really not going to object."

"What are you planning on doing about the rest, Sheriff?" Frank asked.

"Well, Deputy Russell, I'm going to get on that telephone and ruin a couple of politicians' suppers," Mark replied with a great big smile on his face and sarcasm in his voice. "Ain't no need in us having all the fun, now is there."

Mark stepped into the outer office where Mrs. Florence Jenkins was busy typing some kind of legal summons that would need to be processed and served tomorrow. That's the thing about the office, Mark thought, we may have a strange death to get resolved, but the mundane day-to-day operation has to continue.

"Florence," Mark said, "see if you can get the coroner on the phone for me." Mark noticed that Mrs. Jenkins never looked up or spoke. She just checked her telephone file and began dialing. By the time Mark returned to his chair his phone was ringing. As he picked up he could hear the voice of Mrs. Jenkins telling the coroner that the sheriff wanted to speak with him.

"Dewey," said Mark in a very cheery voice. "How are you today, family doing OK? Look Dewey, I've got Frank Russell on the other phone. We've got a bit of a problem that we need help with."

"Mark, don't start that with me'" replied Dewey Chambers. "Every time you call me this late in the evening it's midnight before I get back home. So tell me where the body is and I'll be on my way. You people seem to forget that I got a service station to run. That's how I make my living. I ain't got a cush job like y'all."

"Slow down, Dewey," Mark said. "You ain't gonna have to leave home to night. I wouldn't do that to you if I didn't have to. I just need you to make a few phone calls before you go home, that's all. Tell him, Frank. We're not trying to take him away from home tonight."

"That's right, Dewey," Frank said.

"What kind of phone calls?" Dewey curiously asked.

"Dewey, I need for you to call for an inquest and an autopsy," Mark said. "That's all."

Dewey felt relieved. He really didn't mind helping the sheriff's office at all. It was just a little game that he and the sheriff played on almost every call that he received. "No problem, Mark," he replied, "I'll drop by your office tomorrow and get the details and then we can get the ball rolling. Will that be OK?"

"I'm afraid not, Dewey," Mark said. This time there was no mirth in his voice. "I need an inquest to convene no later than ten tomorrow morning and an autopsy to follow immediately. And Dewey, whoever you get to do the autopsy, make sure they know how to look for poison."

"OK Mark, you got my attention, now talk," Dewey said. He too was stone-cold serious and listening attentively.

Mark went over the entire day's investigation in less than fifteen minutes. When he finished he asked the coroner, "Any questions so far?"

"Have you run any of this by Henderson yet?" Dewey asked.

"Well, it's really your baby, Dewey. Thought I'd get you on board first, then I'll talk to the solicitor," Mark answered. "I know that he'll turn right around and call you anyway, but you won't have to hear everything secondhand."

"I'm sure I'll hear from him shortly," Dewey said. "Think I'll just wait right here till he calls. See you in the morning, Mark."

"That wasn't too bad, was it?" Mark asked.

"After I talk to Henderson I'll be up for awhile getting everything lined up. But that's my job and I don't mind."

After the phone call ended Frank left the Courthouse and headed once again for the Jail.

Mark leaned back in his chair. He thought to himself, now I've got to call the solicitor. Normally the Coroner handled the entire inquest, from front to back. But Henderson and Dewey had reached an agreement several years ago to work together on these things.

It wasn't that Henderson Lanham wasn't a good prosecutor. He was actually pretty good. But he had already unofficially announced for Congress in the fall.

Mark knew that he wasn't going to be real keen on getting involved in an investigation that might not go anywhere. If there was anything that comes out of the autopsy indicating foul play, and if we're not able to solve it, then Henderson is going to look a little weak in the eyes of the public. At least that's the way the politician in him will see it.

Mark decided to go upstairs and talk directly to the Solicitor-General. When he reached the solicitor's office, he noticed the door was open and he walked in unannounced.

"Well, I see that the Sheriff's working late," Henderson Lanham said, grinning at Sheriff Mark Horton as he entered the office. "That means that the taxpayers are getting their money's worth. We certainly don't want to short the taxpayers, now do we, Sheriff?"

"I need a coroner's inquest and an autopsy, Henderson," Mark said. "and I need them first thing in the morning. I've already called Dewey and made the request, and he's waiting on you to call him now."

"Why don't you just come straight to the point, Sheriff?" Lanham asked as he straightened up in his chair and pushed his glasses back on his head. "Are you going to tell me why, or make me guess?"

"I'm getting there," Mark said. One more time, he thought, I've got to relay the facts as I know them.

Henderson waited until Mark finished explaining the details of the request then asked, "What's your gut feeling Sheriff? Do you think that young man died of anything other than natural causes?"

"Honestly, I'm not convinced that he did. But it is strange. And I've got Russell and Doc Elmore thinking that something ain't right. Henderson, both of them old boys got better noses than a blue tick hound. I can't just rule it out."

"All right Sheriff, here's what we're going to do." Henderson replied. "I'll call the Coroner and let him know that we're available for an inquest at ten tomorrow morning and he can follow that immediately with an autopsy. Did you say that Jennings was Dewey's choice?"

"Yes I did. Jennings is always Dewey's choice. It's close to his service station in North Rome and he isn't gone as long as he would be if he comes down here. He'll want to conduct the inquest there also. He ain't been coroner that long and he gets J.W. Jennings to kind of help him along." Mark replied. "Anything else you want me to do?"

"I'm going to get Chastain Parker and Graham Wright to handle the inquest," Lanham replied. "I want to meet with them and you in your office at nine tomorrow morning.

"I'll call the Health Commissioner and have him there to testify. You have Russell attend this meeting. He's a key witness. Also, I don't want to get a permit to seize the body at this time, that's not gonna be a problem if we need it. I don't see any real reason that the widow would object, do you?"

Mark shook his head.

Lanham continued, "And I agree with you on Dewey wanting to hold the inquest at Jennings, partly I think because he has trouble climbing all the stairs around here with that wooden leg. But this time I'm going to insist that we come here to your office for that meeting, and we can do the inquest in the grand jury room."

"That's fine with me, and I don't think Bertha will object either. I was just trying to cover all the bases," said Mark. "And there's one other thing, Henderson."

"What's that?" Lanham asked.

"We're both working late," Mark said. "The taxpayers are really getting their money's worth now."

Sheriff Horton was grinning as he left the solicitor's office. He didn't say bye, Mark thought.

Henderson Lanham

Dr. B. V. Elmore was the first to suspect that
Leroy Hill had been murdered.

# Chapter 4

Frank walked back to the jail from the courthouse. As he walked he thought, *This has turned out to be a long day and it ain't over yet.* Bertha had said that the funeral home promised to have Leroy's body back before dark, but Frank knew he couldn't rely on that. He figured they'd get him back that night, but it might be late.

He told the jailer on duty to find Deputy Harry Davis and have him bring a car around. Frank walked into his apartment and told his wife, Christine, that he didn't really know what time he would be back.

"Frank, you've been gone all day," she stated. "Is what you're working on dangerous? Is this something that I should worry about?"

"I'm not in any danger, Chris," Frank said. "It just seems to be getting more complicated and tangled up the more we dig. I'll fill you in on what's happened as soon as I can. Right now, Harry and I have got to go back to Armuchee."

"Be careful Frank," Chris said, as he walked out the door.

Frank walked out of the jail and jumped into the waiting car with Deputy Davis.

"Where to Frank?" asked Harry.

"Head up toward Pleasant Valley," he replied, "and I'll let you know where to stop."

"Frank, you gonna clue me in, let me know why I'm heading up to Armuchee?" Davis asked. "I don't mind getting out of the jail one little bit, but I kind of like to know what I'm facing."

Russell filled Harry in on everything that he knew and had been told since he had got the call earlier in the day.

"Wait a minute Frank," Davis exclaimed. "You're telling me we're fixing to do a stake-out for a hearse?"

"I hadn't thought about it that way Harry, but that's exactly what we're gonna do," Frank replied chuckling to himself.

"You know, I've spent days sitting in cars waiting for whiskey runners to show up. Spent I don't know how much time laying in the woods watching liquor stills and waiting for some moonshiner to return and hoping all along that I hadn't been spotted and wasn't doing it for nothing. Staked out buildings when it had been reported that it was gonna be broken into during the night. Some of those stake-outs actually panned out. Most didn't. But I ain't never staked out the road waiting for a hearse with a dead man to come by."

Harry was really amused by the thought of intercepting the Jordan Funeral Home Hearse. Frank watched Harry as he drove up the road chuckling and wondered just what the deputy was thinking. He had Harry pull into a gas station and get over on the far side so as not to block any customers that might come in.

He tried to get comfortable and reached into his jacket pocket, took his plug of chewing tobacco out and cut himself a healthy chew. That always relaxed him. It said right on the wrapper "a doggone good chew" and Frank couldn't agree more. Whoever invented Bloodhound chewing tobacco needs a statue built in their honor, Frank thought as he offered the plug to Harry.

"Let me ask you a question, Frank." Harry said. "Do you reckon they call this northern third of the county Armuchee cause that's the name of the Creek that flows through it?"

"I hadn't thought about it Harry," Frank replied. "But I imagine you're right. All these little communities used to be completely separate from each other. But as more and more people move up in these parts the closer they seem to get. I expect someday that most of those individual names will all disappear into a large community called Armuchee."

"I know that's an Indian name," Harry said. "So why do we pronounce it Armerchee instead of the correct way?"

"I don't know, Harry. Maybe 'cause we ain't Indians."

It seemed like hours to Frank (all stake-outs seemed to last that long) before he saw the long black hearse go by. It only took a minute to pull the vehicle over, and it had hardly come to a stop when a startled ambulance driver bailed out and almost ran to the police car.

"What's wrong officer?" he asked excitedly. "We weren't speeding, I know."

Frank exited the car and walked around to where the young attendant was and said, "You haven't done anything wrong. It's just that we're redirecting you to Jennings Funeral home. We're going be doing an autopsy on Leroy first thing tomorrow."

"Well, I don't know," said the young man. "You'll have to wait about that till I talk to my boss over in Centre. And I'll have to tell the deceased's widow what y'all are doing, too."

"You're going to Jennings now," Frank said. "Once you get there you can use their phone and call Mr. Jordan and tell him what's been decided. I don't think he'll have any problem at all. And I'm going to the deceased's house and inform his widow. You don't have to worry about that."

Frank motioned for Harry to get out of the car and come to where he was.

"Harry, I'll drive from here on. I want you to climb in the back of the hearse and ride with Leroy up to Jennings and wait for me there. Mr. Jennings ought to know by now that we're on the way and he should be expecting us. I don't think these ole boys mind at all, but I want to make sure that they find their way to North Broad."

"Frank, you know I don't want to be in the back of that thing with a dead man. I don't like being around dead folks. How about you do that and I'll drive?" Harry asked sheepishly.

"No can do, Harry," Frank said. "I gotta go and tell Bertha what's going on and that the funeral is going to be postponed for a while."

"Well, you're gonna owe me one, Frank," Harry said. "And I ain't about to forget it."

"I'm sure you won't, Harry," Frank said with a big smile on his face. "Now climb on in and get comfortable. It's not that far to ride. And if you get a chance, Harry, you might ask ole Leroy what happened?"

"You ain't being funny, Frank. Not funny at all."

Russell drove the short distance to Bertha's house. As he pulled into the yard he noticed some of the same neighbors he had seen earlier in the morning were still at the house. I guess, he thought, they're waiting for the hearse with Leroy to arrive.

Frank walked up to the front door, had a few words with Mr. Watkins and then went on inside. Bertha was sitting in a chair by the kitchen table. When she saw Frank she got to her feet and came quickly to meet him.

"Deputy Russell," Bertha said with just a touch of surprise in her voice. "What a pleasant surprise. What brings you back out here again so late?"

Frank ignored the questions and made a little small talk. "Mrs. Hill, are you feeling better now?" he asked.

"Why yes I am deputy," she replied. "And I thank you for asking. And now that we're beginning to get so well acquainted, please call me Bertha. I really do prefer that.

"Bertha," Frank said, "because of the conversation that you and I had, and the one between you and Dr. Elmore earlier this morning, we have decided to conduct an autopsy on Leroy. We can't find any logical reason for such a young man to be as sick as he was and not want to see a doctor. So I came up here to let you know that we have taken Leroy to Jennings Funeral home on North Broad Street. Is that all right with you?"

It was a long moment before Bertha spoke. "I really don't think Leroy would have wanted to be autopsied, Deputy Russell. But if you think it best, then it's all right with me."

"Hopefully we will get the autopsy done sometimes tomorrow and then it's just a matter of time till we can get a report back. I'm really sorry that the funeral had to be postponed." Frank replied.

"I am too," Bertha said. "But you'll let me know what the report says as soon as you get it, won't you Deputy Russell? And can we have the funeral as soon as the autopsy is over tomorrow?"

"I can't promise anything at this point, but I really don't see any reason that would prevent it. Let's just wait and see what the doctors say tomorrow," Frank replied.

As Frank was leaving the house a man he'd never met stepped forward, and holding out his hand, introduced himself. "Deputy Russell, I'm Ruben McClung and this is my wife Plemma," the man said. "Plemma is Bertha's aunt. She and Zola were sisters."

"Who's Zola?" Frank asked.

"Zola was Bertha's mother," Ruben said. "She died last summer herself. But the reason I stopped you was to let you know that me and Plemma are gonna be staying here with Bertha for awhile, at least till she gets herself settled down."

And if there's anything we can do to help you, just let us know. We ain't real sure that Bertha's herself right now. She had Mr. Watkins drive her to our house in Coosa this afternoon and asked us if we would come and stay with her awhile."

"That was right nice of y'all," Frank said. "I'm sure you'll be a big help to her. And I'll take you up on your offer to help. If I need anything up here, I'll certainly let you know."

Bertha walked over to where Frank was talking to the McClungs. She paused for a brief minute and then said," I'm sorry that I didn't introduce my aunt and uncle to you Deputy Russell. I thought you'd already met."

"Well it doesn't matter Bertha, we've met now, and they seem to be right nice folks."

"Yes they are, and they came up here this afternoon to take care of me. Wasn't that nice of them?" Bertha answered in that soft, yet suggestive voice of hers.

"It certainly was," Frank said. "You can't beat good friends and family, and it looks like you're blessed with both."

"I really am, Deputy, I'm truly blessed," Bertha said, looking deep into Frank's eyes. Then she repeated very softly, "Truly blessed."

Frank said his goodbyes to Bertha and the McClungs, promising to let them know something as soon as he had the results or permission for the funeral to take place.

Frank was mystified as he drove back toward Rome. She didn't seem to be to upset about the autopsy, he thought, but then what could she do about it?

There's was something about her eyes, he thought, it seemed that he could look into them for about a mile, and at the bottom they were smoldering. And he couldn't read her face.

He remembered a picture that he had seen once before in a book. A portrait from France called the Mona Lisa. In that picture, you couldn't tell if that woman was smiling or not. He got the same feeling with Bertha.

She had a crooked little smile or smirk, and Frank realized all of a sudden that he couldn't tell which one it was. And then he wondered if she really was the saint that she seemed to be.

Put that on the list, Frank, he said to himself as he pulled into the parking lot at Jennings. *I don't even remember coming through town. This thing's starting to rattle me. Or maybe I've just about had it for tonight.*

Frank got out of the car and walked in the back door of Jennings. Harry was in deep conversation with some of the ambulance drivers and attendants who were on duty. I'd like to bet on who's lying to whom, he thought. And I'd place all I had on Harry. "You ready to go?" Frank asked.

Harry didn't see Frank come in and jumped just a little at the sound of his voice.

"Didn't see you, Frank! You scared me," Harry said. "Yeah, I've been ready since I got here. What took you so long?"

"Wanted to give you plenty of time to question Leroy about why he up and died. Figured by now you could just solve this whole mystery and we could wrap it up." Frank said as he threw Harry the keys to the car and climbed into the passenger seat. "Put this thing in the barn."

"Sorry about that Frank, Leroy didn't tell me nothing. Looks like you're still on your own," Harry said.

"Nope, you got it just a little wrong. *We're* on our own," Frank said.

"Whoa, Frankie boy, I've done my good deed. I just want to go back to the jail and work my shift. Besides, Mark ain't said nothing about me getting involved in this thing any deeper," Harry said with a big pleading look on his face.

"I can fix that as soon as we get back," Frank said. "Look Harry, unless I miss my guess, there's gonna be a note for me at the jail from the Sheriff telling me to be in his office early in the morning for a meeting and then to testify at a coroner's inquest."

"That means there will be an autopsy right after that. By now Dewey's already got the doctor to report to the Funeral home and be ready to go as soon as he makes the call. I'm gonna run up here as fast as I can after the inquest, but I want someone here before the doctors arrive. I need someone to witness everything that goes on. So you see Harry, I really need you."

"Frank, are you telling me that you want me to witness an autopsy?" Harry said very quietly.

"Absolutely. I plan to be with you but you never can tell, and I want to make sure that the department has a representative. If this thing goes bad, we've got to have somebody here that can testify in court."

"Court? What are you talking about?" Harry asked. "We haven't even had the autopsy and you're already talking about court."

"I just want to be prepared for all possibilities," Frank said. "I'd rather plan for something that we may never need, than need it and it not be available."

"You don't make sense half the time, Frank." Harry said. "If I listened to you for more than thirty minutes I'd go crazy. But I'll be your witness, that is, if there's a note waiting like you said."

When Harry stopped at the jail to let Frank out, he could hear someone shouting to his boss.

"Hey Frank!" came a voice from inside the jail. "You got a note here from the sheriff."

Frank, standing on the jail portico, was conversing with two other deputies who were waiting for the car. Harry Davis recognized the voice of Deputy Bill Payne, the night jailer, and he heard Frank answer, "I'll be right there, Bill." Frank looked at Harry and said. "Pick up a car and be at Jennings by eight. That ought to be early enough."

"And you're coming as soon as you can, right?" Harry asked.

Frank didn't waste any time getting to bed. He lay there in the dark, looking to where he knew the ceiling was. As tired as he was, he couldn't sleep. His mind was running wide open. *What have I missed? What have I missed? Those eyes and that smile! Or was it a smile?*

Finally, rest, sleep--peaceful sleep--once again conquered his acceler-
ated mind, and slowly but surely, turned everything black.

₪    ₪

Johnny Jacobs was in a hurry. It was already five thirty and he didn't have a
pot of coffee ready. He knew that the breakfast crowd would be starting to
come in to his restaurant by at least six. Usually there would be a few that
might even get there early. And the ones who did were going to want a cup
of coffee immediately. He went about the restaurant hurrying everybody
but the cook. The cook was his mama and he didn't dare speak harshly to
her.

Johnny's family had opened The Partridge on Broad Street back in the
early thirties. And from the first day Johnny had loved it. He referred to
the restaurant as his Partridge and it was his intention to have a place where
people could get a good meal for a decent price. He kept the restaurant
open every day of the year except Christmas. He started the business with
a printed daily menu from which customers could circle their order. There
was never a ticket brought to anybody's table. Johnny believed that given
a chance people were honest and would not beat him out of a dime. The
customer simply told the cashier what he had ordered and that was what
was rung up.

As it neared six o'clock, the opening time of the Partridge, his first
customer of the day walked in. And as usual, it was a member of the early
morning breakfast club. The club had begun shortly after the Partridge
opened and continued over the years. It was a very informal gathering.
Members came and went. Some moved away, others became ill, died, or
simply stopped coming. By and large it was made up of local business men.
There were media personalities, insurance executives, lawyers, government
officials and manufacturing supervisors in attendance at any given time.
Also there would be a doctor or local preacher from one of the downtown
churches usually dropping by at least some of the time.

Cecil Rhodes was the first to arrive. The manager of Belk-Rhodes Department store slid into the customary breakfast club booth near the rear
of the restaurant. He took his first cup of coffee from the waitress with a
big smile, and with a glint of mirth in his voice, he said, "Good morning
Johnny, I see you're up mighty early this morning."

"Now Cecil you know that I'm up early every morning. Have to get the
coffee ready for all you folks."

Johnny had his waitress bring a pot of steaming, hot, black coffee to the table and leave it there. He knew that his waitress would have to refill that pot several times before the men left for their respective businesses.

Next Macon Brock, owner of Brock's Jeweler's, and Hix Sims came in one right after the other. Hix was the president of Owens-King, a top of the line men's store on Broad. Dr. B.V. Elmore, the Health Commissioner, was next followed by John Moss owner of Moss Hardware, Jack Harris a local lawyer, Ben Rainwater manager of Georgia Automatic Gas, Bud West a route salesman for Coca-Cola, and finally John Powers the manager of Allen's Five and Dime, came through the door.

Dr. Elmore was glad that his nemesis, Happy Quarles, hadn't made it this morning. But his happiness was short lived. Happy came through the door with a big smile for everyone. He lived up to his name on a daily basis. Dr. Elmore wondered how anyone could feel that good all the time. Happy broke the ice with a question for the Health Commissioner.

"Hey Doc, I just left the jail and there seems to be something going on that ain't nobody talking about. My usual sources say that they ain't heard exactly what it is, but your name keeps coming up in the conversation. Would you like to tell us what the Health Commissioner's doing hanging around with the Sheriff for the better part of yesterday?"

"No sir, I would not," B.V. said, as he poured a cup of coffee and slowly took a sip to gauge the temperature of same.

"Come on, Doc. I've got to make a living same as you," Happy said with a noticeable plea in his voice.

"You can read it in the paper then," he replied looking up and nodding to Ben Cooper, the City Editor of the *Rome News*, as he slid into the booth.

Ben was usually the last one to arrive and usually did so by coming in through the rear door. The *Rome News Tribune* was located on the street behind the Partridge, so Ben parked his car at the *Tribune* headquarters and simply walked up the street, coming through the kitchen rather than walking around the block.

"Read what in the paper B.V.?" Ben Asked.

"Can't tell you right now Ben, call me later in the morning," B.V. answered.

"I'll do'er doc," Ben said as he poured that first cup of coffee.

"Wait a minute, that's not fair Doc," Happy said with just a twinge of sorrow in his voice. "You know my boss will have a fit if I let the paper beat me to a story. Anything he reads in the paper, he says, should have already played twice on the radio."

"Happy, who told you that life was fair?" Doc Elmore asked. "Obviously he hadn't spent much time riding around out in the country visiting folks with me."

"Hey Doc, let me change the subject for a minute. I got a question for you," Cecil Rhodes chimed in. "I had to order another shipment of maternity clothes yesterday. We can't seem to keep them on the rack. Now mind you, I'm not complaining, but is every woman in Rome and Floyd County expecting?"

"Sure looks that way, doesn't it?" Doc Elmore answered. "Almost every physician I've talked to recently has a very large patient pool of women that are in a family way. I've already been delivering quite a few babies out in the country, especially among the poor and just plain old country folks who don't see a doctor until the labor pains begin.

"What do you reckon's causing that, Doc?" Happy Quarles asked, trying to get in the good graces of the health commissioner.

Dr. Elmore and most of the breakfast club members all looked at Happy and rolled with laughter.

"I didn't mean it that way," Happy stated. "I know how women get that way. I was asking why so many at one time and why now?"

"Well, I'll tell you, Happy. When you take several million young boys and girls that haven't seen each other in three or four years, and you let them get back together all of a sudden, it seems to me that all they want to do is jump between the sheets. The result is what you see walking up and down Broad Street every day."

"You think we are going to have us a baby boom Doc, like after the last war?" Hix Sims asked from the far end of the table.

"Yes I do, Hix," Elmore replied. "But not like the last war, about ten times greater. And it's going to last for years. Cecil, you better stock up on baby clothes to go along with the maternity stuff."

"Way ahead of you there, Doc. We've already placed that order. But so has every other department store in town. It seems like there aren't enough manufacturers to supply everybody, but we're on the waiting list."

As Johnny's waitresses were bringing breakfast to the table, the city clock from atop its lofty tower overlooking the downtown area begin its customary striking. As it finished with seven strikes every member of the breakfast club crew, as if on cue, pulled out their pocket watches and checked the time. This had become a morning ritual. After the time check, each member would nod to Macon Brock. He not only owned a jewelry shop but was a certified clock and watch maker. Rome contracted with him to maintain the operation of the giant city clock perched on top of one of Rome's seven hills.

"Everybody says you're right on the money, Macon," John Powers said as he held his watch out for Macon to see. "And since I bought this watch from you, I'm concerned to know that it and the city clock are several minutes apart."

"That was a pretty cheap watch I sold you, John. It might be a little bit off," Macon replied chuckling. "We've finally started getting in a lot of Swiss watches. Just couldn't get them when the Germans had the whole country over there surrounded. But if you come in the store now, I will fix you up with a first class time piece, that I can guarantee."

"Didn't you go to Switzerland right before Christmas, Macon?" John Moss asked.

"Yes I did. Had to make sure my suppliers had survived the War and get some good watches headed this way. In fact, while I was there I bought my first shipment and had them air mailed to Rome. They beat me back to the house. We sold all of them before Christmas, but we have a steady stream coming now. Y'all come by."

"Believe I'll just keep this one for a while, Macon. It isn't doing all that bad," Powers said. "But when I need another one I'll certainly look you up."

As the seventh hour of the morning wound down and breakfast was over, all the participants reached in their pocket and retrieved a coin. Here I go again thought B.V. Elmore. As the flip progressed, Dr. Elmore was elated when he was one of the first out. He looked over toward Happy and grinned, so as to say, you're not going to get me this morning.

Most of the men began leaving the restaurant soon after the flip. Dr. Elmore saw that Cecil Rhodes had stopped at the cash register and was paying the bill. He seemed to be having a chuckle with Mary Johnson, the cashier. B.V. noticed how Cecil towered over Mary. He was six foot six or better, and thin as a rail. But he was a mighty good man. His employees adored him and for good reason. He worked as hard as they did, maybe harder, and they loved him for it. He had more than an employee/employer relationship.

Soon every one of the morning crew had left the restaurant except Dr. Elmore. Johnny came over to the table and sat down with him.

"You hanging around for a reason Doctor? Was everything OK this morning?" Johnny wanted to know.

"You know it was, Johnny," B.V. said. "I've got a meeting at the courthouse at nine and I'm just killing time."

"I heard what Happy said about something going on, Dr. Elmore. Guess there must be for you to wait for all of the news folks to leave without telling anybody."

"Johnny there is, although I'm not exactly sure myself what it is and what's going to happen."

"Well I guess you were right. If there is anything to it, we'll read it in the paper."

"Yes you will Johnny, you surely will," B.V. answered as he headed for the entrance.

# Chapter 5

By the time the men had all gathered for the morning meeting, Mrs. Jenkins had been in the office for over an hour. When she knew that the Sheriff had scheduled an early morning meeting she was always first to arrive, and made sure that note pads and pencils were available. She had perked coffee and stopped at the Broad Street Bakery and picked up pastries. She had almost forgotten how much these men folks loved bakery treats.

During the war, sugar had been rationed and everybody in the courthouse supported the war effort one hundred percent. Goodies like these had just not been available for the last several years, but now that they were, she loved to splurge every chance she got. The pastry spread was ready on the table when the sheriff arrived.

"Mrs. Jenkins, you're going to have to be a little tighter with our budget," Mark said as he poured a cup of coffee and picked up a glazed do-nut.

"Fiddlesticks," Florence Jenkins said. "We've been tight for the last three years; war's over, time to loosen up the reins a little bit."

"Just don't get too extravagant, please?" Mark pleaded with his seventy year old office manager.

"Mark Horton, you worry too much," Florence said. "My daddy was elected sheriff back in 1904. My husband was a deputy most of his life, serving under several sheriffs, and I've been around this department for nearly fifty years. Do you want me to run this office or not?"

Before Mark could answer, Frank Russell, followed by Dr. B.V. Elmore came through the door. Frank stopped for a cup of coffee, but B.V. simply walked into Mark's office, found a chair and had a seat.

"Doc, you want a cup of Florence's coffee?" said Mark, "Best in town."

"Just left the Partridge, Sheriff, probably drank too much already. Believe I'll pass for now, but I do thank you anyway."

Henderson Lanham came into the office next, followed by Chastain Parker and Graham Wright. Frank watched all three as they poured coffee and helped themselves to Florence's spread. He couldn't help but think how high-powered these guys were. Lanham was a good attorney. Frank knew that. But Parker and Wright are as good as it gets. It was obvious that Lanham was not going to allow any slip-ups at all. There might be something to that unannounced run for Congress that the sheriff was talking about. Sure looked that way.

The coroner was the last of the invited guests to show up. Frank sat in his chair and watched all the informal pleasantries take place. He was ready for the meeting to start. He wanted to get this thing over with and get back to work.

Finally the Coroner spoke. "I appreciate each and every one of you being here this morning. I think you already know that the health commissioner and the sheriff have asked for an inquest into the death of Leroy Hill. But just for the record, let me ask both men if that is correct."

"That's correct," Mark Horton replied.

"I didn't know that an autopsy was being discussed until Henderson called me last night, but I wholeheartedly agree and do formally make that request at this time," Dr. Elmore replied.

Dewey Chambers once again addressed the group. "Yesterday evening I randomly selected six names from the present jury pool. Five will serve as jurors and one will serve as an alternate for obvious reasons. I will swear in the jury and then administer the oath to the foreman once they choose one from among themselves. Henderson's staff will call and question our three witnesses and then I will charge the jury. Does anybody have any questions about the procedure?"

None of the men in the room said a word.

"Good," Dewey continued, "Sheriff Horton, Dr. Elmore and Chief Deputy Frank Russell will constitute our witness pool. And now Mr. Solicitor, I will turn this meeting over to you."

"We'll use the grand jury room upstairs," he said. "Chastain will question the witnesses and Graham will sum up before the jury.

"Thank you, Mr. Solicitor," Dewey said. "Does anyone have any further questions?"

"I've got one Dewey," Mark said. "Is the autopsy set for later on this morning at Jennings funeral home?"

"Sheriff let me answer that this way," Dewey said. "If the members of this inquest jury recommend an autopsy then one will be held immediately."

"That's clear enough," Mark replied. "Is everyone ready to go upstairs?"

Frank led the way as the group climbed the stairs to the second floor of the courthouse and made their way to the grand jury room. He could see several men milling around in the hall next to the door of the room itself. He and Dr. Elmore, along with the sheriff, proceeded down the hall to the solicitor's office to await their call to testify.

Frank figured that he would be the last witness called and he was. The whole procedure lasted less than an hour and the witnesses were excused. Frank had been told by the sheriff as he had left the jury room after testifying to come straight to his office as soon as he was finished. Frank eased into a chair in the Sheriff's office and asked, "What do we do now?"

"We wait, "Mark said. "But I don't think it will be long. This thing was short and sweet. You had the longest testimony and once you finished, all they had to do was sum up. Dewey said that he would be down to see us as soon as the jury made a decision."

Less than thirty minutes had passed when Dewey Chambers and Henderson Lanham walked into the Sheriff's office and took a seat. "OK boys, we got the recommendation from the jury," Dewey said adjusting his glasses and raising the paper to eye level. Let me read it to you. 'The death of Leroy Hill was from causes unknown as of this hearing, but under suspicious circumstances that the death was caused by poisoning, we recommend that an autopsy be performed on the deceased and that the hearing be adjourned on the matter until such time as a report of the autopsy is received.'

"The foreman signed the verdict," Dewey said, "And that not only clears the way for an autopsy, but pretty much orders it. The solicitor could ignore it if he was a mind too, but I highly doubt that he will."

"How about it, Mr. Solicitor," Mark said. "Do we continue?"

"Absolutely, I've already told the coroner that I concur, and he made the call from my office to Jennings. By now it's in progress."

Frank retrieved the report and re-read it one more time. The only thing he noted that Dewey left out was that the foreman was Dr. Lee Battle, Jr. That was smart, Frank thought. This had turned into a complicated matter based on a medical evaluation which had led to this point. Who would be better than a local physician to be the foreman? And once the autopsy was finished and the report was back, he would be invaluable in interpreting the findings and explaining them to the rest of the panel.

"Gentlemen, let me complete my report to you and I'm going to head to the Funeral Home to assist," the coroner continued. "Mark, you said yesterday to make sure that whoever I got to do the autopsy could look for poison. Well, really any of the cutters that we use are skilled in surgical matters. Then Henderson says on the phone that he wants someone qualified as an expert in case it comes back bad and at some time in the future we have a court case.

"Taking all of that into consideration, I called Dr. Warren B. Mathews of Atlanta to come and do the autopsy. He will take back samples of various organs to Dr. George T. Lewis, of Emory University, who is in charge of the chemistry department, actually now it's called bio-chemistry I think. But anyway, he's a noted pathologist in Atlanta and does this sort of thing on a regular basis. We should get a first class job in about two or three weeks. So with that, gentlemen, if there are no further questions I'm going to Jennings."

"I'm right behind you Dewey," Frank said as he vacated the office and actually got ahead of the coroner. Frank was moving fast as he crossed the street from the courthouse and walked the short half block back to the jail. He grabbed a patrol deputy and had him drop him off at Jennings Funeral home.

What was it the solicitor had said? When he came into the sheriff's office he said that the coroner had made the phone call from his office and had given the order for the autopsy to commence. Poor Harry, Frank thought with a wide grin on his face, doubt if he'll ever forgive me.

Frank jumped out of the car at the rear of the funeral home and went straight to the back room where the autopsy was underway. In fact it was almost over. Harry looked up at him as he entered the room. What was it they said about 'if looks could kill?' Harry had a look of total animosity on his face. Just a few minutes after Frank entered the room, Dr. Mathews announced to the funeral home staff that he was finished and they could close him up.

Frank introduced himself to the man and said, "Doc, I'm sorry that I couldn't get here any sooner. I had to testify at the inquest and I was last to go. But I hope that Deputy Davis was able to witness the entire operation for the sheriff's office."

"Oh, he was," the Doc replied. "In fact he was here when I arrived this morning. Everything went real well."

"Anything you can tell us that might save us a long wait on an official report?" Frank asked.

"I understand from talking to Deputy Davis, that you have been proceeding on the assumption that death was not from natural causes," Dr. Mathews said. "Would that be correct?"

"Yes, it would," Frank replied.

"Then that's what I would continue to do Deputy," Dr. Mathews answered. "I can't make an official report until a lot of tests have been completed. But I have done a lot of these in the past and it looks very suspicious to me."

Dr. Mathews shook hands all around and headed for Atlanta. The funeral home attendants closed Leroy up once again and then asked Frank, "What do we do with Leroy now, Deputy Russell? Should we call Jordan to come and get him or take him back to the home place."

"Just leave him here until I call you and let you know," Frank said.

Frank and Harry left the parking lot and headed back toward the jail. Frank noticed that his deputy wasn't saying much. That certainly wasn't like Harry.

"What's the matter buddy? You look a little pale," Frank said, trying to sound sincere.

"Frank," Harry said. "That doctor pulled Leroy's fingernails and toenails off. Not all of them but some on each hand and foot. Then when he cut him open, he started packing up his insides. He would hold each piece up and announce what it was so that one of them funeral home guys could write it down. He'd just turn it over and over, poke on it some and then put it in a bag. I know that he took samples of stomach, liver, kidneys, and intestines and then he got hair samples. It was awful, just awful."

"Guess I owe you one, Harry," Frank said as he stopped for a light on Broad Street.

"You're mighty right you do," Harry said. "And it ain't gonna be cheap, either."

"Wouldn't want it to be," Frank said. "Tell you what I'm gonna do. I got a call this morning before I went to the sheriff's meeting from Chief Wood Quarles at the Rome P.D. He said that they was having a supper this Friday night at a cabin down near the lock and dam and he wanted me to come. He said that I could bring a deputy or two with me. I think the sheriff will be there, too."

"Frank, I ain't feeling real good. Don't want to talk about food right now."

"Well, I gotta let them know, Harry. And Joe Adams is doing the cooking. Gonna be a big chitling supper. I know you love chitlings. I can remember watching you eat a hog gut a mile long, and you know Joe. He boils them first. A lot of cooks don't. I ain't crazy about the smell of boiling hog guts. But after he gets them good and tender he cuts them up in six-inch pieces or so and fries them good and brown. They're great, unless you get a kernel of corn that didn't pass through. But you know that Joe takes his hog guts when they're fresh and cleans them real good. They're creek-flung and stump-whupped."

"Stop the car, Frank!" Harry exclaimed in a crisp, harsh voice.

"Harry, you all right? You're kinda turning green around the hairline, buddy," Frank taunted.

"Stop the car Frank!" Harry said again.

Frank pulled up to another stoplight. He was still several blocks from the jail when Harry opened the door, jumped out of the car and started walking down the street.

Frank pulled alongside Harry and said, "He always has big old biscuits and onion gravy, too."

Harry refused to look at Frank and just kept walking toward the jail. Frank was driving at the same speed that Harry was walking and kept asking him to get back in the car.

"Frank you got me this time," Harry said. "I'm forty-three years old and I ain't never seen nothing like that, And I ain't never going to another one of them things if I can help it. And I ain't going to no supper with you. Right now I doubt if I'll ever eat again. Now go on and leave me alone. I'll walk back to the jail."

Frank parked his car at the jail and walked once again back across the street to the sheriff's office. As he entered the office, he heard the sheriff tell him to come in and be seated, that he'd be right with him. Mark was on the phone with someone Frank noticed and was doing a whole lot of listening. After what seemed like an hour he finally hung up. Looked at Frank and just shrugged his shoulders.

"Frank, that was Dewey. He said that it didn't look good. Said that Doctor Mathews didn't like the way the stomach lining was inflamed and that the liver looked horrible. His best guess is that Leroy was poisoned. And that he was not prepared to make a guess if it was intentional or accidental."

"He so much as told me the same thing," Frank said. "I guess we keep digging."

"Got to," Mark replied. "Frank do you think Leroy could have had some kind of problem that would cause him to want to kill himself?"

"No I don't, Sheriff," Frank said. "From everything I've learned so far Leroy loved living, and Leroy loved Leroy. Killing himself is just about the last thing in this world he would do.

"Besides, when men kill themselves it's almost always with a gun to the head. Poison is for women, and it's usually sleeping pills or something similar. If a woman does shoot herself, it's in the chest. Most women don't want a closed casket funeral.

"Have you ever noticed, they clean their house real good, put on their best night gown, get in the bed and take a bottle of pills. A couple of times I've found them in the bathtub with cut wrists, so as not to get blood all over their clean house.

"Colored folks don't kill themselves at all. Hard times ain't nothing new to them. If you see a colored man dead, start looking for his killer if it ain't from natural causes.

"Suicide is a white man's game. But it wasn't Leroy's. He didn't kill himself. I'd bet on it."

"You told me that Joe Adams said that he ran with some shady characters up there in Pleasant Valley. Think they might have poisoned him?" Mark asked.

"Nope, not gonna happen," Frank answered. "Sheriff, there's all kind of outlaws up in Armuchee. There are moonshiners, bootleggers, and a heck of a ring of car thieves. I've heard rumors that back in the late twenties and early thirties that some of them old boys made their way to Detroit and were members of the Purple gang for awhile. They're there too.   There are guys that can strip a car and have the parts labeled and in the bin for sale in thirty minutes. Beer joints are all over the place and enough customers to keep them all busy.

"Sheriff, this country just fought the biggest, costliest, most vicious war that's ever been in recorded history. We trained millions of men how to kill, and then gave them three and a half years to practice. Then all at once it's over and we send them back where they came from. A lot of them can't just turn it off. If you make somebody like that mad, they will kill you and quickly. If Leroy made one of those Armuchee boys mad, they'd a shot him full of holes. They wouldn't have bothered with poison."

"I see your point, Frank," Mark said. "So what happened to Leroy?"

"Sheriff, I just don't know at this time. But I'm going to, before I'm through."

"You still haven't talked to those hospitals have you?" Mark asked. "I'd like to know what Leroy was being treated for."

"Me too, Sheriff, and I saw that Jack Highfield was in jail. He and Leroy were buddies I understand. I'm going to have a little talk with Jack today. But right now I'm going back to Bertha's house and ask her a few more questions. Besides I promised to let her know when the autopsy was finished. And she's going to want the body released to her for a funeral this evening. What do you want to do about that?"

"Tell her that the coroner has to release the body, and that I'll try to get that done this afternoon. That shouldn't be a problem."

"Sheriff, I'm gonna take Harry with me. Is that all right?" Frank asked.

"Thought he was already with you?" Mark asked.

"He was just at his first autopsy. Wasn't feeling too good, decided to walk most of the way back. He should be at the jail by now." Frank replied.

"I remember my first one," Mark said. "It was a little worse than not feeling good. I was sick as a dog."

Leroy Hill, probably a mug shot

# Order Autopsy In Death of Leroy Hill

An autopsy has been ordered by Floyd County Coroner Dewey Chambers, following a Coroner's inquest held here this morning in connection with the death of Leroy Hill, 28, who died early yesterday.

The verdict of the jury was "The death of Leroy Hill was from causes unknown as of this hearing, but under suspicious circumstances that the death was caused by poisoning, we recommend that an autopsy be performed on the deceased and that the hearing be adjourned on the matter until such time as a report of the autopsy is received."

The verdict was signed by Dr. Lee Battle Jr., local physician, as foreman.

The inquest was conducted by Chastain Parker and Graham Wright, a number of witnesses testifying. An investigation had been ordered following Mr. Hill's death early yesterday morning.

above: Leroy Hill dressed for the ladies

right: the house Leroy and Bertha shared for three months before he died

# Chapter 6

Frank picked Harry up at the jail and headed for Bertha's house in Pleasant Valley.

"You feeling any better, Harry?" Frank asked.

"I feel just fine now that I got away from that cutter from Atlanta and you for awhile," Harry said, looking straight at Frank. "I know you're the boss, but that was a mean trick to play on me. You shouldn't oughta done that, Frank. It made me real sick."

"I'm sorry Harry," Frank said. "I tried to get to the autopsy before they started, but they were too quick. Anyway you did a good job. Just make sure that you write down everything you saw, and what you did," Harry said. "It's all here in my notes."

As Frank and Harry pulled into the yard at Bertha's residence, Frank could see that the crowd of neighbors and family members were all still there. As he got out of the car he turned to Harry and said. "I'm gonna have a word with Bertha. Harry, I want you to mingle with the menfolks out in the yard. Have a smoke, and see if you can pick up anything that we don't already know."

"Sure thing, Frank," Harry replied. "I don't want to go in the house with all them women anyway. I'll be right out here if you need me."

Bertha spied Frank immediately as he came into the house. She approached him with a big smile and put her hand out for him to take it.

"I've been waiting on you Deputy Russell," she said. "And here you are. I like for a man to do what he says he's gonna do. Can you tell me anything about the autopsy?"

"It might be a week or two before we get a report back. But I'll let you know as soon as I find something out," Frank said.

"Well what about the body. Are they gonna bring Leroy home today so that we can have his funeral?" Bertha asked.

"Sheriff's checking with the coroner now, Bertha. But I think it might be tomorrow before they bring him up here. Then you could have Leroy's funeral."

"I guess after the autopsy the funeral home has a little work to do on getting him ready again," Bertha said. "Tomorrow will be all right. I just want to get him buried. That's what he said he wanted. Just get it over with quick."

"Please ma'am, I need to know which hospital Leroy was in and what they were treating him for," Frank said as he retrieved his pad and pencil.

"I was hoping that you wouldn't dig into that too deep, Deputy Russell," Bertha said with a deep crimson blush.

"Why is that, Mrs. Hill?" Frank asked.

"Leroy had a disease. He was ashamed of it. He was being treated with penicillin and a prescription. He really didn't want anybody to know. That's why he told me to bury him in our family lot in Alabama if anything happened to him, instead of back at his home in North Carolina."

"What kind of disease, Mrs. Hill?" Frank asked.

"Syphilis," she replied.

"For how long?" he asked. His mind was racing in about four different directions.

"It was in the first stages," Bertha said, "and he thought it was getting better but it hadn't gone away."

Frank knew that the most common form of treatment for syphilis was various forms of arsenic injections and oral supplements.

"Which hospital was he treated in?" Frank asked again. He was trying to get his thoughts together. This was something that he was not prepared for and certainly did not expect. Got to expect the unexpected, he kept telling himself as he waited for Bertha's answer.

"He was in Harbin hospital once and Floyd Hospital twice," she replied.

"When was he in those hospitals?" Frank asked.

"Since back in the middle of January," She said.

*She's not offering much. Only answering exactly what I ask her. I've got to make sure I cover all the bases while she's still talking at all.*

"Were all three times for treatment of syphilis?" Frank asked.

"Well, one of those times he had some food poisoning, said he got some bad shrimp. But they did treat him for syphilis each time," Bertha said.

"Bertha, did you know that there was arsenic in the medication used to treat syphilis?" Frank asked.

"No I didn't, Mr. Russell," She said. "But Leroy said that it made him feel mighty bad."

"Do you think that Leroy could accidentally have taken an overdose?" Frank asked.

"I don't know Deputy. He took shots and pills. I just don't know," Bertha answered.

Frank checked the prescription bottle and got the doctors name and entered into his notes. He told Bertha that he would check with the sheriff about releasing Leroy once again when he got back to the office.

He spoke briefly with the men in the yard, where Harry was the center of attention, and everyone was laughing and seemed to be enjoying themselves. Frank and Harry hurried out to the car and quickly left the property. Frank spent the next ten or fifteen minutes filling Harry in on what had transpired between himself and Bertha.

"How about you, Harry?" Frank asked. "Get anything good?"

"Nah, not really, Frank," Harry said. "I did talk to an old buddy of mine named Harry Fleming. He lives right down the road, works in the mill at Lindale and has for a long time. That's where I know him from. You knew I hang around a lot in Lindale, didn't you?"

"Yes Harry, I know that you spend a lot of your free time in Lindale. So what did he say?"

"Who?" Harry asked.

"Mr. Fleming, Harry, the guy we're talking about."

"Oh, he didn't say nothing really. Just thought it was strange that Leroy and Bud Hardin died in about the same way. And both of them sudden like."

"Who's Bud Hardin?" Frank asked.

"Well his real name was James, I think. But everybody called him Bud. He's Bertha's daddy, or was. He also worked at Lindale. Harry Fleming said that they rode together to the mill, and he shore did miss Bud."

"Guess you knew him too, from all that hanging around in Lindale," Frank said.

"Yeah, I knew Bud from the mill, but he wasn't from Lindale. He was from over in Alabama somewhere. You know Frank, if it wasn't for Alabama folks working at Lindale they'd have to shut that mill down."

"Are you sure he said Bud died. One of them old boys told me yesterday that Zola died last summer," Frank said.

"Was that Bud's wife?" Harry asked.

"I believe so," Frank said.

"Bertha sure has had a rough year. She lost mama, daddy and husband. No wonder that Rueben McClung was telling me that she was struggling with everything," Harry said.

"Yeah Harry, sometime life just don't seem fair," Frank said. "But we have to take the bad with the good, I guess. Didn't you tell me that Jack Highfield was in our jail?"

"Yep, he got drunk and got into a fight up at the Rosemont tavern, but that ain't nothing new for Jack."

"When we get to the jail, go up and get him and bring him down to the office. I'd like to talk to him," Frank said.

"About getting drunk and fighting. Frank you're wasting your time. He won't quit," Harry replied.

"No Harry, not about getting drunk and fighting. I want to ask him about Leroy. I understand that they were buddies," Frank said with a touch of exasperation in his voice.

As soon as they were in the jail, Frank went to his office and waited for Harry to bring Jack down to the office. He was beginning to get a little hungry. It was getting close to dinner time.

"Here he is, Frank," Harry said. "All dressed up in his Sunday clothes."

"Why are you wearing a suit, Jack?" Frank asked.

"I was going to a dance, Russell, and that damn Earl Wilkey laughed at me. So I hit him right in the mouth while he was laughing," Jack said.

"What did he do?" Frank asked.

"What do you think he done? Hell, he hit me back, and more than once. Then we went at it," Jack replied. "That what you want, to talk to me about fighting with Earl? We've had lots of fights. Probably have some more when I get out."

"Jack, how well did you know Leroy Hill?" Frank asked.

"Pretty good. What you want to know for," Jack asked. "And what do you mean 'did know?'"

"Leroy's dead," Frank said. "Ain't sure yet, but it looks like poison."

"Damn, I tried to tell him. I told him to get away from that woman."

"What woman is that, Jack?" Frank asked.

"That'n he was living with, that's who. Haven't you met Miss Bertha yet, Russell? You be careful when you do, and don't let her get to close to you. Now I mean it, you better mind what I say. She's trouble.

"What kind of trouble?" Frank asked.

"Bad trouble Russell, real bad trouble," he said.

"How did you meet up with Leroy?" Frank asked.

"He came here as a truck driver and mechanic with that company that built the airport. I worked out there for a couple of years myself. We used to hit the bars some, and ran into each other all the time. Leroy was a good time. He was always laughing and joking, and man he drew women like honey draws flies. Just hanging around and picking up the leftovers was fine with me.

"I couldn't believe it when he and Bertha hit it off. He had a lot better looking women than her. I mean she ain't bad, but not like some he had. But I'm gonna tell you, Russell, that woman charms men like a snake charms a chicken. I mean she puts a spell on 'em. And they get all wrapped up with her and then they're ruined.

"Hell, it almost ran Neal Gossett crazy, after they broke the plate. He still ain't right. And Leroy does the same thing to women. Something had to give.

Russell, you've ruined my whole day. That's what you've done. Look you need to talk to Dynamite, he's upstairs too. He knew Leroy a lot better than I did. They were pretty close. Dynamite scares hell out of me, but Leroy thought he was funny."

"Who are you talking about, Jack?" Frank asked.

"Caleb Hayden, but everybody that knows him calls him Dynamite," Jack replied. "He's always got a stick of dynamite in his pocket and he don't mind letting you hold it either."

"Is he the guy that got wounded in Italy?" Frank asked.

"Yeah, said he crawled across Sicily and half of Italy before a German shell went off close by and messed his leg up. He still limps a little but he's getting around pretty good. Army taught him how to blow things up and he likes to keep in practice."

"I don't remember seeing him on the roster. What's he in jail for? Drinking and fighting with you and Earl?" Frank wanted to know.

"Nah, funny thing happened a couple of weeks ago. I mean, Dynamite didn't think it was funny, but everyone else did.

"Ole Dynamite said that all the time he was overseas, he kept dreaming about going float fishing like we used to do on Armuchee Creek or over on the river. Couldn't wait to get back and go, then he went and got wounded. He spent all that time in the hospital, going through all kinds of surgery and finally healing up enough to get out.

"His momma bought him a 1940 model Plymouth and had it waiting for him when he got home. It wasn't much, but there ain't too much to pick from, even now. He drove it around for about six or eight months and it got stole.

"About two weeks ago me and him and Billy Ray Haygood got us a jug and went way up into Chattooga County and started float fishing down Armuchee creek. We'd fish and drink, and drink and fish and was just having a big ole time when, …wait a minute, let me back up right there.

"Look Russell, I got locked up last night. I don't have a cigarette or a chew," Highfield said. "Could you help a feller out a little bit?"

Frank cut himself a chew and then tossed the plug of Bloodhound to Jack.

"You can have the rest of that," Frank said. "That's about all I can do."

Jack didn't say a word. He just bit off a healthy chaw and put the rest of the plug in his pocket.

"Russell you can't hardly get down Armuchee Creek any more for the stripped down cars that have been pushed into the thing. There are places where it looks like a damn parking lot.

"Ok, so we're floating along and Dynamite sees his old Plymouth, or what's left of it. He recognized it by a yellow spot of primer on the left rear fender. That was the only fender left. Boy, he got boiling mad. He didn't say a word, just kept on fishing and drinking.

"Everybody knows who was stealing them cars. I mean everybody in Armuchee knows who done it, including ole Dynamite. Day before yesterday me and him were walking down the highway headed to Enoch Salmons beer joint. I mean, we were almost there, when Snake Wilson pulls up. Two of the Duke boys were with him, along with Ben Holcombe and one of them Cunningham boys from over near the Shannon mill village. Snake starts picking at Dynamite. Telling him that walking seems to be agreeing with him since his car got stole. That it was probably helping his old cripple leg.

"All of them was laughing and snickering and just having a big time. Dynamite didn't say a word. He just pulled out two sticks of dynamite that he had taped together. He lit the fuse off of his cigarette and tossed them two sticks into the car with them ole boys. I saw it a-coming and got on down the road a piece before I looked back.

"Hell, Russell, you ever seen five ole boys bailing out of a two-door car? And Holcombe's fat as a hog. When that dynamite went off, they hadn't rolled too far. It burned the clothes off of Snake's back and Jackson Duke still can't hear it thunder.

"They wasn't enough of that car left to throw in the creek. And the funny thing was, Dynamite walked on just as calm as anything into Enoch's and got a draft. Still ain't said a word about the whole thing. 'Course, your boys put him in jail. And that's where he is now. Go talk to him Russell."

Frank had the jailers take Jack Highfield back to his cell and bring

Caleb Hayden down to the office. He talked to Dynamite for the better part of an hour and didn't get much more than Jack had told him. He learned that both men didn't want Bertha around them in any form or fashion. Frank finally told the jailers to take Caleb back to his cell.

"Hey Caleb, let me ask you one more thing," Frank said. "Why did you throw that dynamite in the car with Snake and his boys?"

"Seemed like the thing to do at the time," Caleb said nonchalantly as they led him back to his cell.

Frank finished his dinner in his apartment and told his wife Christine that he was off again. He walked back to the sheriff's office and after making sure that the sheriff was alone he simply entered and sat down.

"Where we at, Frank?" Mark asked. "You got anything new?"

Frank went over everything that he and Bertha had discussed. The only thing new was that there was a possibility that Leroy might have accidentally taken an overdose of his medication. And that two of Armuchee's outlaws didn't think much of Bertha.

Mark picked up his phone and got Florence to call Dr. John L. Garrard. After speaking for several minutes with the doctor, he thanked the man and hung the phone up.

"Dr. Garrard just said that he could have taken the whole bottle at one time and it wouldn't have done much to him. Not much chance of an accidental overdose with that stuff." Mark said looking at his Chief Deputy.

"Mark, while you're using the phone, call the coroner and see what he says about Bertha's mother and father dying last year. See what they died from and what kind of record that he has on them."

Sheriff Horton spoke briefly with the Coroner and then looked up to his deputy with a puzzled look and said," That's odd. Mr. James A. Hardin died last April and Mrs. Zola Dutton Hardin died in July. Both of the old folks were taken over in Cherokee County and buried by Jordan Funeral home. Neither had a Removal from the State permit issued."

"What about the death certificates? That should tell what the old folks died from." Frank said.

"Mr. Hardin didn't have one and Mrs. Hardin was filled out 'undetermined.' Can we call him and find out why he filled it out that way?" Frank asked.

Mark was already looking for the number to Dr. N.L. William's office in the phone book. Shortly he had him on the phone and asked the same questions that Russell had asked him. Mark relayed his comments on to Frank.

"He said that he went to the house and treated Mrs. Hardin for acute stomach pain, more commonly known as food poisoning. That the next day he was in the vicinity visiting with another patient and decided to stop and check on Mrs. Hardin again. When he pulled up, her daughter, Mrs. Bertha Hill, met him outside the house and told him that she had died during the night. He filled out a death certificate in the yard without going in the house and listed it as undetermined."

Frank sat quietly. His brain was trying to process what he'd just been told. It was trying to lead him in a direction that he wasn't sure he wanted to go.

"Frank, that's very suspicious. Now I want to know what Mr. Hardin died from," Mark said in a low but concerned voice.

"I think I know, Sheriff," Frank said. "When we were at Bertha's, Harry stayed outside and talked to the men folks. One of them told Harry that it was strange how Mr. Hardin had died the same way Leroy had."

"Do you think you can find him and question him a little bit more about Mr. Hardin?" Mark asked.

"Yes, we can. His name was Harry too. I remember at the time I couldn't believe that there were two of them. He won't be hard to find."

# Chapter 7

As Frank was standing up to leave and to head back to Pleasant Valley one more time, the phone rang. Sheriff Horton answered it, and after a few seconds, he motioned for Russell to sit back down. Frank pulled up his chair and waited patiently for the sheriff to finish his conversation.

When Mark hung the phone up he looked at Frank and said, "That was a woman that said her name was Mrs. Lacy Beale. She said that she was Leroy's mother and that she had just gotten into Rome and wanted to speak to me or my representative. She is in room 342 at the Grey Stone Hotel."

"I'm on my way," Frank said as he got his hat from the rack and exited the office. Frank decided to walk to the Grey Stone. It was only about four blocks and he felt that the walk and the fresh air would do him good. When he reached the hotel he climbed the stairs to the third floor and proceeded directly to room 342 and knocked softly on the door. When the door opened, he saw a very attractive lady somewhere around fifty, he would guess. It was evident where Leroy had gotten his looks.

"I'm Deputy Frank Russell. I was told by Sheriff Horton that you wanted to speak to someone from our department. That is, if you're Mrs. Lacy Beale."

"I'm Mrs. Olivia Beale. Lacy is my husband's name. And I'm Leroy's mother. Won't you please come in?"

As Frank entered the room he noticed another woman, probably a daughter. She looked to be in her late twenties. He took the chair that was offered him and then asked, "What can we do for you Mrs. Beale?"

"I received this telegram from Bertha," She said, holding a Western Union telegram in her hand. "I'd like for you to read it."

Frank took the telegram and read to himself:

Leroy died. The funeral is to be tomorrow. The burial is to be in our family lot in Cherokee County, Alabama. Rome is in flood stage. You probably couldn't get here, so don't even try to come. Love Bertha.

Frank didn't know what to say. He handed the telegram back to Mrs. Beale, and sat waiting for her to speak. It didn't take long.

"And you can see that we did make it. No amount of water is going to keep me away from my boy. Mr. Sheriff, I don't want Leroy buried here. He wouldn't want to be buried here. I want to take him home to Chatham County, North Carolina. We live in the City of Pittsboro, and that's where Leroy's going to be buried.

"Mrs. Beale, all funeral plans are on hold right now. We conducted an autopsy on Leroy. Unofficially, it looks like Leroy was poisoned. But I can't grant your wishes anyway. Even if I agreed with you, the wife has the final say about burial plans.

"Poisoned?" Mrs. Beale exclaimed, horrified. She turned to the younger woman and said. "What did I tell you, Clara? I knew something like that had happened? Mr. Sheriff, I know that woman has gone and killed my Leroy. I want her charged with his murder."

"And about her having Leroy buried in Alabama. What you told us was exactly what our own sheriff up in North Carolina said before we left. That's why I brought Clara with me. Mr. Russell I'd like for you to meet Mrs. Leroy Hill. This is my daughter-in-law and the mother of my grandchildren."

Every nerve ending in Frank Russell's body was tingling. He was trying to sort out his thoughts, but they were like a puzzle spinning out of control. He knew they were all there but he just couldn't put them together. At least not right now. He couldn't find his voice, and even if he did he wouldn't know what to say to these women. Fortunately he didn't have too. The young woman spoke first.

"Sir, we know who Leroy was and what he was. He and I have had a rocky marriage to say the least. He's been unfaithful our entire married life. But he was a hard worker and never a week went by that he didn't send some money for the boys. Even when he didn't have much or was between jobs, he still found a little to send. I'm not saying that Leroy and I wouldn't eventually divorce. In fact, we talked about it some last year. But at the present time he is, or was my husband, and we're gonna take him home."

"Mrs. Hill, I'm not doubting your word, but did you happen to bring a copy of your marriage license or any other proof that you're married?" Frank asked.

She handed a folded letter to Frank. He knew what it was without having to open it. After scanning the marriage license, he asked the next question.

"And you're not divorced at this time?" asked Frank.

"No sir, I'm not," Clara Hill replied.

"Mr. Sheriff, I want to know about this poison," Mrs. Beale interjected… "I want to know everything that you know."

Frank spent the better part of the next hour going over everything that he knew and had done up to this point in the investigation. At the end of his summation he said, "Ladies, that's it. You've heard everything we've got."

"And we thank you for all that has been done so far," Mrs. Beale said. "Now, more than ever, I want that woman charged with the murder of my son."

"Mrs. Beale," Frank said," I'm nowhere near the end of my investigation. I'm not sure at this time that Bertha is the one that poisoned Leroy, or even if he was intentionally poisoned by anybody. I've got days ahead of me before I can make any kind of determination as to who might have wanted to kill Leroy and why. And we still have to rule out accidental and unintentional."

"But right now she's beginning to stand out, ain't she deputy?" Mrs. Beale asked, looking Frank square in the face.

"Well, yes ma'am, I guess she is," Frank said. "But why would Bertha want to kill Leroy? That's what don't make sense. She had no reason to want to hurt him."

"I don't know about such things as that. All I know was that she cast some kind of spell on Leroy. It was just a few months after he moved in with them people he called me up and was on cloud nine. He said that he had bought a car, a motorcycle, and a horse and saddle. I could just tell by listening to him that he was having a high old time.

"And the money for the boys kept coming in all summer. I asked him where he got money for all that and he said from Bertha. That she had got some insurance money from her daddy. Mr. Deputy, the only way a woman could charm Leroy would be with money. And that's what she did. I guarantee it."

Frank sat silently and listened to Mrs. Beale rave on about Bertha. He glanced occasionally to the younger woman. She seemed to have shriveled up in her seat. Her hands were folded on her lap, her eyes were downcast and Frank could almost hear her screaming inside. He could tell that Mrs. Beale's words were pounding Clara like a wild storm pounding the shoreline. It was obvious that this woman dearly loved Leroy.

How many times, he thought, had he seen this same scenario played out. Some scoundrel like Leroy Hill marries a woman like this and doesn't realize what he's got. Frank had a little more than a twinge of sympathy for this lady. Still somebody or something killed Leroy and it was his job to find out who or what that was.

"You're saying that Leroy told you that he and Bertha were spending Mr. Hardin's insurance money?" Frank asked.

"Yes sir, that's what he said," she replied.

"I didn't see a horse or a motorcycle at the house yesterday," Frank stated. "I wonder what they did with them? Bertha said that Leroy sold a car at the end of the summer. But she didn't mention a horse or motorcycle."

"I can tell you what they did with the motorcycle. They were on a little week-end trip, according to Leroy and he hit something in the road. Both of them got a messed up leg, and had to call somebody back here to come to Chattanooga and pick them up. Bertha missed two or three weeks of work according to Leroy. They were lucky that it wasn't worse. But the motorcycle wasn't that lucky. It got tore all to pieces."

"I'll make a note to check into that and what happened to the horse too," Frank said.

"Alright Mr. Deputy, you gonna charge her with murder or do I need to go to the courthouse and talk to a judge or somebody else?" Mrs. Beale demanded, her eyes glued to Russell's face.

"Mrs. Beale, I'm going back and talk to the sheriff right now. You just stay here till I get back." Frank said.

"Don't be long. I ain't gonna wait forever. And I'll tell you this much, too. When I take my boy back to North Carolina, that woman's not gonna be running around down here scot free. When I leave Rome, I'm gonna have the satisfaction of knowing that she's in jail where she belongs.

"And I forgot to tell you this. Right after I called the sheriff, I called up to the number I had for her. It was some store. But in about five or ten minutes she called back. I told her that I was able to get here and wanted to know how to get to her house. She told me the funeral had been put off till tomorrow and that she would come down here late this evening and we could talk things over. But now, with this poison and everything, I don't want her anywhere around me. So you need to go and tell her to stay away from me tonight."

"Mrs. Beale, just sit tight until I go and talk to the sheriff, can you do that?" Frank asked.

Frank left the Grey Stone at a brisk walk. *The one time that I wish I had my car, I left it at the jail. Gonna take you a nice little leisurely stroll, weren't you Russell, and now look what's happened!* Frank criticized himself all the way back to the courthouse. As he came into the sheriff's office, he was very excited and his speech was quick and rapid. He was blurting out everything that he and Olivia Beale had discussed at one time. Nothing made sense.

"Hold on Frank," Sheriff Horton said. "Sit down and take a deep breath or two and just relax for a minute."

Mark Horton knew that this was unusual. Frank Russell was not easily excitable. In fact, it was almost impossible to get him rattled. Mark was more than interested in what had gotten Frank so excited.

"Alright Frank, from the beginning," Mark said. "You left here to go and talk to Leroy's mother at the Grey Stone. Start right there and tell me everything that took place."

Frank spent the next half hour or so briefing the sheriff on the entire afternoon.

At the end of the report, Sheriff Horton leaned back in his chair, picked up his pipe and re-lit it, and let everything Russell had told him sink in. Finally he straightened up, looked at Russell and said, "Let's let her take a warrant for Bertha. From what you've just told me about the insurance money, we may have a motive. Especially if we find that Mrs. Hardin had a policy and that Bertha had insured Leroy. And I just got a gut feeling that we will."

Mark took several pulls on his pipe and then continued. "But you're gonna have to eliminate the first husband as a suspect. I've heard that at times former spouses do crazy things to get back at former loved ones. Or maybe he might have wanted her back, you never can tell. So tell me what do you think?"

"You took the words right out of my mouth," Frank said." I'm not ready to charge her with anything specific. But if we let the mother of the deceased take an open felony warrant, we can hold her on that till the investigation is complete and the autopsy report comes back. If it all turns out like I think it will, then Henderson can take it to the Grand Jury and ask for an indictment."

"So how do you want to do it?" Sheriff Horton asked.

"I've been up to her house in Pleasant Valley three times and every time I go the crowd gets a little bigger. Friends, neighbors and family members are all over the place. I'd rather not arrest her there if we can help it. Mrs. Beale says that Bertha told her that she was gonna pay her a visit this afternoon late at the Grey Stone. I thought that Harry and I could simply be waiting in the lobby and make the arrest there."

"I got no objection to that, as long as Mrs. Beale or the other Mrs. Hill don't come in contact with her," Mark said.

"We'll make sure of that, Sheriff," Frank said. "This is turning into something else, ain't it, Mark? We've got doctors saying that Leroy had syphilis and now it appears that he was a bigamist on top of that. And maybe he was murdered by the sweetest little thing you ever saw, or a woman that is cold as ice and has no emotions at all. Just depends on who you talk too. And all Leroy wanted to do was have a good time."

"Yea, Bertha's complicated alright," Mark stated. "And I'm sure that Leroy didn't have a clue as to what he'd run into. You're just gonna have to sort it all out Frank. It's not gonna go away. In fact, I think it may even get more involved than it is now."

"I hope you're wrong, Mark," Frank said. "But I tend to agree. By now it's obvious that we don't know what's coming next."

Frank left the courthouse where he picked up a car and Deputy Davis. As he drove the short four blocks to the hotel, he informed Harry of what they had in mind.

Mrs. Beale and her daughter-in-law were waiting in the lobby. Frank introduced both ladies to Deputy Davis and then escorted them to the waiting car. As he drove back to the courthouse he explained that he and Harry would arrest Bertha in the lobby of the Grey Stone and that both ladies should remain in their room until after the arrest was made.

At the courthouse Mrs. Beale was taken before a magistrate judge and was allowed to take out an open felony warrant for Bertha Hill. Then they were taken back to the hotel. The whole trip lasted less than an hour.

Frank and Harry settled down in the lobby to await the arrival of Bertha. Several hours passed before they saw her enter the main doors of the hotel. As she crossed the lobby she spotted Frank and Deputy Davis approaching her. She stopped and with a big smile on her face said, "Deputy Russell we just seem to keep bumping into each other. What brings you to the Grey Stone so late?" Bertha asked.

"Well Bertha, I have bad news. I have a warrant for your arrest," Frank said fixing his eyes directly on Bertha.

"Whatever for, Deputy Russell?" Bertha asked as her eyes darted nervously about.

"It's an open felony warrant to hold you while the investigation is ongoing into the death of Leroy," Frank said.

"I'm not going anywhere Mr. Russell, and you know where I live. You can find me there at any time," Bertha said her voice beginning to crack. "You aren't really going to take me to that stinking old jail, are you?"

"Yes ma'am, I'm afraid we are," Frank stated. Gently taking Bertha's arm, he slowly began to walk her to the hotel entrance. Harry had placed himself on the other side of Bertha and was also using his hand on her elbow to guide her from the lobby onto the street.

Bertha could feel her heart beating all over her body. It seemed it was in her throat preventing her from speaking. She thought for a minute that it would choke her to death or that she would pass out. As she began to regain a little control of her emotions she once again asked Deputy Russell, "I don't understand why I'm being arrested. Why did you take out a warrant for me?"

"I didn't," Frank said, "Your mother-in-law, Mrs. Beale, did. She insisted on you being arrested. She's absolutely convinced that you poisoned Leroy. And she wouldn't have it any other way."

"Couldn't you have told her the truth, Mr. Russell?" Bertha replied.

"What *is* the truth, Bertha? I don't know the truth. But I will, and that's a promise."

Harry placed Bertha in the back seat and crawled behind the wheel. Frank had spotted Mr. and Mrs. Watkins parked in front of the hotel. He felt sure they had driven Bertha to town and he walked over to where they were waiting in the car.

Although he didn't have to, he explained what was taking place with the arrest of Bertha. He felt that these two would spread the word throughout Pleasant Valley and he wouldn't have to make a trip out there tonight. But he fully expected that he would hear from the McClungs bright and early tomorrow morning.

As he got back in the car, Bertha leaned forward and said, "Deputy Russell, are you telling me that you can just up and arrest somebody for nothing. And that you can put somebody in jail without charging them, on the say so of a crazy old woman?" Bertha asked, as she was going into full panic mode.

Tears were now streaming down her face and there was no way to staunch the flow.

"What makes you think she's crazy, Bertha?" Harry asked, interrupting the conversation, as he steered the Ford onto Rome's Broad Street.

"Leroy told me so. He said that she was crazier than a Bessie bug. He said that he loved his mother, but that she just ran him crazy every time he went home."

Bertha was trying to regain control of her emotions. So far it wasn't working.

"It's not for nothing, Bertha," Frank said as leaned over and looked her straight in the face. "I told you it's for investigation. And if it turns out that Leroy didn't die by your hand, you'll be released."

"Well he didn't," Bertha said as she leaned back in the car and looked out the window. She was still looking away from Frank as they passed McClellan's ten cent store. Once again the tears were uncontrollable as she thought about her job, her co-workers and Mr. Cantrell, her boss who had been so nice to her over the years. And now she wondered if that was all over.

Frank and Harry stopped at the jail and escorted Bertha inside and up to the booking desk. The jailer on duty began to fill out the booking information. It was evident that he had done this hundreds of times and his nonchalant attitude unnerved her. She realized that he was just doing his job, but it was her life. He obviously didn't care. To him it was just another run of the mill booking. But to her it was the most traumatic thing she had ever been through in her life.

She wanted him to feel what she did. He could at least look up and acknowledge that she was there and was a real person. She felt like some object that was being discussed in her presence and that for the first time in her life she had no control over the situation.

After the booking process was complete, the jailer looked up and said to her, "We don't do fingerprints and mug shots on second shift. They'll come and get you and do that in the morning. Please follow me and watch your step. We're gonna climb some stairs and go to the second floor. That's where the women's cells are."

Bertha felt herself start to shake. By the time they reached the second floor she was shaking uncontrollably. She knew the jailer had made the same little speech thousands of times, but it wasn't to *her*. She also knew that she couldn't expect any sympathy, but she had to try.

"Please don't do this to me. Let me call my aunt to come and get me. I'm not leaving Rome. They know where to find me." Bertha said in that soft, pleading, almost little-girl voice that seemed to come from somewhere deep inside when she needed it.

"You're talking to the wrong guy, lady. I just work here and do what I'm told," the jail deputy said as he opened the door to a cell and motioned for her to step inside.

Bertha eased into the cell. There were four bunks.. The light was not very bright, and it took a few minutes for her eyes to adjust. The two bottom bunks were occupied and there was another woman stretched out on one of the top bunks. Bertha realized that she didn't have a place to sit. She could hear the jailer as he walked down the corridor and slammed the steel hallway door. She turned her back to the women in the cell, grabbed the bars and sobbed uncontrollably.

Finally one of the women on the bottom bunks said, "Queenie, you might as well stop all that blubbering. It won't do any good no how."

Bertha ignored the woman and continued sobbing into the bars.

"Mama, I don't believe Queenie heard you or she ain't paying no attention, one or the other," the second woman said.

"I believe you're right, Baby Girl. Don't look like we'll get no sleep tonight. We got a lady in our house. And I don't think she's ever visited around here before."

Bertha turned and faced the two women. It was then she could see one was probably twenty years or so older than the other. The one on top hadn't said a word. Bertha looked at the older of the two and said, "Would you please be quiet and just don't talk to me! I don't want to have anything to do with you. I don't want to talk to either of you. Just leave me alone."

"Yes ma'am, Mama, it's gonna be a long night. Would you hand me that can of Bruton on the back of your bunk?" Baby Girl said.

The older of the two opened the snuff can, took a big dip, then passed the can to her daughter and said, "Look Queenie, me and my daughter don't mean nothing. We ain't trying to mess with you or anything like that. It's just that we don't see your kind here in the Riverside Hotel very often."

"'At's right," Baby Girl said. "Just think of us as your welcoming committee."

Bertha squeezed the bars until her knuckles were white. She listened to the mama and daughter team for as long as she could stand it. She thought she was going to explode. After what seemed an eternity to Bertha, she turned and screamed at the top of her lungs, "I told you two to shut up! I don't need no Cotton Block whores telling me nothing."

The cell got quiet for a minute or two.

Bertha was standing with her hands balled up into fists. Her eyes were aflame, and she was gritting her teeth so hard that her jaws hurt. The sobbing had turned into pure anger. And she was taking it out on these women.

Finally the woman on top rolled over onto her side and looked straight at Bertha and said, "We're all whores lady, just depends on what you're selling and how much you charge for it. Climb up on this other bunk here, lay down and be quiet. You probably won't sleep much tonight, but you will in a few days. In the meantime try to be as respectful as you can. None of us want to be here either. It won't get any easier if you keep beating yourself up."

Bertha did as she was told. It was early in the morning before she was able to doze off. And it was just after daylight when she heard Mama and Baby Girl tossing around below her. She was startled for a moment, but then reality brought her back to the present. She remembered all too well what had happened last night, and then an awful sinking feeling slowly came over her.

# Chapter 8

Mr. and Mrs. Watkins were silent as they headed back toward Pleasant Valley. Both were in deep thought about what they had just witnessed. Deputy Russell had approached their car where they were waiting for Bertha and told them that they could go ahead and go home because he was arresting Bertha on investigation. He had said that they believed something was strange about the way Leroy had just up and died. And until they completed their investigation, Bertha would be in jail.

About half way home, Ollie turned to her husband and asked, "Marvin, do you think it's possible that Bertha could have poisoned Leroy intentionally?"

"I don't know Ollie. I've tried not to think about it at all, but it's all I can think about."

"Me too," said Ollie, "It sure has made me think about some of the things I saw and heard."

"I guess it has," said Marvin. "You know, I heard Harry Fleming talking to the other deputy, Davis I think. He said that it was strange that Leroy died just like Bud did. I can't get that off my mind. And from everything I heard about Mrs. Zola's death, it sounds just like the other two."

"Well, we weren't there when Zola and Bud passed away," Ollie said. "But Carrie Poole and Jessie Lynch sure were. Just as soon as we get back I'm gonna get those two off to myself and compare some memories."

As Marvin pulled into the yard at Bertha's house, no one seemed to notice at first that Bertha was not in the car. After a few long moments Plemma McClung asked, "Ollie, where's Bertha? Why didn't she come back with you and Marvin?"

"Mrs. McClung, the Sheriff's Department was waiting at the hotel for

Bertha. They arrested her and took her away," Ollie said, about to break into tears.

"Took her away where?" Plemma asked, her voice getting louder and louder the more excited she became.

"To jail, Mrs. McClung. They took her to jail."

Plemma McClung turned toward the house and yelled for Ruben to get out there.

"What's the matter, Mama?" he asked, as he came bounding down the steps. "Are you ok?"

"No I'm not ok! Ollie said the sheriff's done took Bertha and locked her in the jail for killing Leroy," Plemma said. "Now you run along to Rome and get her out and bring her home."

"Mrs. McClung, I didn't say that the deputies arrested her for killing Leroy. She was arrested pending the investigation of Leroy's death. Deputy Russell said that she couldn't get out till the investigation was over, and then if she was cleared, he would personally drive her home."

"Well, ain't that the same thing?" asked Plemma. "They ain't never gonna let her out on their own. We'll have to make them. I promised my sister that I would look after her baby, and that's what I'm gonna do. Ruben, you go and talk to a lawyer in the morning and get Bertha out."

Plemma turned abruptly and stomped into the house, slamming the door behind her.

"I'll go and calm her down. It'll take a little while, but she'll be alright in the morning. Thank you folks for all you did for Bertha. We really appreciate it. I want everybody to know that Plemma's not mad at y'all, just what happened."

Ruben McClung walked up the steps to the porch, he turned and waved at the small crowd of folks still gathered in the yard, then went inside gently closing the door.

The neighbors and friends gathered in the yard that had been with Bertha for the past few days were slowly coming out of a sense of disbelief. They all said their farewells to each other and headed toward their own houses. As they were leaving, Ollie Watkins looked at Carrie Poole and Jessie Lynch and said, "Ladies, I'm gonna be serving coffee at my house in the morning right after breakfast dishes are done. Sure wish y'all would join me. Carrie, I know Louise works late, but if she's up in the morning please have her join us. I'm gonna have Missy there."

"She'll be there," Carrie said, "And so will I."

"Count me in," Jessie replied as she turned and walked up the road.

ℼ     ℼ

Henderson Lanham burst into the Sheriff's office without a word to anyone. As he approached the Sheriff who was sitting peacefully behind his desk, he blurted out loud enough for the courthouse workers several offices down the corridor to hear.

"Horton are you out of your mind? Who gave you the authorization to arrest Bertha Hill? What do you think you're doing, putting that woman in jail? Have you forgotten that her husband hasn't even been buried? I've listened to your and Russell's crack pot theories till I'm just about sick of them. I want her out. You get Russell to drive her home and apologize. And I mean right now."

The veins on Lanham's neck were standing out like ropes, his face was blood red and his breathing was shallow and rapid. Mark thought the man was fixing to have a first class heart attack right here in his office. But right now he just didn't care. Lanham had infuriated him by barging into the office in such a fit of rage.

Sheriff Horton knew that he too had a short fuse and a quick temper. Most cops do. The trick is being able to control it. If you can't, you won't last long in police work. And right now, Mark was biting his tongue to keep from giving the solicitor the thrashing that he wanted to. He was standing now, leaning over his desk and facing Lanham. There was less than a foot between their faces when Mark said, "I don't have to get authorization from you or anybody else to make an arrest in this county. And the jail is where we put those people we arrest on my authorization. Yes, I know Leroy ain't buried yet, and he probably won't be for a few more days and most likely not in this state. And you ain't even begun to hear all of our theories yet. So sit down, shut up and listen for a few more minutes. After you hear me out, if you still want, I'll have Russell take her home. Is that a deal?"

Lanham stood for a long time without saying anything. Then he flopped into a chair like the air went out of him all at once. He reached into his watch pocket, pulled out his railroad watch and looked at the time.

"You got ten minutes, Horton," he said. "You might oughta get started."

The sheriff began with the phone call from Mrs. Beale and repeated everything that he knew had transpired after that. He ended up with Lanham rudely barreling into his office without a howdy-do to anybody and making a fool out of himself, an event that would be all over the courthouse by now.

Lanham ignored the last comment, but not the previous ones.

"Mark, let me get this straight. You're saying that Leroy was a bigamist. You're also saying that Mr. and Mrs. Hardin both died under similar circumstances. And at least one insurance policy was in force and that

Bertha and Leroy spent it. Is that right?"

"Well, not exactly. We don't know for sure that Leroy and Bertha were married. She has said that they were, but until now we haven't had any reason to doubt her."

"Mrs. Beale was the one that stated Leroy and Bertha spent Mr. Hardin's insurance money. That's one of the things that Russell has to check out today."

"Did Mr. and Mrs. Hardin die from similar circumstances? It has been reported to us from neighbors that knew them very well and that were with them when they died and that it was awfully similar. And there's one more little item Henderson..."

"And that is…?" he asked.

"Neither of the old folks had a Removal from the State permit. Mr. Hardin died without having a death certificate and Mrs. Hardin's was filled out as undetermined."

The solicitor sat quietly for a long time, his eyes absolutely glued to Sheriff Horton. He was deep in thought about all of the latest facts he had just heard. Finally he began to stir in his chair. Still focusing on the sheriff he asked, "Mark are you gonna need more help with this thing?"

"I've already thought about that and right now we don't. Russell and Harry Davis have everything under control. If the investigation grows, and it very well may, we could possibly need more manpower."

"What's Russell's plan of action today, do you know yet? Henderson asked.

"There's several things he's got to do, and I don't think it matters which one is first. Why do you ask?" Mark replied.

"I'd personally like to verify the fact, if possible, that Bertha and Leroy actually got insurance money from somewhere. And try to find out if all that was true about the car, horse, and motorcycle. You said that you told Russell that it might be a motive, and I agree. I'd like to know that as soon as possible."

"Alright, I'll tell Frank that you would like for him to get on that as soon as he can."

Henderson continued, "And also, somebody mentioned a first husband. You're right about that too. We need to find out where he was during all of this, if nothing more than to eliminate him."

"I've already got that down, plus Frank's got to go back to Armuchee and talk to the neighbors a little more. Now that Bertha's been in jail for a night and the folks up there have had a chance to think about things, we might get a little more information from them."

"Yes, I suppose we will," Henderson said, changing the conversation. "You know the *Rome News* and *Floyd County Herald* are gonna be all over this today, don't you?"

"They already are. They were at the jail early this morning, and it's been on the radio since daylight."

"Sheriff, how did you book her? Even if she was married to Leroy, and he was still married to the woman from North Carolina, then their marriage wouldn't be legal. What name did you use?"

"We booked her as Bertha Gossett. Actually more people on Broad Street and in the community know her by that name than by Hill," Mark replied.

"Well, I'm going back to my office and see if I can hurry that autopsy a little bit. Once again, I'm sorry about the intrusion earlier this morning."

"Don't worry about it. There is one final thing I'd like to ask," Horton said. "Do you have any reason not to release the body of Leroy Hill to his wife and mother and allow them to take him back to Carolina?"

The solicitor stopped at the door and looked back at the sheriff and said, "I can't think of a single reason why we need to hold the body any longer, can you?"

"Not a one," Mark replied.

₪    ₪

Ollie had been up since daylight. She knew that her neighbors would be here bright and early this morning. Missy had already arrived and was drying the breakfast dishes and putting them up. She had gotten hold of Missy, now Mrs. L.E. Holloway, after the short meeting in Bertha's yard and told her to be here by breakfast time in the morning. Ollie still had a hard time accepting the fact that Missy was married and had been for some time. *Lord, I'm getting older every day*, she thought and then laughed. *Of course I am and so is everyone else!*

As Missy put the last dish in the pantry, Ollie took a pan of tea cakes out of the oven and set them on top of the stove to cool. She hadn't moved more than a couple of feet when Marvin was already at the stove reaching for one of the fresh baked cakes.

"Get away from there, Marvin Watkins," Ollie said in a rather stern voice. "Them tea cakes ain't for you. Besides you just had breakfast and you eat enough to feed Cox's army."

"Now, Ollie, I live here too, and you're making me feel that you don't want me around this morning."

"I'm making you feel unwelcome, is that what you're saying?" Ollie retorted.

"Yes you are," Marvin said once again.

"Well Marvin, you're getting smarter and smarter in your old age. You're not welcome. Now get out of here."

"Where do you want me to go Ollie?" Marvin asked.

"Marvin you can go out and play in your compost pile, check that salt pork in the smoke house and make sure that it ain't gonna turn. You can fool around in your little tool shed, or walk down to the grocery store and sit around and tell lie's with Cyril Lynch. I don't care where you go, just get."

Missy Holloway was laughing so hard at the antics of her mother and father that she was about to wet her pants. She knew better than to laugh this hard and lord help her if she started coughing. But they were so funny she couldn't help it. They had always been this way.

She remembered one time when she was a little girl and the flood waters were rising. Her dad had burst into the house real excited and said, "Ollie, I just heard on the radio that the river was rising twelve inches to the foot."

Ollie's hand went to her mouth and she said, "What are we gonna do Marvin? Are we in danger?"

"Don't think so, but I'm gonna go listen some more. I'll let you know shortly."

It had been nearly an hour, Missy remembered, before it dawned on her mother just what her dad had said. And boy, did she get mad! Marvin ran from the house that day with Ollie right behind him waving a frying pan and threatening to bust his head. Missy remembered that she'd been rolling in the floor laughing at those two that day.

Life had been good growing up here. They never had a lot. But they had enough to get by. And their little house was always warm and toasty. It smelled like gingerbread, apple butter, cinnamon, cloves or any number of kitchen spices that her mother might be cooking with.

In cold weather her dad kept a crackling fire going in the fireplace and the smell of wood smoke just filled the house. When she thought about it, she realized that her parents house was full of love. That's what she tried to do with her family now.

Marvin hiked up the road to Lynch's grocery like he was told. Along the way to the store he passed Jessie Lynch heading to his house.

"Morning Marvin, Ollie run you off?" she asked.

"You mighty right she did," Marvin said as he kept walking. "Jessie, y'all save me some of those tea cakes."

"Oh, Ollie made tea cakes! I sure do love tea cakes, especially the way

Ollie makes them," Jessie replied as she passed Marvin and continued to the Watkins house.

"That ain't right Jessie, and you know it." Marvin said, looking back over his shoulder.

He could hear Jessie laughing as he continued toward the store. On the way he was joined by Henry Poole and they entered the store together.

"Come on in boys," Cyril Lynch said, "I've been expecting you. There's a pot of coffee on the stove."

For the next hour the three men went over all that had happened in their community. The three deaths at the Hardin/Hill household were the main topic of conversation.

Occasionally, Cyril Lynch had to stop and wait on a customer but he hurried right back to the group setting as soon as he could. Harry Fleming joined the group after an hour or so and put his two cents worth into the conversation.

The men soon realized that they had no answers and were no closer to finding out what really happened when a sheriff's car pulled up out front. Deputies Frank Russell and Harry Davis came into the small grocery.

Cyril had them pull up a chair and then said, "I kind of thought we might see you boys today. I really thought you might be a little earlier than you are."

"Well Ruben McClung came by the jail. Wanted to know if Bertha was going to have a bond or get a hearing. He asked a lot of questions that I couldn't answer so I sent him over to the courthouse to talk to the sheriff. Guess by now he's in some lawyer's office down town."

"Let me ask the same question so that we'll know," said Marvin Watkins. "Is Bertha gonna be allowed to make bail?"

"I doubt that she will. Really that will be up to the judge, but the Solicitor is going to fight it, I can guarantee that," Frank replied. "I don't think she will be allowed to get out until the investigation or the autopsy clears her."

Harry Davis had given Cyril a dime and was quietly sipping on a Nehi Orange and munching on a moon pie. Cyril asked Frank if he wanted anything to eat or drink and he also bought a Nu-grape and a pack of salted peanuts. He took his pocket knife and cut the top of the peanut pack and poured them into his drink. He gave them a minute to fizzle and settle in the grape drink and after the first taste, he asked the group, "Mrs. Beale told me that Leroy had come into some money. She said that he had bought a car, motorcycle and a saddle horse last year. She also said that the money came from Mr. Hardin's insurance money. Do y'all know anything about that?"

"That's right," said Henry Poole. "Everything she told you is the gospel truth."

"Bertha told me that Leroy sold the car at the end of the summer. What happened to the motorcycle and horse?" Frank asked.

"They took a little motorcycle trip last July." Cyril Lynch said. "That's when they got married. And while they were on their trip Leroy dropped the motorcycle and tore it up. It busted him and Bertha up something fierce. Harry had to go all the way to Chattanooga and bring them back from the hospital. Bertha didn't work for nearly a month. And while they were laid up they sold that horse to one of them Trapp boys up in Floyd Springs. At least that's the way I remember it."

"That's right, Cyril," Harry Fleming said. "I went and got them in Tennessee and brought them back, and it was a mighty uncomfortable ride for both of them too."

"Does anybody know where Mr. Hardin was insured?" Frank asked.

"Probably down at the mill," Fleming said. "Lindale has a policy they pay on everybody that works there. They call it a group policy. I know mine is a thousand dollars. I'll bet Bud's was too."

"Who would we need to see at the mill to verify that?" Frank asked.

"Dick Hand would be my guess," Fleming replied, looking toward Harry Davis. "You know Dick, don't you Harry?"

"Sure do," he said putting his empty bottle in the rack next to the drink box. "I know right where his office is, Frank. He's a nice guy. He'll help us all he can."

Harry returned to his chair, leaned back, and fired up a Lucky Strike.

"Any other insurance policies on Mrs. Hardin or Leroy that y'all know about?" Frank asked once again.

"Mr. Russell, I took Bertha to Ruben McClung's house in Coosa the morning that Leroy died." Marvin Watkins said. "It was right after you left the house the first time. But before we went to Coosa she wanted to stop at an insurance office on Broad Street. Now I wish you'd go down to my house and ask Ollie and Missy about that insurance thing, 'cause I don't want to get it wrong. All the women folk are down there having a hen party and they'll be glad to tell you anything they know."

Frank and Harry finished up their conversation shortly with the men and headed to the Watkins house.

They pulled up in the yard, parked the car, and walked up on the porch. By the time they reached the door, Missy already had it open and invited them in. They went through the front room and continued to the kitchen where the women had gathered. Once again a chair was provided for the deputies and they were invited to sit a spell. Mrs. Watkins gave them a hearty welcome, poured them a cup of coffee without asking and immediately wanted to know how Bertha was this morning and was she going to get out. Frank covered the same ground that he had with the men at the store then asked, "Do you ladies know anything about any insurance policies on Mr. or Mrs. Hardin?"

Mrs. Lynch was the first to repeat some of the information that Frank had already gotten from the men. He did not interrupt or attempt to stop her in any way. He knew from experience that it was entirely possible that she might add a little tidbit to what he already knew.

After she finished, she turned to Missy and said, "Go ahead, baby, tell him what you told us this morning."

"Mr. Russell, after Leroy died, Mama walked up to the Lynch's to get Jessie," she said. "There weren't nobody but me and Bertha in the house working on Leroy. You know, trying to clean him up and such. Bertha went to the cabinet in the bedroom and came back with papers in her hand. She told me it was a good thing that she had her insurance policies 'cause medical bills had just about broke them'."

"Mrs. Holloway?" Frank asked. "Did you happen to notice a company name on the policies?"

Missy looked down and answered in a quite shameful voice, "After Mama, Jessie and the Pooles were all there, I took the policies out of the cabinet and looked at them. I know I shouldn't have done it and I'm very sorry that I did."

"What company was it, Missy?" Frank asked again.

"State Mutual and Liberty something or other were the two names that I saw," she said.

"So you saw two insurance companies, is that right?" Frank asked.

"Yes sir," she said.

From his chair at the table where Harry Davis was sipping on his coffee and working on his second tea cake he asked, "Missy, did you notice how much the policies were for?"

"They were a lot of money. One was over two thousand dollars. I couldn't tell how much the other one was," Missy replied. "I'm sorry I looked, Mr. Davis, I know it was wrong."

"Missy, you shouldn't go snooping around in other people's houses, but I sure am glad you did this time," Harry replied.

Frank asked the women to describe the last few days of Mr. and Mrs. Hardin's life. Carrie and Louise Poole, Jessie Lynch, Ollie Watkins and

Missy Holloway all had a story to tell. By the time they finished he and Harry had several pages of notes. Frank thanked the women as they rose to leave and he informed them that at some point they may have to testify in court. Harry got one more tea cake as he thanked the women and headed toward the car.

"What do you think, Frank?" Harry asked.

"I think we're going to Lindale right now, and then we'll go back to the sheriff's office and fill him in on what we learned so far."

"Do you think that she really did poison ole Leroy, Frank?" Harry asked.

"I'm thinking that if these insurance policies pan out, we sure do have a strong motive. I really wish that we could hurry that autopsy up a little."

"You think Bertha will tell us any more now that we know about the insurance?" Harry asked.

Frank remembered the last time that he and Bertha talked at her house. He recalled that she only answered the exact question that he asked. She didn't add or volunteer anything else.

"I doubt it Harry," Frank said. "But she sure is gonna get an opportunity."

# Chapter 9

It was just after daylight when Bertha heard the key turn in the steel corridor door. She glanced over to the woman on the top bunk across from her with a questioning look.

"Breakfast," the woman explained. "If you can call it that."

The trusties were going to each cell and handing each inmate a tin plate. In the plate they put a dipper of watered down grits and a slice of greasy boloney. That was followed by a slice of store bought bread and a cup of black coffee. Bertha stood in the cell looking down at her plate and then back at the woman on the top bunk who was dipping her bread in the boloney grease and eating slowly as if to keep from gagging.

"They expect us to live off of this?" Bertha asked disgustedly

The older of the two drunks on the bottom bunks replied, "They don't care if you live or not, Queenie. It's all the same to them."

Bertha took a bite of the grits and spit it back into the plate.

"I could make better grits than this when I was ten years old," she said, "and what kind of meat is this?"

"It's fried boloney," said the top bunk woman, "and you should try and force it down. The grease will give you strength and you're gonna need it 'cause dinner's worse."

"It don't look like no baloney that I ever cooked." Bertha said. "I just ain't hungry enough to eat this slop yet. My daddy fed his hogs better than this."

A half hour after breakfast the jailer and trusties come back around and collected plates, cups, and spoons. As they left the area around Bertha's cell, the jailer looked to where she was sitting on her top bunk and asked, "Are you Bertha Gossett?"

"I used to be Bertha Gossett, but my last name is Hill now," she replied. "Have I done something else?"

"The Identification Officer said to tell you that he'd be around shortly to take you downstairs for printing and mugging," he replied.

Bertha sighed. *I don't have any make up, lipstick or anything. I don't even have a hairbrush or a mirror and I know that my hair must look like a stump full of grand daddies. This is gonna be a great picture.*

The woman on the top bunk looked at her and said. "I've got a little make-up and a hairbrush. You can use it if you want. We've all been through printing and mugging."

Shortly after Bertha got her hair in some kind of order, she heard the steel corridor open once again. A tall slim man with a polite look on his face opened her cell door and said, "I'm Deputy Frank Perry, the ID officer. Did the jailer tell you that I'd be by this morning?

"Yes he did, Deputy Perry," she said in her sweet little girl voice. "And I'm as ready as I'll ever be."

"Good, then you lead the way. Just go to your right, and I'll be right behind you."

The booking, printing and mugging didn't take very long. Bertha thought that Deputy Perry treated her with respect and she liked him immediately. Before he locked her back in the cell she asked, "Will I be allowed visitors this morning?"

"I don't think they have any restrictions on you, so I wouldn't think that's a problem," Deputy Perry said. "I'll check and see. If there are restrictions I'll come back and tell you. If I don't come back you'll know they ain't none."

"I sure do thank you, Deputy," Bertha said sweetly. "Can I ask you one more question?"

"Go ahead," he replied waiting at the cell door.

"Why are they calling me Gossett instead of my real name?"

"That's the way they got you booked in. You'll have to ask Chief Deputy Russell why they're doing that, 'cause I don't know."

Bertha looked around the cell and noticed immediately that Mama and Baby Girl were gone. She kind of shifted her eyes to where they had been and back to the other woman, who was now sitting on the bottom bunk, as if to say 'where are they?'

"They were only here for a public drunk charge," she said. "They got out."

Bertha was glad they were gone. They had both stunk, and the small cell made the odor all that much worse. She didn't understand why they had four women in one cell to begin with. On her morning walk to the ID room, she had noticed that the cell next to hers was empty. There were only two cells on the second floor and they both were for women. She didn't understand why one would be empty and the other have four women packed in it.

"I'm glad they're gone," Bertha said to the other woman.

"So am I," she said, holding out her hand to shake. "You had them pegged right last night. They're just a couple of dollar-a-ride mattress backs. Look, let's start all over. I'm Mattie Weaver."

"I'm Bertha Hill," she said, "and I'm glad to meet you. Just wish it was under different circumstances."

"Ain't that the truth," Mattie said. "What was all that mix up about your name?"

"I don't rightly know," Bertha said. "Guess I'll have to wait and ask Mr. Russell, if he ever comes around again. Gossett was my first husband's name, but we divorced a year ago this month. I married Leroy Hill in July of last year."

"Bertha, you look so familiar. I'm sure I ran into you somewhere before," Mattie said.

"Well your name sounds familiar, I just can't remember where I know it from either," Bertha replied.

"Probably read it in all the papers. They wrote it up real good about a month ago. I was the teller that helped herself to the bank's money. I got real popular there for awhile. It was kind of like they didn't have anything else to write about."

"I do remember that," Bertha said. "It did seem like it went on forever and ever. Were you charged right away?"

"Nah, they put me here in jail for a week or two on what they call an open felony warrant. Deputy Russell kept talking to me almost every day. I tried to keep my story straight," she said, laughing, "but he kept getting me confused. He said, 'Mattie the truth ain't in you. All you do is lie, lie, lie. I think you've told more lies in a week than I've heard in a year. And I mean you're doing it with a straight face'."

"Well, did you ever admit to it?" Bertha asked.

"Hell no," she said, "and don't you either. My lawyer says that all kind of stuff can go wrong at a trial. But if you've confessed you ain't got a Chinaman's chance."

*A trial! I don't want to have anything to do with no trial. I got to get out of this place somehow.*

"I had a job at McClellan's," Bertha said. "But I don't know if I do now or not."

"That's where I know you from." Mattie said, "I used to come in there all the time."

Mattie adjusted both bottom bunks the best she could and motioned for Bertha to pick the one she wanted. Both women sat down facing each other and continued their talk.

"You know my story. Now what are you doing here, that is if you want to tell me. It really ain't none of my business."

"Mattie, I really don't know at this time. Everything is so full of holes. I was arrested on one of them felony things that my mother-in-law took out. See, my Leroy died day before yesterday, and they did an autopsy. The report ain't back yet, but the doctor's told the sheriff that it looked like he was poisoned. Mr. Russell told that to my mother-in-law and right away she thinks I did it. And here I am."

Bertha and Mattie heard the big steel door open and Mattie put her finger to her mouth indicating for Bertha to hush. She then pointed to her ears to let Bertha know that a lot of listening is done in this place.

The jailer appeared in front of their cell, followed by her Uncle Ruben. Bertha's eyes began to tear up just seeing him standing in the hallway. He looked at her and said, "Bertha, are you alright?"

"Uncle Ruben, I'm in jail, I'm not alright. Can't you get me out of here?"

"I tried to Bertha," Ruben said, "But Deputy Russell said that he doubts that you'll get a bond till the investigation is over. Then if you're cleared, you'll get out. Guess you'll have to wait it out. He said it shouldn't be long. Can me and Plemma bring you anything?"

"Go see a lawyer, Uncle Ruben. I don't want to stay in this place even for one more night."

"I'm gonna do that before I go back home. But if I can't get a lawyer to see about getting you out, do you need anything?"

"Uncle Ruben, I need everything they'll let me have. I ain't got nothing. They took my pocketbook away from me last night and kept it. My brush and compact are in it. Just tell Aunt Plemma to pack me some clothes and y'all get it back as soon as you can. I ain't gonna run off."

The jailer told Ruben it was time to leave and they headed down the corridor. Before he left he told Bertha that he would check and see if it was alright for her to have her personal things.

"Thank you so very much Mr. Jailer, I sure do appreciate it," Bertha said in a very sensual voice.

"Well, you sure are welcome, ma'am," the jailer replied.

"You sure are nice to these deputies Bertha," Mattie said, "That's two out of two that you've been sweet to this morning. These guys are not your friends or buddies, you know."

"How old are you, Mattie?" Bertha asked, turning to Mattie with a cold hard stare that caught her by surprise.

"I'll be twenty two September 15th," she said with a puzzled look. "Why?"

"And how old is the man you stole the money for?" Bertha asked.

"How did you know that?" Mattie asked sitting up on her bunk and looking at Bertha with big wide eyes. "He's in his early thirties, I guess."

"The papers indicated that there was possibly someone else involved in your theft, I remember that much." Bertha said. "And I can just bet that a cute young thing like you working at a bank drove the men crazy. I'll bet that they were all over you like ants on candy. That is till you fell for one of them, lies and all. And then I'd bet you a dollar to a doughnut that he talked you into stealing the money. He probably showed you how to do it, fixed it where he couldn't get caught, and kept all the money himself. Am I right or not?"

Mattie dropped her eyes to avoid contact with Bertha. She looked like she had just been caught with her hand in the cookie jar.

"I been thinking about telling Russell everything. Bertha, you oughta be the detective around here." Mattie said.

"Don't you think Russell already knows everything I just said?" Bertha asked. "I guarantee he does. He just needs you to tell him who it is, and then testify."

"What do you think I oughta do?" Mattie asked.

"You got any job prospects when you get out?" Bertha asked.

"No," she replied.

"Got any money?" Bertha asked.

"No," she replied once again.

"Then look, if he goes to jail, it ain't gonna do you a bit of good. Maybe you'll make a deal and get probation for your testimony. But if you ain't never been charged before, then your lawyer's gonna get that for you anyway," Bertha said.

"Well, I ain't never been in trouble before," Mattie said. "I never even got a parking ticket."

"When you get out, you're gonna need a few dollars now and then to make ends meet. That is until you get a job and even after. Your boyfriend gets to keep his job, family and career. Come on honey, think about it, you got a cash cow. Shut up now and milk it later."

Mattie sat silently staring at this woman. A strange feeling came over her. She didn't know what to think. *What kind of person could plan everything out in such detail, and so quick? And did she really kill her husband? Am I locked up with a murderer?*

Bertha broke the silence between them once again.

"Mattie, if you'll pat them on the head every now and then, maybe scratch'em behind the ears a few times and promise them a treat later on, they'll follow you anywhere. That's why I'm nice to the deputies, sweetie. And they are gonna be friends and buddies. After all, they're just men."

₪      ₪

Frank and Harry slowed the Ford as they entered the cotton mill village of Lindale. Frank never failed to marvel at the two story mill houses with the steep roofs. He never understood why the Massachusetts's Mill Company had built houses for North Georgia with a New England style. Maybe they figured on heavy snow here like up north during the winter. The village had been founded back in the 1890's and had grown for the next thirty years or so.

As they approached the two sets of railroad tracks that ran through the village, Harry began to wave and yell at people he knew along the sidewalks.

The village was only about six or seven miles from downtown Rome. A little too far to walk for everyday needs, but close enough for week-end or monthly trips to the Broad Street stores. Frank knew that the Rome merchants depended on the mill workers to purchase their wares and the Rome government had gotten the Georgia Power Company to put Lindale on their bus line.

Years before, when Rome ran street cars, they had run one all the way to Lindale just to help those shoppers get to the big city. The Rome papers were filled with advertisements that were aimed at not only these workers but the ones at Anchor Duct, Shannon and Celanese. Those were the other textile villages that surrounded Rome. All of these had their company-sponsored housing and amenities. But none had everything that this village did.

Lindale had its on school system, doctor, dentist, school nurse, barber shop, beauty shop, carpenter shop, shoe shop, gas station with mechanic, auditorium that showed good movies and it had an indoor swimming pool in the basement. There was a department store, drug store, hotel and an inn all supplied or encouraged by the mill.

The company kept the houses in tip top shape, picked up the garbage, and supplied water and sewage. They had a pasture for your cow and a pen for your hog. There were garden spots for those that wanted to grow their own vegetables.

Most of these workers had grown up on farms, or their parents had, and they were used to tilling the soil. During the Depression their very survival depended on their ability to grow and can vegetables. And of course during the War they all had victory gardens. Yes sir, Frank thought, the mill provides everything that you need to live. Grinning to himself he also thought of the funeral home in town and added, everything you need to die also. And yes, there was a cemetery at the edge of the village. It too was provided by the mill of course.

Frank crossed the second track with caution. It was banked in such a way that you could easily tear something up under your car if you hit this track with any speed. As he eased over the track, he could see the baseball field to his right. Already the middle of February, he thought, it won't be long till that thing will be packed every game day.

Baseball was big in the textile leagues across the south, and nowhere was it bigger than here. He knew that the big league teams up north used the textile teams as a training and instructional league. But you could see some mighty good baseball played around northwest Georgia and the edge of Alabama.

Frank had seen Rudy York play in the league and Leon Culberson was in the Major Leagues right now. And he had already heard Harry talk about this young hot shot pitcher that Lindale had who was gonna be a sure fire big leaguer. He had said that the youngster would be there in no more than a couple of years. Frank made a mental note to come and watch this kid pitch Lindale's opener this year.

"Hey Harry, what's the name of the young hot shot pitcher?" Frank asked.

"Willard Nixon," Harry replied. "What brought that up?"

"Just saw the ball field over there and thought it ain't that long till the season starts."

"You dang right it ain't," Harry said. "All the real good ball players are back from the war too. This is gonna be a season to remember. Don't think Lindale can be stopped this year. They should win the league championship."

"You know I hear that Shannon is loaded also. And Atco, Celanese and Anchor Duct might have something to say about it too, don't you think?" asked Frank.

"Well I'm sure they're gonna try," Harry said. "That's what makes it so doggone good. You're right about Shannon, that's gonna be a real battle when they meet."

"Frank, I'm telling you, Nixon's fastball looks like an aspirin tablet coming sideways. And the umpires call his curve by memory, 'cause they're ducking out of the way. He can't be beat. And it ain't just Nixon. They got Shorty Hall, Bo Sheppard, Jack Gaston, Jimmy Jordan, Gene Baggett, J.W. Mathis and a whole host of real honest to goodness ball players. It's gonna be a tremendous season."

As Frank passed the auditorium on his left, he was hoping to see the Lindale Band out in front practicing. But he knew that it wasn't likely that director Paul Nixon, no relation to the pitcher, would have them out in February. The band was better than good, Frank thought, and Paul Nixon is superb. They did a lot of free concerts in the summer and always drew large crowds whereever they played.

They crossed the bridge over Silver Creek and turned into the mill office parking lot. As they went inside all of the ladies in the office turned and spoke to Harry. Mrs. Marble Henderson stood up and welcomed the deputies to Lindale, then said, "Mr. Hand is gonna be glad to see y'all. He was just saying this morning that he was going to have to find a new police officer,"

"Has somebody quit the department?" Harry asked.

"Nope, gonna add on, we don't have but four officers. And with a rough and ready crew home from killing Germans and Japs, it can get a little out of control around here on the weekends. I heard one fella say last weekend that the American Legion post up on the hill was almost as dangerous as the Battle of the Bulge."

"The whole county's that way right now, Mrs. Marble," Harry said. "Maybe they'll settle down in a few more months."

"Maybe they will," she said. "Do you want to fill out an application? I know he'll hire you, probably both of you."

"Didn't come looking for a job. Mrs. Henderson. We gotta little Sheriff's Department business with Mr. Hand," Harry said. "Is he in this morning?"

"Yes he is, Harry. Let me go and tell him you're here."

It was less than a minute till she came back into the room followed by Dick Hand, the Office Manager of the mill.

"What can I do for the Sheriff's Department?" Dick asked as he shook hands with both men and motioned them into his office and waiting chairs.

"Mr. Hand, do you recall a James Hardin working for the company. I believe he was known as Bud?" Frank asked.

"The name sounds familiar. I don't remember right off. Let me check some paper work and I'll get right back to you."

Mr. Hand was only gone for a few minutes and returned with a file folder in his hand.

"I do remember him now that I've looked at his file. What do you want to know about him?" Dick asked.

"Anything you can tell us," Frank said.

"Well, he worked for us the first time back in the late thirties for awhile. That was before my time, but it says that he lived over in Alabama and lost his ride to work. That he was subject to rehire anytime he wanted. Now I remember a few years ago that Harry Fleming came and asked if we would hire Bud back. He said that Bud had moved in with his daughter in Armuchee and was going to ride to work with him if he could get the same shift."

"And it's pretty obvious that he did," Harry said.

"Boys, we were in the middle of a war and good, experienced male employees were hard to find. He could have come and lived at my house if he'd wanted to. I would have put him on any shift that he asked for, and did."

"What happened after that?" Frank asked. "Did he stay with the company till he died?"

"Yes he did. And the company hated to lose him. Not only was he a good man, he was an excellent worker. His supervisor said that it was almost impossible for his co-workers to equal him for an entire shift. He had worked on the railroad sometime in his life and had gotten used to working without breaks. And since we didn't have a water boy to bring a bucket around every now and then like the railroad does, he just worked straight through."

"Was he insured through the company?" Frank asked.

Dick checked through his files and made a little note on his scratch pad before replying.

"He was. All our employees are covered by a group policy from Metropolitan for one thousand dollars at no expense to them. Of course a lot more have private coverage also."

"Who was the beneficiary?" Frank asked.

"His wife was," Mr. Hand replied, "but the check was made out to his daughter. That's what I was jotting down. I want to double check that."

"Then you really don't know who the insurance company paid?" Frank asked.

"Well, we have a note from them saying that the check was paid and that Bertha Hill endorsed the check. But you're right. I don't actually have any idea who got the money."

Both Frank and Harry had been writing notes since the interview began. Both looked at each other to see if there was anything else to cover. They stood up and thanked Mr. Hand and informed him that at some time he might be a witness in a trial and that they would appreciate his confidence on their questioning.

Mr. Hand nodded his understanding and said, "You know, policing sure looks interesting from a layman's point of view. I kind of wish I had tried it myself."

"It's never too late," Frank said. "We'd love to have you involved."

"And remember Harry," Dick said. "I got a job for you whenever you want it."

"That's good to know Mr. Hand. I'll keep that in mind," Harry replied.

They drove back to Rome and parked the car at the jail. After going inside reviewing their notes Frank said, "Harry, I want you to make a list of insurance companies on Broad Street. That's should take care of most of the ones in the city. And then canvass all of those and ask the same kind of questions that we asked Dick Hand. Let's find out if she had anymore insurance on Bud, Mama or Leroy. I'm gonna talk a little more to Jack Highfield and Bertha."

₪    ₪

Frank took a long look at Bertha as the jailer brought her into his office and seated her in the chair across from him. Her night in jail was already starting to wear on her. She looked very fragile and haggard. Being unkempt was to be expected of jail inmates, and Bertha was no exception. Frank was trying hard to read this woman and once again he felt unable to do so.

"Please come in and sit down, Bertha. I'd like to ask you a few questions if you don't mind. Would that be all right?" Frank asked.

"Oh Mr. Russell you know it would. And I have some for you too," Bertha cooed, fixing her eyes squarely on the deputy and not looking away for any reason.

"Well, why don't you go first then," Frank said.

"Thank you, I will," she said. "Have I been charged with anything yet?"

"No, Bertha, you haven't." Frank said. "We're still holding you on an open felony warrant."

"Mr. Russell, somehow that just don't seem right. Am I going to be allowed to make bail?"

"You're uncle Ruben's trying to get you a lawyer, but I don't think any judge will set you a bond till the investigation is complete and the autopsy report is back. Anything else you want to know?" Frank asked.

"Why yes, there is, Deputy," Bertha replied. "Can you tell me why I wasn't allowed to have my personal things last night? I still don't have my purse, hairbrush, compact and other items. And the other women had theirs. The nice jailer this morning said that he would try and get them for me, but he hasn't yet. And why was I put into a cell with three other women when the one next to us was empty?"

"We have a concern of suicide when someone who is being investigated for possibly being involved in a wrongful death is placed in custody. I'll see that you get your personal things today."

"Mr. Russell, I'm not going to kill myself, and that's a fact," she said, giving Frank just the hint of a smile, and then changed the subject.

"Is it possible to get something to eat other than jail food? I do believe the Japanese fed our prisoners of war better than this."

"Bertha I admit, it ain't like granny fixed it, but it will keep you going and most of our inmates aren't here that long. You can have all you like. Just ask for more."

"It's not more that I want. I can't eat what they bring now," she said disgustedly. "Can my family bring me some things from home? I have some preserves at home that I canned last fall. Would that be OK?"

"Yes it would," Frank replied. "Are you finished with your questions now?"

"Deputy Russell, you know that a woman's never finished, but I'll stop for now," Bertha said with that smile or look on her face.

Frank looked into her eyes and they were dancing. It was the same trance-like feeling he got when watching an open fire in the fireplace on a cold winter day. He sat back in his chair. *She likes this. She's enjoying every moment. Be careful Frank Russell. Remember what Jack Highfield said. You're gonna wind up as the mouse instead of the cat.*

"Bertha would you like a co-cola or a cup of coffee?" Frank asked.

"Oh Deputy Russell, thank you so much! I'd love either one or both," she said.

Frank summoned the on-duty jailer and asked him to check with his wife and see if she still had hot coffee. If so to please bring Bertha a cup, and ask her if she has any apple cobbler left after her younger brother got through with it. If so please have her send me a helping.

"Bertha, your father had an insurance policy through Lindale mill, is that right?"

"Yes, it was for one thousand dollars."

"Who was it made out to?" Frank asked.

"It was made out to my mother originally. But she couldn't read or write and the company didn't want me to sign a check for her. So they came to the house and she told them to make the check out to me. And that's what they did."

"What happened to the money?"

"We paid off a few small debts that my daddy owed. Mama loaned some to her sisters to help them out a little bit. And we bought some things for around the house." She said.

"Did you have big funeral expenses?" Frank asked.

"Not at all. Papa had joined an insurance burial association through the Jordan Funeral home. He had paid on it for years. Just a few pennies here and there until it was all paid up. Me and Mama were also paid up."

"Leroy bought a car, motorcycle and saddle horse last spring. Was that part of your father's insurance money?"

"I'm afraid it was," Bertha said. "Leroy told Mama that he would pay her back as soon as he got a job. But she died before he could."

"Are you saying that your mother loaned Leroy the money for those things?"

"That's what she did," Bertha answered. "I told her to save some of the money. But she had faith that Leroy would pay her back."

The jailer brought Bertha a steaming cup of coffee and a very generous helping of cobbler.

"Oh Mr. Russell, thank you once again," she said. "And thank you, too," she hollered after the jailer.

"Bertha, was your Mama or Leroy also insured?" Frank asked.

"Mr. Russell, I'm not trying to be mean, but I don't want to talk about insurance anymore. I'm not sure what you're trying to imply," she said.

"What do you mean by that?" Frank asked.

Bertha took a sip of coffee, washing down a mouthful of cobbler and then asked, "Mr. Russell, do you have insurance on your wife and family?"

"Yes I do, Bertha, but they're still alive," Frank replied.

"Deputy Russell, I didn't kill him," Bertha said looking Frank in the eye and taking another bite of pie. "And my family was alive when our policies were taken out."

Frank thought that this would be a good time to shift gears. But before he could bring up another point Bertha asked him, "Why was I booked in under my first husband's name instead of mine?"

"Mrs. Beale said that Leroy wasn't divorced from his first wife. And she had her marriage license to back it up. That means that if you and Leroy were married, yours ain't legal."

"He said that his divorce was final. What's a girl to do? We got married in Rossville, Georgia. You can check it out."

"I don't think you would make that up Bertha. It just ain't all that important," Frank said.

"Well, it is to me, Mr. Russell," she said.

"But speaking of your first husband, when's the last time you saw him?" Frank asked.

"I don't rightly know. It was some time before Christmas. He came in the store. We spoke. He was pretty nice to me. Asked how I was doing and all. The divorce wasn't final then, in fact it hadn't even been filed. I filed for divorce right after the first of the year."

"What kind of married life did you have with your first husband?" Frank asked.

"Not good. If it had been, I'd still be married to him," she replied.

"Tell me a little about your life with Neal. It was Neal wasn't it?"

"Yes sir, Neal Gossett. He wasn't much, and ain't a lot to tell. I was fifteen when I married Neal. He was twenty-one. I can look back on it now and see that it was a big mistake. And I mean for both of us. Life was hard out in the country in the thirties. You oughta know that Mr. Russell. And Cherokee County was a hard place to try and scratch out a living. Neal worked hard enough to start with. But as he got older he drank more and more. Then he started beating on me when he came home drunk. I weren't no saint either. Do you understand? If you go over there and ask around, most folks ain't gonna speak to highly of either one of us. Most thought that we deserved each other."

"What about family?" Russell asked.

"I didn't have any brothers or sisters. Papa was a lot older than Mama. So they just had me. Mama had a house full of sisters and a couple of brothers. I got a ton of aunts, uncles and cousins. Papa had a pretty big family too. Not as big as Mama's, but it weren't small."

"What about Neal's?" Frank asked.

"By and large they were good, hard-working people. Neal's Daddy, Fred Gossett, was a mighty fine man. He helped me and Neal out several times when times got hard and things didn't look so good. And he didn't have too. He let me work in the store some and we lived in one of his houses. Neal was one of the oldest of a whole bunch of brothers and sisters. Couple of his brothers and he don't get along. And he's got some pretty mean sisters."

"What kind of mean. You mean they get in trouble a lot or what?"

Frank asked.

"Oh no, I didn't mean like that, me and Neal had a big fight a few years back, and one of his sisters threatened to beat my eyes in if anything happened to Neal. That's what I was talking about. That kind of mean"

"What did she mean, if anything happened to Neal?" Frank asked.

"I never did figure that out, Deputy Russell. I didn't know what she meant."

"So the drinking and beating is the reason that you divorced Neal," Frank said as he continued writing down the names of family members Bertha was mentioning.

"That was the reason. I tried to stay married to him. All the older women in my family feel like that when you make your bed, you're supposed to lie in it. I just couldn't do it any longer. After our baby died, I moved to Rome, got a job at McClellan's, then moved Mama and Papa over here where I could take care of them. We were separated for a long time. Oh he'd come around and stay awhile but it wasn't the same. So several years ago, we separated for good. I finally got around to filing for my divorce after I met Leroy. I thought he did too."

"You had a baby that died, Bertha?" Frank asked. "I didn't know that."

"It was such a tiny little thing. It just quit breathing one day not to long after it was born. Then Mama shipped me off to her brothers down in Americus, Georgia. I stayed about a month I guess. I shared a room with my cousin. She was a lot younger than I was, but she kept me from going crazy at night by talking to me and telling me that everything would be all right. You know, like a little girl would do. That was when Neal and I really split the blanket. Things were never the same anymore."

Frank sat and watched Bertha as she told the story of her life. Her divorce and the death of a child were all tragedies to Frank. But he didn't pick up on any remorse in her voice or her actions. She might as well have been reading from a book.

"Bertha, I'm truly sorry for your loss. Is there anything else you'd like to ask me before I send you back upstairs?" Frank asked.

"I don't think so Mr. Russell. I'm sure we'll talk again. But I do thank you for the coffee and cobbler. Please thank your wife for me. And also thank your nephew for not eating it all."

"You're welcome Bertha. And yes, we'll probably talk again."

"I look forward to it, Deputy," Bertha said with her eyes dancing as she stood up and followed the jailer from the office.

Bertha Hill, mug shot

the Floyd County jail at the
time of Bertha's incarceration

# Chapter 10

Frank thought he would stretch his legs before he talked to Jack Highfield. He headed across the street to the courthouse to report in to the sheriff. It was already getting late in the afternoon. He hoped that Harry had a little luck with the local insurance companies. He intended to go over the case, talk to Jack Highfield and call it a night unless something else came up. He wasn't sure that the sheriff was going to be in his office this late on a Saturday afternoon, but he was.

"Come in Frank. Ain't nobody here but me, so it's a good time to catch up on a little paperwork." Sheriff Horton said.

"Thought I'd fill you in on what went on today, unless you're in a hurry to get out of here," Frank said.

"I'm in a hurry all right, but I can't leave for awhile yet. I got too much to do here. This Leroy Hill thing has got the whole office backed up."

"What have I missed?" Frank asked.

"It ain't nothing you've missed. I mean, I got a superior court judge wanting to know when we're gonna officially charge Bertha. Two different lawyers have inquired about setting bail or at least having a hearing. The solicitor-general is getting real nervous. We've had family members come by wanting to know details of the arrest. The news paper and radio guys are camping out on the doorstep. I'm just trying to keep the lid from blowing off."

"Well I've got a little information for you that may help with the solicitor," Frank said.

For the next thirty or forty minutes Frank covered all of the day's events. First he discussed the trip to Pleasant Valley. Then he went over the trip to Lindale and the interview with Bertha that afternoon. He also mentioned the mission Harry was on and that he still hadn't reported in yet, so he didn't know for sure what he might have found out, if anything.

"Maybe I can help you a little bit with that," Mark said. "I was down on Broad for a late dinner when I bumped into Harry coming out of the Busy Bee Café. He told me what he was doing on the street. He said that he still had a lot to do, but he had already hit pay dirt. That's all I got out of him, but I thought I'd throw that out there for you to chew on."

"That's good," said Frank. "That's real good."

Frank ended the discussion in record time and headed back across the street to his office. He really wanted Harry to check in now so he could find out what he had learned on his Broad Street trip. When he got back to the jail, he poured a cup of coffee and headed to his office. Things were already starting to pick up on Saturday evening. The office itself was close enough to the booking desk that most of the noise was impossible to keep out. Still Frank sent for Jack Highfield. He wanted to ask him a few questions about Neal Gossett. Frank desperately wanted to rule Neal out of the investigation if he could.

"Sit down Jack. Would you like a cup of coffee?" Frank asked, motioning the jailer to bring him one even before he answered. He then tossed Jack an un-opened plug of Bloodhound which he put in his pocket without even saying or nodding thanks.

"What do you want this time, Russell?" Jack asked as he picked the coffee up and took a sip.

"I want to go over some of the same things we covered the other day. Hoping you'd remember a little more now that you are not so fuzzy headed as last time." Frank replied.

"I don't know any more than I told you the other day. Why are y'all still holding me? My brother said that I couldn't get out till next week. And that the sheriff was going to try to send me to the chain gang."

"Jack, Earl came and took a warrant for you for knocking out one tooth and breaking another. You're gonna have to go to trial for this one, and your record ain't real good. I don't know if you'll get a bond hearing or not. And if the judge does set one, it'll be pretty high, you can bet on that."

"I don't see what all the fuss is about, Russell. I mean, it ain't like Earl don't have no more teeth. He's got plenty, and if he kept his mouth shut he'd be able to keep them. You go tell that sheriff that I been in the chain gang. He don't scare me none."

"Maybe you won't have to go back Jack," Frank said. "Tell me again what you know about Neal Gossett."

"Not much to tell, Russell. Neal is an alright feller. He's kinda like the rest of us when it comes to drinking. He don't handle it real well either."

"You ever know of him beating up on his wife?" Frank asked.

"You mean that damn bitch Bertha," Jack said. "She deserved whatever she got. I promise you that."

"Just answer the question, Jack," Frank asked again. He could feel himself getting a little agitated.

"I don't know much else, I never seen him beat her up. I've seen her with a shiner or two. Somebody gave them to her, but I don't know who. Gossett hardly ever came up to Armuchee. He hung around over in Cherokee County, Alabama where he was from. And I almost forgot, he came to Cave Spring a lot. If you'll go down to Booger Holler and talk to Jake Wade or one of his kin, they should be able to tell you everything you want to know about Neal. And Russell, better tell'em I sent you."

"That all you got, Jack?" Frank asked one more time.

"That's about it Russell. Except you can tell that sheriff that I will get out someday. He can't keep me here forever."

Frank sat in his chair and thought about everything that had transpired during the day. At just about the time he was getting ready to call it a night, Harry came in. Frank just sat back down and let Harry go. When he finished, Frank got up and told him to have a good week-end and to come in bright and early Monday morning and be ready for another thirty yard dash.

Frank walked into his apartment, kicked off his shoes, hung up his coat and hat, turned to Christine and said, "The devil's running wild in Rome, Georgia. If ever a man needed to go to church tomorrow, it's me. I don't know yet what tonight might bring. It must be a full moon. The town's already going crazy.  But don't let me sleep late and miss services tomorrow."

ℸ    ℸ

Frank made it to church Sunday morning. As he and Christine, her sister and brother Danny entered the North Broad Baptist Church Frank felt like he was being watched. Already the local media was getting the feeling that something was going on in the city. He knew that rumors traveled fast. It was common knowledge by now that Bertha Hill was in jail and that her husband wasn't even in the ground. Although most folks didn't know Bertha, they knew where she worked. He knew that within a week everybody would know Bertha Gossett Hill. He felt that this investigation was going to generate a lot of press before it was put to bed.

He tried to keep his mind on the preacher's message, but it kept drifting to things that were unfinished. He wished he had his notebook with him so he could jot down a few of his thoughts. But he knew that even if he did have it with him, he wouldn't jot anything down. After the service he took his family back to their apartment in the jail. After dinner Frank settled down in his chair and began to read the *Rome News Tribune*. Sunday was the only day of the week that the paper ran in the morning. Reading the Sunday paper had long been a habit with Frank. He read the entire paper. He was not one to just read headlines, sports or even the funny papers. Then he saw the announcement in the obituaries.

> *Funeral services for Leroy Hill, who died at his residence on the Summerville Highway early Thursday morning, will be conducted this afternoon at 4:30 from the Hickory Mountain Methodist Church, Chatham County North Carolina. Interment will follow in the church cemetery. The remains were sent to the residence of the parents in Pittsboro, North Carolina by the Jennings Funeral Home.*

Frank read over the announcement several times and it brought him back to reality. No matter how much he wanted to relax today, this would be a wonderful time to completely re-write his notes and make sure that they were current. He told Christine that he would be in his office if she needed him.

As he sat down at his desk, the funeral announcement kept coming back to him. No matter how wild Leroy Hill was, or wasn't, somebody had killed him. Frank was positive of that even though no reports were back. *And I think I know who it was. I've just got to prove it.*

ℵ   ℵ

Monday morning came awful early. Frank was up before daylight. He knew what this day was going to bring. After breakfast he carried another cup of coffee with him to his office. The main thing that Frank liked about living in the jail apartment was that he didn't have far to walk to work. He was at his desk going through the duty rosters and the jail population report when the sheriff came in.

"You're up early Frank," Mark Horton said as he poured a cup of coffee from the jailer's pot.

"Got a long day ahead of me today, Sheriff. I wanted to get the morning jail business out of the way before we get started."

"Did Harry finish with the insurance companies on Broad?" the sheriff asked.

"Almost. There were a few that closed up before he got to them," Frank said. "We'll finish that up today."

"What else is on your schedule besides the insurance question?"

"I hope we're gonna find out where Neal Gossett was when Leroy died. I simply want to eliminate him. After talking to Jack Highfield again, I'm pretty convinced that Neal just ain't gonna be involved in any way. Oh by the way, Jack don't like you much," Frank said with a big grin on his face.

The sheriff turned blood red. He almost choked on the coffee he was trying to swallow. "What did he say?"

"He said something about you personally trying to put him in the chain gang."

"Well, he's got that right. I'm tired of fooling with him and his crowd every weekend. The next time he hits one of my deputies, he's going under the jail."

Harry Davis walked in and poured himself a cup and joined the group. He had stopped at the Broad Street bakery and gotten some doughnuts. He passed the sack around before getting one out and then placed them by the pot.

"We were just talking about Jack Highfield, Harry," Frank said. "Jack don't seem to like the sheriff to much these days. Says that the sheriff don't like for him and Earl Wilkey to fight."

"Aw, Jack'll get over it. He's just got a temper, that's all," Harry said as he finished his first doughnut and reached for another one.

"Well he better get over it," the sheriff said. "And you can tell him I said that he's going in front of a judge this time.

"Boys, it's been nice chatting with y'all but I got to get to the office and see which way the wind's blowing today. Y'all keep me abreast of where you are and what's going on with the investigation."

"Harry, would you make the morning jail check for me? I want to finish up this paper work before we get started today. Go ahead and drink your coffee, and make the check when you're through."

"No problem. Which way we going today?" Harry asked. "and Frank, thanks for letting me tag along. I don't get to do this kind of police work often."

"You're doing more than tagging along Harry. And none of us do this kind of police work often, thank goodness."

Harry finished his jail check, brought the car around, made sure that it was full of gas and was waiting out front when Frank came out and climbed in.

"Which way, boss?" Harry asked.

"Head down Twenty-Seven till you get to Six Mile and turn toward Cave Spring."

"I love Cave Spring. Are we gonna have time to stop at the cave and get a drink of water?" Harry asked.

"I don't know, Harry. We might," Frank said.

As they approached the Cave Spring turn-off, Frank told Harry to continue on down Highway 27 toward Cedartown. About a mile past the Cave Spring turn, Frank told Harry to take the next road to the right.

"That's the Booger Holler Road, Frank," Harry said, his voice rising in excitement.

"I know that Harry. I've been policing almost as long as you."

"Well why are we going down this road? You didn't say nothing at the jail about going down the Booger Holler Road."

"The reason I didn't is I knew how you was gonna act when I told you. But we're going to talk to some folks. That's why we're going down this road."

"Who are we gonna talk to, Frank? Ain't nobody down there I want to talk to. I'll tell you that right now."

"Jake Wade."

Harry stopped the car, turned in his seat, and looked at Frank with a little more than concern on his face.

"Dirty Jake Wade? We're going to see Dirty Jake? Frank, are you trying to get us killed?"

"Nope, I don't want to get killed this morning no more than you do," Frank replied. He loved to pick at Harry and he knew this would do it. But he wanted to put the Neal Gossett theory to rest and he hoped that Jake could do it.

"Frank, you know how we talk about all them outlaws up in Armuchee that Leroy ran around with."

"Yeah I do Harry. Why do you ask?"

"'Cause they won't come to Booger Holler, Frank, that's why. Big Cedar Creek winds its way through the Holler and them old boys have been making whiskey along the banks since Adam got run out of the garden. You're gonna get us shot and we ain't even gonna see it coming."

Harry stopped the car and drew his model 10 Smith & Wesson thirty eight special and checked the load. When he was happy that all the charge holes were filled he put it back in his holster and drove on down the road.

"What was that for Harry?" Frank asked. "I thought you kept your sidearm loaded all the time."

"I do, but I usually leave a cylinder empty under the hammer. Today I want all I can get. That one bullet might make a difference."

"Harry, you're being ridiculous. Jake ain't gonna shoot at nobody for just pulling into his yard."

"I know he ain't. But I heard that some of his kin was always in the woods with rifles trained on who ever stopped, just in case anything went wrong."

"Well we would've heard about it if somebody got shot, wouldn't we?" Frank said.

"Not necessarily. They just disappear and you never hear from them again. That's what I was told."

Harry arrived at the Wade household and pulled into the yard. Old man Jake was sitting on the front porch with his legs hanging off whittling on a cedar stick. He looked up at the deputies, turned his head and spit a big stream of tobacco juice. He then looked back down at his blade paying them no attention at all. He continued pulling foot long cedar curls with his pocket knife. Curls that were paper thin and never broke until he reached the end of the stick. It took a razor sharp knife and years of practice to be able to whittle like that. Harry noticed immediately how the pocket knife seemed to be nothing more than an extension of Jake's arm. It was like it belonged there.

"What y'all want?" he asked, still slowly pulling curls.

"Want to ask you a couple of questions, Jake," Frank said as he walked over to where he was sitting.

Harry had gotten out of the car but was lingering back behind Frank and he was looking in about four directions at once. Frank thought that Harry was going to spin his head off if he don't quit all of that nonsense.

"I'm pretty good at listening. Can't say whether I'll answer or not. But it's your dance, lead on."

"How well do you know Neal Gossett?" Frank asked.

"He comes around every now and then," Jake answered.

Frank told Jake the story about Leroy being dead and it looked like he was poisoned. He then told him about Bertha and that he had her in jail. He wanted to know where Neal was at the time of his death.

"What makes you think I know?" asked Jake.

"I was talking to Jack Highfield. He said to tell you that he sent me, and that you'd help if you could," Frank said.

"Jack Highfield, huh?" Jake said. "How's old Jack doing?"

"Looks like he might have to go bust rocks for awhile," Frank said. "He's in jail now awaiting trial. He knocked Earl Wilkey's teeth out."

"There's lots of rocks on The Bluff Road need busting," Jake said. "It won't hurt him none.

"Look, there's two things I'm gonna mention to you," Jake said. "Last week some of my boys were in Cave Spring and they saw Neal downtown near the Green Hotel. They talked a little bit and invited him to come out to the house. He had some woman with him, but it weren't Bertha. We know her, too.

"Drive over in Alabama and go to Bill May's grocery and ask them where John and Pauline Black live. Then you ask John where Neal was last week. That's his best friend."

"You said that you knew Bertha. How well do you know her?" Frank asked.

"Well enough," Jake answered, "I'll see you boys later." He looked back down at his whittle stick and then back at the deputies. Looking straight at Harry he asked.

"What's wrong with you? You've been acting like a long tail cat in a room full of rocking chairs."

"I heard stories about rifles in the woods," Harry said.

Jake grinned and then put his stick down and said, "My grandpaw's daddy said that back when the Yankees came, they wouldn't send no scavengers in the Holler. 'Fraid a Booger might get'em. Confeds didn't send no conscript officers either. Even though they were losing, they didn't want soldiers that bad. We've always been a peace-loving bunch of folks. Don't want no trouble from anybody, an ain't gonna tolerate none either. What's yore name deputy?"

"Harry Davis."

"Well, I'll tell you Harry Davis, since you look like such a brave young man and all, I'm gonna give y'all one more little tip. In Cave Spring at the Deaf School there are a couple of teenage girls, the Searcy twins, and they see things.

"Somebody dropped them off on the school's doorstep when they were three or four years old. Had a note saying they were the Searcy twins and that was all. It's been said that they can tell you all kinds of things if'n you really want to know bad enough. Just don't let them spook you."

Harry was as white as a snowball. He was having trouble catching his breath. He turned to Frank and said, "Frank, I don't want to go see no witches."

"He didn't say they were witches. He said they see things. They're seers."

"That's the same thing to me. And I ain't going," Harry said. "And if they're deaf, they can't talk anyway. How they gonna tell us anything?"

Jake had climbed the steps to his front porch and just before he went in the house he looked at Harry and said, "They got great big eyes. They talk with them."

Harry drove the car away from Jake Wade's property as fast as he could. He didn't say a word till they were at least a mile down the road.

"I'm not kidding Frank. I don't like being around fortune tellers and witches."

"Harry, I don't believe in that stuff, but what could it hurt? I'd like to see what they say. They're just teen-age girls."

"I don't care Frank. I don't want to do it."

# Chapter 11

Frank and Harry stopped the car in front of the Green Hotel. The two story frame building had been there for over a hundred years but wasn't an active hotel anymore.

There were however, several families that occupied apartments in the building. Rumor was that it started out as a Cherokee trading post and tavern. The building had been added on to so many times that if a cabin existed it was well covered and nobody remembered it.

Frank and Harry walked the short block to the Cave Spring Café and ordered a plate lunch. After they finished eating they asked the cashier if he knew Neal Gossett and had he seen him recently. The cashier stated that he did know Neal, but he hadn't seen him since last week. They left the café and crossed over the Cedar Creek Bridge and turned into Rolater Park.

They parked the car and walked to the entrance of the cave from which the city got its name. Water was pouring from the mouth of the cave into a small pond at the cave's mouth. Frank knelt down and picked up a dipper that was lying on a rock near the stream. He swished the water around in the tin dipper, washing it out, then took a long drink of the cold spring water. He refilled the dipper and after he finished that one, he handed the dipper to Harry. Harry repeated the process and placed the dipper back on its rock and followed Frank toward the car.

"I never get enough of that water," Harry said.

"Best in the state," Frank replied. "Harry, drive us up to the Deaf School."

Harry did as he was asked, but Frank could see that his heart wasn't in it. At the school they explained who they were and why they were there. They were ushered into a large class room setting which had a good fire going.

February was finally trying to act like a winter month. Frank had noticed that there was a chill in the air that had been missing for the past two weeks. A tall friendly man came into the room and introduced himself as Clayton Hollingworth. Frank repeated the same conversation that he had just had with the receptionist and wanted to know if it was true about the twins.

"Mr. Russell, sometimes they astonish me and the staff with their insight. I truly believe that they have a gift."

"Could we ask the girls about two questions, if you don't mind?"

"I've already sent for them. They'll be here in a few minutes."

Frank could see that Harry was very nervous and was ready to leave. He looked up and two beautiful identical twins came into the room. Frank estimated their age at about fifteen. Both girls took their right hand and made what looked to Frank to be a letter C and then placed it over their left breast. Frank was told that it was the sign for police officers. The girls moved simultaneously. It was uncanny how two girls moved as one with no communication. Little trickles appeared on Harry's face.

Mr. Hollingsworth explained to the girls that the police officers were working on a case where an individual had died. The officers were trying to establish if the death was from natural causes. The girls took each other's hand and stared long and hard into Frank's eyes. After what seemed to be an eternity, both shook their head no at the same time. This really scared Harry. Frank was afraid that his partner's knees were going to fail him at any moment.

Frank then asked the superintendent if the girls could tell him who killed the person.

The request was made once again to the girls in sign language and they immediately turned as one person and walked to the fire and knelt in front of the flames. Both reached at exactly the same time and took a poker and scraped some ashes out on the hearth. After four or five minutes of moving ash around, and staring into the fire, the girls got up on cue and faced Frank and Harry once again. They signed to the superintendent that this man had died from something that he ate. And that the officers should look for a loved one. As soon as they finished, they were gone. Frank thanked the superintendent and administrative staff and he and Harry left the building.

"Where to now, Frank?" Harry asked.

"Head over into Cherokee County. Do you know how to get to Bill May's Store?"

"I think I can find it. I know about where it is. Hey Frank, how did them little girls do that?"

"I don't know, Harry."

"I mean we didn't even know ourselves that we were gonna stop here. We didn't tell anybody at the school nothing. They didn't even know it was a man that was dead. Much less that he died from something he ate."

"The last part is what got my attention," Frank said. "Look for a loved one."

After only a couple of wrong turns, Harry stopped in front of May's Store. Harry stayed in the car while Frank went inside and got directions to John and Pauline Black's house.

"We got to backtrack a little bit, Harry," Frank said, "The Blacks live over on Mud Creek. That's where John rents some land to farm."

Ten minutes later the Ford was in the yard of the Black's house. Both deputies were invited inside after knocking on the door and telling John who they were. Mrs. Pauline asked both men to sit and asked if they would they like a cup of coffee and a fried pie. It was well after dinner and both men were glad to accept.

Frank asked John as he sipped the coffee, "I understand that you're probably Neal Gossett's best friend, is that right?"

"I'm certainly one of them," he replied.

"And we're friends with Bertha, too," Mrs. Pauline interjected. "We all used to run around together, back in the old days."

"Have you seen Neal in the past week?" Frank asked.

"Yes sir, he was up here a couple of days last week. He helped some on my wood pile. There's a lot to do on a farm and the sooner I get caught up, the better off I'm gonna be. I'm trying to get it ready for planting season. It ain't that far off, you know."

"What days was he here?" Frank asked.

"Let's see, I believe it was Wednesday and Thursday," John Black said.

"You're sure about that? He was seen in Cave Spring on Tuesday or Wednesday with some woman." Frank said.

Both John and Pauline started laughing.

"You're right again, Deputy. We were all in Cave Spring on Wednesday morning. I had ordered some new harness and trace chain for my mule and plow coming in by rail to the hardware store."

"And while John was paying for the parts and making sure they were all there, Neal and I walked around downtown and then got a table at the cafe," Pauline said.

"Did you notice if Neal talked to anybody while y'all were walking?" Harry asked.

"I don't remember anybody," Mrs. Pauline said then corrected herself. "Yes I do. Some of them bootleggers, that Wade bunch, stopped and talked to Neal for a minute or two. Said they had some real good stuff they had just run off. They said it won't last long and invited him to come by the house later that day."

"John, Bertha told me yesterday that she and Neal weren't that well thought of over here in this community. That most folks thought they deserved one another."

John slumped down in his chair. He looked up at the deputies with pleading eyes and Frank recognized that look. He had seen it many times before. He knew that John didn't want to say anything bad about Neal or Bertha. But he didn't know how to get out of it.

"Mr. Russell, I never had any trouble with either one of them. Like Pauline said earlier, we're friends with both. Now I've known Neal a spell longer and I guess I like him a little better. That's actually how I became acquainted with Bertha. Neal and I played a lot of baseball on Sunday's in whatever pasture we could.

"Both of them have a reputation around here. Most folks don't trust either one of them as far as they can throw them. In fact, around here they got a saying: if Bertha will hold the sack, Neal will fill it up. I never knew Neal to have that kind of reputation till he met up with Bertha. Now mind you, I've never witnessed nothing like that. But it is the talk."

That set Frank back. That was not what he was expecting at all. He looked over at Harry and he was writing as fast as he could.

"She also said that a couple of his brothers wouldn't have nothing to do with him. What can you tell me about that?" Frank asked.

"Same thing, they won't let Neal on their property. It's just a family fight. Really it's only one brother and that was an argument over money." John said.

"What about Neal's father, Mr. Fred Gossett? Bertha says he's the salt of the earth. How does he figure in this?"

"She's right; he's a good old man. And she oughta like him. He kept her and Neal out of jail. Years back the sheriff came out to the store and had some checks from Mr. Toll Price that somebody had traced his signature on. They totaled around three or four hundred dollars, I was told. Mr. Fred paid them off right then and there to keep Neal and Bertha out of jail."

"She also said that one of Neal's sisters threatened to beat her up for having a fight with Neal. Do you remember anything like that going on?"

"I was there when that happened," Pauline answered, and then added, "Bertha sure has been talking a lot. And that's pure Bertha. She leaves out a lot, or changes it around to suit herself." Pauline took a quick look to where John was fidgeting in his chair and then continued. "It wasn't a fight with Neal at the time. He had come home drunk and knocked her around a little bit. A few days later he was working in the fields and Bertha took him a fruit jar full of lemonade just as sweet as she could be. Neal apologized on the spot for hitting her and drank his lemonade.

"For the next three days, we thought he was gonna die. Mr. Fred had to get a doctor to check him out and give him some medicine. He pulled through it but was a mighty sick puppy for awhile. About a week after the lemonade thing one of Neal's sisters stopped me and Bertha in the store. She told Bertha that she knew what she had done and that if anything happened to Neal she guaranteed that Bertha would be buried right beside him. I believed her and Bertha did too."

"What did the sister think Bertha did to Neal?" Harry asked.

"It's pretty obvious don't you think?" Pauline said, "She thought Bertha put something in his lemonade. Lots of other people did too. Then there was some that thought he deserved it for hitting a woman. And you know, he might have just gotten sick and Bertha didn't have nothing to do with it. I mean, we don't really know."

"Mrs. Pauline, Bertha said that she and Neal had a baby to die, and that put the final blow on their marriage. Was she telling me the truth this time?" Frank asked.

For a long time John and Pauline sat and stared at each other. Finally John took a deep breath and said, "Deputy, we're friendly folks out here in the country. But danged if you ain't just about ruined our day. It ain't nothing you done, mind you. It's just that you're making us remember things we don't want to. They had a baby and it died. Neal said that it was fine when he went to the fields to work. Granny Garner went to visit Bertha and the baby and also said it was fine. About an hour later Bertha came running down the road saying the baby was dead.

"A lot of the Gossett family and other folks hereabouts think that Bertha did something to it. Granny saw the baby after it was dead and said that it had a spot on the top of its head that wasn't there earlier. There was some talk about a hat pin going in the soft spot to the brain. No investigation was done and Bertha seemed to be just as tore up as Neal, maybe more. She had to go to South Georgia and stay with kin for a month or two."

"So that was what really ended their marriage. Bertha was right about that," Frank said.

"I didn't say that," John said. "You've had a good dose of Bertha, it seems like. You see that baby died way back in 1934. It was in June to be exact. Neal and Bertha got married in July of 1933, and the baby was born toward the end of May. It was a little girl and they named her Mary Francis. Bertha was only fifteen when she got married, and had just turned sixteen when Mary Francis was born. They both took it mighty hard when she died.

"Neal and I were young men and I had to stay with him as much as possible to keep him from going crazy. Mrs. Zola shipped Bertha off to south Georgia to stay with her brother for awhile. I used to see Neal standing up in Howell cemetery by little Mary Francis' grave. After Mr. and Mrs. Hardin died they were also buried real close to the baby. Neal thought a lot of them too. He still goes to the cemetery a lot."

"Bertha said that she didn't have brothers and sisters. Tell me a little about her growing up?" Frank asked.

"Bertha was spoiled rotten," John said. "Her Mama and Papa worshipped that girl. I'm gonna tell you something, Mr. Deputy, that my daddy told me. He said that the railroad was hiring back in the twenties over near Cedar Bluff. They were doing some track repair. A bunch of the local men got a job with them and was making decent money. You know the old saying that it don't rain on the railroad? Well the sun don't get too bright, either. There were men waiting for your job if you couldn't hack it. My daddy said that he saw Mr. Bud Hardin work a ten and twelve hour shift and never take a break. He said that sweat would run down his legs soak his socks and fill his shoes. At the end of the day he would squish all the way home and it was two or three miles.

"When he got to the house Bertha would pitch a fit for a piece of candy and he would walk another mile to the store and back just to get it for her. I'm telling you, Deputy, as much as I like her, if she done something to that old couple, she deserves anything she gets."

Everybody sat in total quiet for what seemed the longest time. Frank finally stood up and thanked the Blacks for their hospitality and left the house. As they walked out on the porch Frank thought Harry was going to be sick. His face was pale and he looked like he was going to throw up. They started back to Rome and after several miles, Harry was the first to speak.

"Did you expect anything like that, Frank?" Harry asked. "Can you imagine a hat pin being stuck in a baby's head? I hope that wasn't right."

"Me too," Frank said. "But we sure learned a lot today. A lot of my questions got answered. And some more have popped up."

"What are you saying that you learned?" Harry asked.

"That Bertha can lie with a straight face, and it's believable," Frank said.

"And that Neal Gossett had nothing to do with Leroy Hill's death."

"Well, Mrs. Pauline said that she was sweet as pie most of the time," Harry said.

"It's the other part of the time that I'm worried about," Frank replied. "She also said that Ginny Knight was her best friend growing up. Remember that name, Harry. We're gonna talk to Mrs. Knight one of these days."

"It's in my notes, Frank. What do you think John Black meant when he said 'if she done anything to those old folks'."

"You know, Harry. You know."

₪   ₪

It was Monday morning at the Partridge and the breakfast club was all assembled. The newspaper folks were here early trying to pick up any tidbit of news from the weekend that the radio folks might have missed. Both were anxious to hear from the Health Commissioner.

"Doc, are you gonna tell us what's going on at the courthouse?" Happy Quarles asked. "I can understand why you didn't tell us last Friday, but the coroner's inquest is over now."

"Happy, you know about as much as I do," Doc Elmore said. "I testified at the inquest. You know that. And the jury ordered an autopsy and it was done up at Jennings by some doctor that Dewey got out of Atlanta. You know that too. The report ain't back yet and when it gets here, you'll probably know about it before I do. I'll most likely read about it in the paper."

"Well, why are Russell and Davis going door to door on Broad Street, and driving all over Armuchee asking questions?"

"Why don't you ask them?" the doc said.

"'Cause they ain't there, they're always gone," Happy replied.

"Well I don't know where they are," Elmore said, turning to Cecil Rhodes and refusing to answer any more questions from Happy. "How was business this weekend, Cecil?"

"It was pretty good," he replied, "I did what you said last Friday. I went back and doubled my order on baby clothes. Maternity clothes too. We're gonna have the best supply in town."

"What about that little store on the other side of the street up in the 300 block?" John Moss asked. "The Lad and Lassie, they don't do nothing but kids clothes."

"Different price range, John," Cecil said, "That's like us and Hix's place. Owens-King sells a higher dollar line of suits than we do. No real competition."

"Yeah but Kessler's and Penny's don't," Macon Brock said. "You're gonna have to have some big sales to compete with those folks, Cecil."

"Just what we're gonna do, Macon," Cecil replied. "We've always been able to compete with them. We have to keep a good selection, decent prices and a quality product. Plus maintain a good reputation. We all have that right now.

"The working woman who comes to Broad goes to all three stores before she usually makes a purchase. We just gotta make sure she comes back to us after she's looked around."

"I can't believe you guys are talking about baby clothes with a woman sitting in jail for maybe killing her husband. And him buried yesterday in North Carolina and ain't even thirty yet." Happy Quarles said.

"Dang, I almost finished my breakfast before you got wound up again," Doc said.

Johnny was laughing at Dr. Elmore and Happy Quarles when he said, "Don't you two ever let up on each other? Everybody knows y'all don't really mean anything."

"They do look like some kind of chicken fight, don't they?" Jack Harris said.

"They're always circling each other looking for an opening to jab at the other fellow."

"He is right though, Doc," Ben Cooper said, "This could be the biggest court case in our part of the country in a long time. That is, if it goes to court. At the paper we're probably gonna have one reporter follow every little detail real close, and if something breaks, then hopefully we'll be ready."

"Good idea Ben," Doc said. And then looking down to the end of the table where John Powers was apparently deep in thought, he asked, "What's wrong with you this morning John? The dime store business not doing as good as you want?"

"Doc we're doing pretty good at Allen's," Powers said, "But we've got a lot of competition. I was trying to think of a way to capitalize on this baby boom you've predicted. I've been thinking about it all week-end."

Johnny Jacobs walked back over to the table and said, "I heard that, John. Don't you sell bibs, rattles, playpens and those kind of things. I'll bet they're gonna take off too."

"He's right, John," Dr. Elmore said. "Any of the things that Johnny mentioned are gonna be big sellers. Plus teething rings and anything you can think of for the newborn. Load up now and avoid the rush."

"And don't forget the *Rome News* wants to handle all of your advertising,"

Ben Cooper added. "And that goes for everybody here."

"That's a good idea," John said. "We carry all of that but it's usually a slow mover. But now I think I'll take the plunge."

"You won't regret it, I promise," Doc said.

"Boys I gotta head out. Y'all ready to flip?" John Moss said.

# Chapter 12

Frank walked into the jail and went straight to his office. He wanted to rewrite his notes into a more sensible ledger. Most police officers simply put their notes on scratch paper and if a court case did come up, they would try to decipher them on the stand. Frank had insisted that the sheriff's deputies make good notes and have them written and accessible to the solicitor if he wanted to see them before court.

Frank felt that this case was only just beginning and he had started to prepare himself for court. The last thing he wanted to do was get so far behind with the paper work that he couldn't remember or catch up when the time came to make a presentation to a grand jury or testify in court. Just as he was beginning to write, Harry came into his office. He had just put the car up and was looking for further instructions.

"Where do we go from here?" Harry asked. "What's next on the schedule?"

"Harry I know it's late," Frank said. "But I want you to try and finish up with the insurance companies today if you can. If not, you can start back tomorrow morning. We've got to get them out of the way before we get started again.

"Before you do anything else though, I wish you'd make the jail check for me while I get started on my paper work."

"Will do," Harry replied. "I saw that Bill Payne's already here. Think I'll get him to help me. That way it won't take so long."

"Good idea," Frank said. "Just let me know if there's a problem. Take the roster and make sure it's been updated and that everybody's where they're supposed to be."

Frank was busy with his paper work when Bill Payne stopped at his office door and gave a quick knock.

"You don't have to knock, Bill," Frank said. "You know that. Just come on in."

"Chief, that little preacher's back and he wants to see Bertha and Mattie. I told him that this wasn't normally a day we allowed visitors but since you were here and he insisted, I thought I would ask."

"What little preacher and why does he want to see the women?" Frank asked.

"He says that his name is Reverend Lemuel Abbott and he's the pastor of a small Baptist church down toward Seney, right before you go into Polk County. He's been coming around for the last several months, Chief. I'm sure that you'd recognize him once you see him."

"Why is he here today?" Frank asked. "I don't understand."

"Says that he has some money for the women, and he wants to speak with you," Deputy Payne said.

"Bring him in," Frank said, "And let's see what he wants."

Frank stood and greeted the Reverend and the lady with him. He then asked them both to please come in. The preacher introduced the woman as his wife Maeleigh Grace. Frank extended a cordial welcome to Mrs. Abbott and asked them both to please have a seat. As soon as both parties were seated he asked Bill to remain in the room and he sat down and asked, "Reverend Abbott, why do you want to see the women prisoners on Monday?"

"Mr. Russell, I was here yesterday and had a chance to talk to Miss Mattie and Mrs. Bertha. We had quite a lengthy prayer upstairs. After I got home I told Maeleigh Grace about it and nothing wouldn't do but for her to fry a chicken and fix some greens and cornbread and have me and her drive all the way back to the jail and see that they got it.

"'Course she couldn't go into the jail and I wouldn't expect her to, but she told me that she sat in the car and said a prayer while I brought the chicken in. Your deputy was kind enough to take it up to the ladies and bring her basket back down.

"When we got back to the church right before Sunday night services, Maeleigh Grace got her women's prayer group off to one side and they had a little group meeting of their own. I told the congregation what all went on up here Sunday afternoon and right then and there somebody said that we ought to take up a love offering to help these poor souls along their way.

"That's exactly what we did, and I got almost forty dollars that I want to get to those poor women. And the ladies of the church sent along another basket. There are some pear preserves, fried pies, a chocolate cake and a bowl of pinto beans and mashed potatoes with a pone of cornbread to go with it. Maybe a few other food items. I don't really remember.

"I know there is a sewing kit. Mrs. Bertha said that she loved to sew. The ladies sent her some needles, thread, and scraps to work with. And we want to be able to bring them some things to help them at least once a week, if it's all right with you."

Frank was speechless. For a long moment he just looked into the grinning faces of Lemuel and Maeleigh Grace Abbott. *If this is the kind of people heaven's populated with, I want to go. They ask nothing in return. Go out of their way to try and help somebody who may not deserve that help. But they follow the book and refuse to judge. So who am I to refuse their charity?*

"Bill, go through the basket, count the money and take it up to the women," Frank ordered. "Make a notation of the money on the jail docket."

"I'm on the way, Chief," Bill replied.

Frank pushed forward in his chair and addressed the Abbotts.

"I think it's a wonderful thing that y'all are doing. I don't mind if you bring a small basket of selected items once a week and I'll tell the jailers that you may be coming. But I hope you understand that once a week is all that we can allow, and I wish you'd limit that to Sunday visiting hours. We have extra deputies during those hours and are better prepared to receive guests in the jail on the proper day."

"Oh, Mr. Russell, we thank you so much," Maeleigh Grace said. "You know our Lord asked His disciples if they fed Him when he was hungry, clothed Him when He was naked and visited Him when He was in prison. Although they asked when any of those things pertained to Him, He replied that when you do any of those things for My children you do them for Me. And you've allowed us to do those things for some of His children, may God bless you, Deputy."

"Thank you ma'am, Frank said. "I appreciate that."

Frank was waiting for Bill to return when he decided to ask the Reverend about yesterday.

"Reverend Abbott, you said that you had a lengthy prayer meeting with the ladies, is that right?" Frank asked.

"Yes it is," Reverend Abbott replied.

"I don't know exactly how I want to phrase this," Frank said, "Don't get me wrong. I know we have preachers in the jail every week, but how did you happen to have a lengthy prayer with Mattie and Bertha."

The Reverend grinned from ear to ear, looked at Frank and said, "You feel it too, don't you Deputy Russell?"

"Well, I feel something, although I'm not too sure what it is," Frank said.

"Deputy Russell, let me explain," Reverend Abbott said. "I've been coming to this jail now for several months. I also visit the jail in Polk County. Most of the times those jail visits are all the same. I ask the prisoners if they want to have prayer. And of course some do and some don't. I try to testify to the ones that I can and always ask if they know Jesus as their Lord and Saviour. I have been able with the Lord's help to lead a few prisoners to Christ. I just try to give a little spiritual guidance whenever possible.

"That's what I was doing when I got to Mrs. Bertha's cell. When I asked her if she wanted to have prayer, she jumped at the chance. As soon as I began to pray she joined in. Mr. Russell I want you to know that woman can pray. She began to testify and praise the Lord, and then the tears started rolling. I couldn't stand it any longer and I was crying as hard as she was. She said that she was saved but hadn't lived for Christ like she should and re-dedicated her life right there in the cell.

"While we were on our knees with only the bars between us, she reached up and pulled Mattie down beside her and she got to crying too. I asked Mattie if she knew Jesus as her Lord and Saviour. She said she didn't, but she wanted to. She is going to be praying with Bertha this week and hopefully Bertha will lead her to the Lord.

"Anyway, while we were praying, I guess we got a little loud, another visiting preacher heard us and he came running and joined in. There were also a couple of trusties that joined our session and one of them got saved right there in the floor.

"After the prayer session was over, I just stayed and talked to the women for the better part of an hour. Mrs. Bertha did most of the talking. Mattie just shook her head in agreement. That's when I found out that Bertha had been locked up without a dime, no personal things and that they were about to starve to death. She also informed me that she was a poor orphan and widow with no family to help her. When I told Maeleigh Grace and my little flock what happened, well you know the rest, and like she done told you, we're very appreciative to what you've done."

"Thank you for sharing that with me, Reverend," Frank said." You've helped open my eyes as well."

"You're welcome, Deputy, and if you're ever out our way, please stop in and see us. We'd love to have you visit. And Mr. Russell, I understand about jailhouse religion. I've been doing this kind of ministry for a long time. It's not for me to decide if a prisoner is trying to con me or not. God will take care of that in due time. All I'm supposed to do is spread the word."

Frank walked to the jail door with the Abbott's and wished them a safe drive back to Seney.

"Thank you once again," Maeleigh Grace said. "We'll see you Sunday evening."

"I look forward to it," Frank said. Turning and going back into the jail, he spotted Bill Payne at the booking desk.

"Go upstairs and split Bertha and Mattie up. You can leave them next to each other but not in the same cell. And I don't want any other women put in the cell with either one of them in the future."

"On the way Chief," Bill said as he vanished into the bowels of the jail.

ℕ    ℕ

"What's on the agenda today, Boss?" Harry asked as he finished his second cup of coffee and continued to make love to a doughnut.

"Harry, you're gonna have to work by yourself today. I've got so much jail work to do it ain't funny and I can't spare anybody to help you. Really it would take too long to have another deputy brought up to speed on this case anyway."

"What do you want me to do?" Harry asked, finishing the dough-nut and licking the glaze off of his fingers.

"Ever since this case started I've wanted to check with the hospitals about the treatment Leroy received while he was there. For one reason or another we got sidetracked along the way. I want you to go to all three hospitals and find out why he was there, when he was there, how long he was there, and who treated him. Bertha told me he was at Harbin Hospital once and Floyd twice. We've established the fact that she will lie and is believable. I want you to check at McCall Hospital also and ask all three about Mr. and Mrs. Hardin. Get the same information on each of them."

"Frank, that might take longer than just today. You realize that, don't you?"

"Yes I do, Harry," Frank said, "It may take a couple of days, maybe three, but that's OK. I want doctors' names, how to get in touch with them for court purposes, same with hospital record clerks. When you do get finished I want to see your notes so I can bring myself up to date. Can't have you getting too far ahead of me, plus I gotta report to the sheriff."

"I still got a couple of insurance companies left to contact. You want me to just forget them?"

"Let me ask you something Harry," Frank said. "Suppose you're on the stand and the defense attorney asks you if you checked with all of the insurance companies in Rome. You say almost all of them, there were just a couple I didn't get to. What do you think he would say next?"

"I get your point, Boss," Harry answered. "I'll finish them first. Then I can put that to bed before I start on the hospitals."

"That's what you need to do Harry, and remember to make good notes on everything. I know I'm repeating myself but just remember the five things you want to find out are, who, when, where, why and how. You answer those things and you're gonna have the beginnings of a good case file."

"I never made a case file before, Frank. The last time I was in court I had made a few notes on a match book cover and I read them off of that. I'm learning a lot about police work on this case."

"This has the makings of a once-in-a-lifetime case, Harry. And if it is, I don't want to lose it for lack of something we didn't do. It may blow over and fizzle into nothing, but it ain't yet. And until it does, we're gonna treat it with the respect it deserves.

"The way I see it Harry, is this way. This case is gonna have a lot to do with medical reports and findings. And once the lawyers all get involved on both sides there's gonna be all kinds of motions flying. Them doctors and lawyers all have about seven or eight years of college. The average police officer has about ten years in a cotton mill or service station. We're the red-headed stepchild in this family.

"I heard a City of Rome Commissioner say one time when I was working over there that he didn't need to educate or pay police officers any more than bare minimum. That he could find them anywhere. In fact he said that when a man got too sorry to drive a cab he could always hire him as an officer. I wanted to hit him right in the mouth. But the problem is that's the truth of the matter. I worked with officers on the Rome P.D. in the thirties that couldn't read and write. But they could go in the Bumble Bee or the Triangle and clean it out. Yes sir, them old boys could stand toe to toe with anybody. But if it wasn't physical, they were lost.

"Law enforcement's got to change Harry. We won't be able to keep up with the other members of the criminal justice family if we don't. The trouble is I don't see that happening in our lifetime. So I have to look at it this way. This case is mine. I've brought you in to help me with it, and we ain't gonna be the ones that lose it. We might get blamed for it if it goes down the drain. In fact, I'm pretty sure we will, but we'll know better. I didn't intend to make no speech this morning. I just want you to see the importance of this case the way I do. If we're together on this thing, and check each other constantly, we'll be just fine."

"Wow, and I thought we were just trying to find out what happened to Leroy," Harry said. "I didn't know you thought it might turn into something that big."

"It might not Harry," Frank said, "But if it does, we won't get caught with our pants down."

"I'll see you this afternoon Chief," Harry said as he left the office and headed for the street.

Frank scheduled a meeting with his jail staff for later in the afternoon and began to read through the stack of papers on his desk. *I got at best two or three days before all hell breaks loose.*

# Chapter 13

Bertha rolled over on her stomach and asked Mattie, "Well, how was your first night alone?"

The jailer had split them up the night before. He had also brought a basket of food and they had halved that. Bertha had asked why they were being moved apart and the jailer had told her that he didn't know. Even in different cells they were only separated by a steel wall. The bars of the cells opened toward the hallway and as both women lay in their bunks, they were actually closer than they had been when they were together.

"Bertha, you're a genius," Mattie said, "I never would have believed that they would give us our own cell."

"They wouldn't have if we'd have asked," Bertha said, "That little preacher threw 'em a curve. Bless his heart. They don't know what we're up to, or what to do with us, so splitting us up is their solution. We're easier to watch."

"I been locked up for two months and last night was the first time I've been alone since I been here. It sure was nice. I mean if you gotta be in jail, being by yourself is a lot more comfortable."

"I'll say," Bertha replied, "And that preacher's wife sure can fry chicken. I can't do much better myself. What did he say her name was?"

"Maeleigh Grace," Mattie said. "Maeleigh Grace Abbott."

"Well, bless her heart, too," Bertha said. "I'm gonna make that old girl a quilt top if I can get enough scraps. And I believe I can."

"What kind of scraps?" a small voice asked from the hallway.

Both women reacted swiftly and looked toward the hallway. Standing before the bars in front of Bertha's cell was a small, very cute little boy.

"What's your name, cutie?" Mattie asked.

"Danny," the little boy said.

"Got a last name?" she asked.

"Danny Garrett," he replied.

"Well Danny Garrett, I been here for a pretty long time and I ain't never seen you up here before. What did they lock you up for?" Mattie asked with a big smile on her face.

"I'm not locked up," he replied. "Frank Russell is my married to my sister Christine. We live in the jail.

"The big door is usually shut. Besides, Frank told me I couldn't come up here 'cause the ladies might be using the bathroom or something."

"Hey Danny," Bertha said, "we've hung blankets in front of our toilets, now that we're by ourselves. You can come and visit as often as you're allowed."

"What kind of scraps?" Danny asked again.

"Let me show you," Bertha said as she broke out a handful of colorful cloth scraps in all sizes and shapes. "These are the scraps that ladies have left over from making dresses and things like that."

"Chris has got all kinds of scraps like that," Danny said, "You want me to get you some."

"I sure do, if Chris don't mind."

"She won't," Danny replied.

"Danny, I already owe you for one big favor," Bertha said.

"What's that?" Danny asked.

"The other day I was downstairs talking to Mr. Russell and he had the jailer bring me a saucer of apple cobbler. He told the jailer to check with Chris and see if her brother had left any. So I owe you for not eating it all. And it sure was good."

"Chris is a real good cook," Danny replied, "I think she has some cake left from yesterday's dinner. If she does would you like some?"

"Well Danny, we don't want to get you in trouble or anything. But if your sister doesn't mind, we sure would."

Danny was gone as quick as he had arrived. Bertha turned to Mattie and said, "Mattie, we've got to fix a compact mirror on the bars so we can see who's coming down the hall. I don't like getting sneaked up on."

"I'm way ahead of you this time Bertha," Mattie said. "I've got a piece of a broke mirror in my purse and I'm gonna take care of that."

"We gotta be careful about lying on our backs and talking to the ceiling," Bertha said. "Especially if they start leaving that door open.

"Bertha, I been meaning to ask you something," Mattie said, "Why do you think I ain't got a trial date yet?"

"Aw Mattie, they're just trying to wait you out. They're thinking you'll finally break and tell them who your boyfriend is if you stay here long enough."

"Well, they're pretty close to being right. I've about had it. That is, till that little preacher and his flock fed us and give us some money to get things with."

"Mattie, do you want to shake the tree a little bit?" Bertha asked.

"What do you mean?"

"Can you get a note to your boyfriend without him getting caught?" Bertha asked.

"I've got a sister who visits me ever week," Mattie said. "She could do it."

"Here's what you do. Write a note and tell boyfriend to give every bit of the missing money to your sister. I mean have him set up a time and place. Tell your sister to take the money to your lawyer and get a receipt and for him to go back to the bank and make full restitution. Of course tell him to try to work out a deal with the bank first, but even if he can't, when you get in court it's gonna help you if the judge knows that the bank's got their money back."

"What if he won't do it?" Mattie asked." It was a pretty good little sum of cash."

"He'll do it, Mattie," Bertha said. "I guarantee it. Just put in the note that you're beginning to feel more and more like a canary every day."

"Somebody's coming," Mattie said real quietly.

Danny appeared once again before the bars. He carried two bowls full of coconut cake and a paper bag full of cloth scraps.

"I can't stay and talk this time," Danny said. "I'll bring y'all some more scraps when I can."

"Danny, you're a sweetie," Mattie said.

"You sure are," Bertha said, "You're a little dear. You can come and visit any time you want."

"Oh, Miss Weaver," Bertha said very dignified. "Would you like some of Maeleigh Grace's peach preserves to top off your coconut cake?"

"Why yes, Mrs. Hill, I believe I would," Mattie replied, very lady-like.

₪   ₪

The knocking on the door startled Frank. He was used to the jail deputies rousting him out of his apartment on the weekends but they never knocked this long or this hard.

"Hold on a minute! I'm coming," Frank hollered at the door. "What's going on?"

"The sheriff stopped by the jail just long enough to tell us to get you on the way to his office," the deputy said. "He wants you over there five minutes ago."

"What's he doing in the office on Saturday?" Frank asked. "He don't usually work on the weekend unless he's way behind or something's going on."

"Chief, you know he don't tell me. I don't have a clue."

"I was just talking to myself out loud," Frank said. "I gotta pretty good idea."

Frank hustled across the street and went straight to the sheriff's office. As he entered the office Mark Horton looked up at him and said, "Have a seat Frank. I want you to read this." He handed Frank an envelope.

Frank opened up the envelope, unfolded the letter, and read to himself. He already suspected what the contents were but this solidified his suspicions.

"Who knows about this?" he asked the sheriff.

"The report came to Dr. Battle," Sheriff Horton said. "He brought it by my house and gave it to me about an hour ago. He's going out of town for a few days and wanted to make sure that we had the report before he left.

"He said that he didn't know if Henderson or Dewey got a copy or not. Anyway I called them both and they didn't, so they're on their way here. I guess we're going to have a war council this afternoon and see where we're at and where we're going."

"That sounds like a good idea," Frank said. "Did Dr. Battle add anything to the report that you have?"

"I almost forgot. He said that he called Dr. Lewis in Atlanta to ask a few additional questions after he opened the report. Medical stuff I guess. Anyway, to make a long story short, he said that Dr. Lewis told him that Leroy had enough arsenic in him to kill ten men."

"And it wasn't from injections or pills from syphilis treatment. Is that correct?"

"That would be correct and I know what you're gonna ask next, and no it wasn't from being embalmed either. Dr. Battle said that he got this arsenic in him while he was alive, not after."

"That pretty much nails it down, don't it?" Frank said.

"Not quite. All we know right now is that somebody killed Leroy Hill. We got a pretty good idea who, but it ain't all tied up in Christmas wrapping paper just yet."

Dewey was the first to come in. He looked at Mark and said, "Can we hurry this up? I'm shorthanded at the station and Saturday is one of my busiest days."

"Just as soon as Henderson gets here we can get started," Mark said.

About fifteen minutes later the solicitor came in and was followed by Graham Wright. Both men pulled up chairs and took a seat. Henderson Lanham looked at the Sheriff and asked, "Is this what I think it is?"

"We've got the autopsy report on Leroy Hill," Mark replied. For the next fifteen or twenty minutes Sheriff Horton reviewed the entire investigation with the solicitor, the coroner and attorney Wright. He finished up with his conversation with Dr. Battle and what the doctor had told him personally.

"Dewey we'll need to re-convene the coroner's jury as soon as possible. Mark, did you say that Lee would be back on Wednesday?" Lanham asked.

"That's what he said." Mark replied.

"OK, that's fine with us. Does that suit you Dewey?" Henderson asked.

"Consider it done," he said. "Can I leave? I have to make a living."

"Do you need anything else from Dewey, Mark?" Henderson asked.

"Nothing I can think of," Mark replied.

Dewey was up and on his way out when he stopped at the door and told the group that he would see them upstairs in Henderson's office on Wednesday.

Henderson turned to Graham Wright and said, "I want you to make the press release today, and finish up the coroner's inquest next Wednesday. We're gonna be looking for a verdict to hold Bertha Hill pending action by the grand jury."

"You want me to make the press release on the other thing, too?" Graham asked.

"No, I'm gonna handle that. I want you to concentrate on the coroner's jury."

"What other thing?" Frank Russell asked.

"Sheriff, I'm going to ask the Alabama authorities to disinter Mr. and Mrs. Hardin. Actually I asked about the possibility of doing that last week, but they weren't very receptive. I don't think they have much choice now. Also I want to look into the reason Jordan Funeral Home didn't try or check to see if Removal from the State permits existed. Is Frank gonna be continuing with your part of the investigation?"

"Yes he is," Mark replied.

"Frank I wasn't ignoring you. I just had to make sure that Mark wasn't going to move in another way. I didn't think he would, but I had to make sure. You're doing a great job and we expect that to continue."

"That's OK, Mr. Solicitor," Frank said. "I want to be able to finish this case."

"And you will Frank," Henderson said. "I guarantee it."

₪     ₪

Frank returned to his office at the jail and had the deputies bring Bertha down. As she entered his office he could tell that she was in good spirits and was laughing and joking with the deputies. Frank stood as she entered the room and motioned for her to take a chair. He pulled up a chair directly in front of her. This time he was serious. He didn't want a desk or any other item that might serve as a barrier between them. He knew that what he was going to tell her would upset her. How much, he didn't know. He was hoping that the shock factor of his message would shake the truth out of her. He had read many books on interviewing techniques and this one seemed to work when others failed. Especially on hard to reach customers like Bertha.

"Why Mr. Russell, I didn't expect you to be working on Saturday," Bertha said.

"Normally I don't," Frank said. "Unless we have a problem in the jail or on the street."

"So which is it?" Bertha asked, "In the jail or on the street?"

"Well, this time it's neither," Frank said, "I wanted to talk to you."

"Is that why we're sitting so cozy, Mr. Russell? But don't worry, I like it."

"No Bertha, it's very serious and I want to make sure that we understand each other," Frank said.

"It's very serious to me that I'm in jail for nothing," Bertha said. "What else could you tell me to top that?"

"The autopsy report is back on Leroy," Frank said.

"And?" she inquired.

"He was full of arsenic," Frank replied.

Bertha didn't quiver or move a muscle. Frank was hoping for a response of some kind, but it didn't happen. She gave no indication that he stressed her in the least bit.

After what seemed like hours Bertha dropped her head, folded her hands in her lap and said, "Poor Leroy! I certainly hope Deputy Russell finds out how you got all that stuff in you. I just can't imagine." Then looking up at Frank, she said, "You will try to find out, won't you, Deputy Russell?"

"Oh yes, Bertha. I'm gonna find out, you can bank on that," Frank said.

"I do hope so. It ain't right for poor Leroy to be laying in the ground up there in Carolina and us not even knowing how he got that stuff in him. Is that all you wanted Deputy Russell? I do thank you for sharing that with me."

Frank slid his chair a little closer to where Bertha was sitting. His knee was nearly touching her leg. He could reach out and touch her very lightly on the knee, arm, or hand. When he did he could feel her recoil slightly. Now, he thought, we're starting to get somewhere.

He realized all people have a vulnerable personal space. But they're all a little different. The trick is to get as close to the suspect as you can and make that person very uncomfortable. To do that you had to violate the individual's personal space. Frank knew that was usually eighteen inches to two feet. However, there were some people who couldn't stand it if you got with-in three or four feet, and others you had to get within six inches to be effective. It appeared to Frank that Bertha was in this last group.

"There's one other thing that I wanted to tell you, Bertha," Frank said. "The decision has been made to disinter Mr. and Mrs. Hardin."

Frank was studying her face as he told her about the upcoming disinterment. This time he thought he saw a noticeable tick right at the corner of her mouth. And he could feel rather than see any anxiety being exhibited. Her eyes were flashing, searching for just the right words.

"What does that mean, to disinter somebody?" Bertha asked.

"To disinter means to exhume or literally dig them up," Frank said. "And then perform an autopsy on them."

"Why do you want to do that?" Bertha asked, choosing her words very carefully.

"Our investigation so far has revealed that your mother and father died of similar circumstances to Leroy. We're going to check and see just how similar they were," Frank replied.

"I don't really want y'all to do that, Mr. Russell," Bertha said sliding her chair even closer to Frank and laying her hand on his knee. She looked him right in the eye and said, "Don't play games with me, Deputy. If you want to know something, why don't you try asking?"

Frank felt like he was witnessing a different side of Bertha that had come out of nowhere. He thought that he had seen them all, but was caught by surprise at this statement. When he looked into her eyes now, they appeared dead and vacant. They reminded him of two empty black caves, dark and scary. Frank now knew that he would not be violating her personal space. *If we were playing checks it'd be my move.*

"Did you have anything to do with your mother and father's death?" Frank asked.

Bertha never took her eyes from Frank's face. She leaned a little closer and almost in a whisper asked, "Have you ever been with somebody just before they died? You know, when your eyes are the last thing they look into and you wonder what were they thinking?"

Frank felt his blood pressure starting to rise. He felt like he had ants crawling all over him. Her eyes didn't blink and that smile was back on her face. She had reversed this interview and violated his personal space.

She gave him a healthy squeeze on the knee, and not giving him a chance to answer, continued, "Absolutely not, and I'm not going to talk to you anymore today. Take me back to my cell, please."

Bertha entered the cell, climbed up on the top bunk and stared at the ceiling.

"What's wrong, Bertha? What did they want?" Mattie asked from on the other side of the steel wall.

"Mattie, do you remember the little children's book about Chicken Little?" Bertha asked. "I bet I sold a thousand of them at McClellan's."

"Sure I do," Mattie said. "What's that got to do with anything?"

"The sky's falling," Bertha said. "The sky's falling."

# Chapter 14

It had turned cool this Monday morning. "Today's date is the 25th," Johnny Jacobs mumbled as he prepared the table for the breakfast clubbers. "February's gonna be over and we ain't had much winter at all. Bugs will be bad this summer. Sure do need a good freeze for a week or two."

The breakfast club men started drifting in. After a little small chat and the first cup of coffee was poured, Macon Brock said, "Ben, I read your morning article yesterday about the arsenic case. I was just wandering, is there more to this case than we know at this time?"

"Macon, I don't believe we've even scratched the surface of this thing yet. I've never seen it so hard to get information out of the solicitor, coroner, or the sheriff."

"What about Russell?" Macon asked. "He appears to be the handling the investigation. Can't you get him to elaborate a little?"

"Russell never talks to the paper about any case," Ben Cooper stated, "He sure ain't gonna comment on this thing."

"I stopped Harry Davis on the street Saturday," John Powers said. "I couldn't get him to say a word either, and he's usually pretty talkative."

"So when's the coroner's jury gonna reconvene?" Cecil Rhodes asked. "The paper said tonight, is that right?"

"We thought it was," Cooper replied, "But after we went to press we found out that Dr. Lee Battle was out of town and would be until Wednesday."

"Well I don't see why we have to wait," Happy Quarles said. "We've got the Health Commissioner right here at the table. He's the one I hear started this investigation anyway. He could clear up the whole case if he wanted to."

"You know Happy, sometimes you amaze me," Dr. Elmore said. "If your brains were leather you wouldn't have enough to make a saddle for a bug. I'm not going tell you or Ben anything, and I like Ben. You boys are going to have to wait until the inquest is over."

Johnny came back over to the table with the waitress as she brought more coffee. He sat down and asked, "Is everything all right over here this morning? Does anybody need anything else?"

"Johnny I've been meaning to ask you about your coffee," John Moss said. "The Krystal downtown has a sign in their restaurant that says they have the best coffee in town. And it is good coffee, I'll give them that. But this coffee is the best I've ever had anywhere. Have you got a big secret?"

"During the War we had to struggle like everybody did just to have coffee. But I've got a relative in New York City who has a connection with the Waldorf-Astoria. They have their coffee special made. You can't buy it over the counter or from a distributor. That's what you're drinking, John. Let all the other guys put signs up if they want to, but they can't touch this. And I'm glad you noticed it."

"Well it sure is good, Johnny," John Moss said and then added, "Boys, I've been thinking. On this Leroy Hill case the only logical thing the coroner's jury can do is bind this case over to the grand jury, and the sitting jury's term doesn't end for over a month. So I'm thinking we have an ace in the hole."

"What ace is that, John?" Happy asked.

"I'd like to know that myself," Ben Cooper said.

"Well think about it. Who hasn't said one word this morning about the arsenic case?" John replied.

"Hix, you'd better run like the devil," Dr. Elmore said. "The vigilantes are coming."

"Y'all do remember that Hix is serving as clerk on this sitting grand jury, don't you?" John Moss asked.

"And he's gonna get all the information, hear all the witnesses firsthand and run right down here and tell us, ain't you Hix?" Macon asked.

"Not on your life, guys," Hix Sims said, "I like each of you, but I ain't gonna have Henderson Lanham or Judge Porter after me."

"Just keeping us informed won't get you in trouble," Happy Quarles said. "Besides, the public has a right to know."

"They may have a right, but not from me they don't," Hix replied. "There's a lot of other men on that jury. Y'all go and ask them."

"I got my pad and pencil right here, Hix," Happy replied, "Tell me who they are."

"I don't walk around with a list in my pocket, but I do remember most of them. It seems like we've been on this term forever," Hix answered and then said, "Alright, here goes--start writing, Happy--there's William Colquitt, he works at Knight's Department store in Lindale. And speaking of Lindale, G. Howard Smith, the assistant supervisor of the mill is acting foreman right now. The elected foreman Geston Garner has been sick. Also Herbert Roper, Fair Moon, John Whitehead, Carlton McMullen, Robert Ward, and Wallace Lloyd are all on this term."

"Ain't William Willis on this jury, Hix?" asked Dr. Elmore.

"Yes he is. I don't want to forget our city commissioner," Hix said. And there's Scott Hampton, R.E. Ward, Mark Davis, Fred Hunt, and J.D. Kerce. That's all I think, I might have left somebody out unintentionally, but that should give you plenty of contacts when this verdict is handed down. Just don't call me."

"Or me," Dr. Elmore said.

"Sorry to interrupt good conversation," Cecil Rhodes said. "But it's time to go to work. Grab a coin and we'll see who pays Johnny today."

₪     ₪

That Monday morning, Frank had left Harry in the office getting his notes finalized for the re-convening of the coroner's jury on Wednesday. He had also asked Harry to take care of the jail until he got back.

Frank drove up toward Pleasant Valley. *I've missed something. If Leroy had that much arsenic in him, where is it? If it really did come from Bertha it has to be around the house somewhere. She was never alone from the time he died and couldn't have destroyed it. She wouldn't have had any reason to do so. It's got to be there somewhere, but where? I went through the house myself, and the women folk cleaned it from top to bottom. They should have found any container marked poison. Maybe that's it. Maybe she put into a container that would be less conspicuous. Nah, she didn't expect to be caught.*

Frank pulled into Bertha's yard, walked to the door, and knocked. Ruben McClung answered the door and invited Frank into the house and to have a seat.

"What brings you up this way today Deputy Russell?" Ruben asked.

"Mr. McClung, have you heard that the autopsy report came back on Leroy?"

"Yes, I walked up to Lynch's grocery yesterday and they read me what the paper said. Do you think Bertha's gonna get charged with that, Deputy?"

"I don't really know, but I ain't gonna lie to you, it don't look good for her."

"I guess it don't," Ruben said as he dropped his head and looked at the floor. "Deputy, me and the wife are law abiding people, don't hold no truck with them that steal or hurt other folks. I was gonna call you a little later today. One of my young-uns was kicking a ball around yesterday and it went under the house. He was scared to crawl under there and get it, so he came and got me. I slid up under there on my belly till I got the ball and on the way out I noticed a sack up on the foundation support. I brought it out and put it in the back pantry under a quilt where Bertha's canned goods are. I wish you'd follow me and get it out of the house. I don't want it in here."

Frank followed Ruben McClung to the back pantry and watched as he pulled the quilt off of a two foot stack of fruit jars that Bertha had canned all kinds of preserves in. He then saw what appeared to be a five pound bag that had been opened and had about a pound or two missing. Frank picked up the bag and on the side it had the words Calcium Arsenate printed. Frank noted the time and from whom he had received it. He explained to Mr. McClung that he had come to the residence to look for something such as this. He knew it had to be here somewhere. And he was glad that the McClungs had found it and turned it over instead of him having to tear the place apart looking for it.

He said his goodbyes and asked Mr. McClung to please let him know if he had any other information or if anything else turned up.

As he headed back toward the city, he was elated. *I can't wait to hear how she explains this one!*

₪    ₪

Frank had spent the greater part of Monday reviewing his notes. He had copied the ones that Harry had brought him and was trying to get them all in order.

On Tuesday morning he felt ready. He had one more little chore that he wanted to take care of before the inquest was re-convened. He called for Harry and had him bring a car around. As soon as the morning jail roster was complete, he asked Harry to work the jail for him and he headed for Centre, Alabama.

Frank drove straight to the Jordan Funeral Home, parked his car and went inside. After being directed to Paul Jordan's office, he was seated and spent a few minutes alone waiting for Paul. Frank stood up as Mr. Jordan came into the office. They shook hands and both were seated.

"What can the Jordan Funeral Home do for the Georgia law today?" he asked with a big grin on his face.

"There are a couple of things I wanted to talk to you about," Frank said and then continued. "Did you know that the autopsy report came back on Leroy Hill?"

"I think I remember something about that, although I'm not sure," Mr. Jordan said. "Was it determined that he was poisoned?"

"It was," Frank said, "And of course you know that Jennings shipped him to North Carolina after the autopsy."

"Yes, I'm aware of that," Paul said, "Your deputies scared my driver to death when my hearse was pulled over on the way back to the residence. And then had it diverted to Jennings."

"Well, actually, that was me," Frank said. "I didn't mean to scare him."

"That's OK. He'll get over it," Paul said.

"Mr. Jordan," Frank said, "Like I said a few minutes ago, the autopsy report came back positive on Leroy. And we have reports that Mr. and Mrs. Hardin both died of similar circumstances. Last Friday the solicitor said that he was going to ask Alabama to exhume both bodies and hopefully get an autopsy done to determine if they died of natural causes or not.

"I know from past experiences that when lawyers and judges start throwing court orders and motions around all over the place that the police officer sometimes gets left out. I want to be there when that autopsy is done. It's important to me and to my case. I feel quite sure that your company would be the ones to do it. Can you please notify me when a time is set to carry that out?"

"That's not a problem at all," Paul Jordan said. "But I do believe that the papers will cover it closely. We really don't exhume that many bodies, so when we do, the headlines are usually pretty big."

Frank already knew that the papers would be all over the exhumation of the Hardins. But he had broken the ice with Paul Jordan and it was time to find out about the permits.

"Mr. Jordan, our records indicate that Mr. and Mrs. Hardin were brought back across the state line without a permit to remove them from the Georgia.

"Mr. Hardin didn't have a death certificate and Mrs. Hardin's was issued as undetermined. Leroy was done the same way. No permit to remove him from the state and no death certificate.

"Does that fall under the responsibility of the Funeral Home to make sure that all permits and certificate's are in order?"

Paul Jordan leaned back in his chair and took a long minute to just look at Frank Russell. The office was deathly quiet. Frank sat motionless, waiting for Jordan to speak.

Finally Paul straightened up in his chair, leaned forward on his desk and said, "I knew Bud Hardin. I knew his wife, Mrs. Zola, too. And I got to know Bertha. Now Deputy, let me explain something about the funeral home business. I mean these little country funeral homes like mine. Most of the people around here ain't got much. They are in many cases barely able to scratch out a living. That's the way Bud was most of his life. Way back yonder, back in the late '20s, he purchased a little policy from our burial association for him, his wife and daughter. It took years to pay that policy up. There would be times that he would have nothing but a few pennies and maybe a nickel or two to pay on it, but he always paid something."

Frank saw Mr. Jordan drop his eyes like he was reflecting on something that gave him great pain. After a moment or two of silence, Paul continued, "I often thought that folks like Bud Hardin are the greatest Americans we've had in this country. They're loyal to their family almost to a fault.

"Our association says that if one of our members dies within a 90 mile radius, we go get them and give them a first class funeral. If it's over 90 miles then we contribute $100.00 to their funeral expenses. Bud and Zola were well within the association limits. We went and got them and gave them a first class funeral. I owed that to that old man and I was going to make sure he got what he paid for. And I feel the same way about his wife."

Frank thought Paul was getting just a little perturbed about this line of questioning, but he sat silently and Mr. Jordan continued without interruption.

"Now about Leroy. It was the middle of the night and Mrs. Bertha seemed to be in a hurry. She was grieving pretty bad when I was there, and my first duty is to the surviving family members. I had all the best intentions of calling your health commissioner and checking on any necessary permits the next day, but y'all took him to Jennings for autopsy. We didn't know for a few days whether he was coming back to Alabama or not. Then we found out that he went to North Carolina. I felt like that released us from having to inquire about a permit."

Frank now knew that Paul Jordan was in charge of this meeting and he didn't try to regain that control. To have done so would have caused an obstacle that might prove to be a hindrance later on.

"Mr. Russell, I might be guilty of violating the letter of the law, I don't know. But I'm positive that I'm not guilty of violating the spirit of the law. And I also believe that there ain't a jury in Georgia or Alabama that would convict me or any funeral home director for taking care of his customers, which most of the time are good friends."

Frank stood up and offered his hand one more time to Paul Jordan. As he started out the door he stopped and looked at the funeral home director.

"I can see why your friends and neighbors put such faith in your company, Mr. Jordan. I want to thank you for that little testimonial. I really needed that. You see, often we get so tied up in legal bindings that we really can't see the forest for the trees. I'll see you at the disinterment if the State of Alabama grants our request."

"They will, Deputy, and I'll be there myself to make sure Bud and Zola get the respect that they deserve."

Frank drove back to Rome in deep thought. Mr. Jordan had made him remember why he had chosen to be a police officer. It was gratifying to see somebody who was that serious about his profession.

*I have the same responsibility to Leroy that Mr. Jordan felt for the Hardins. I've got to double my efforts if that's what it takes. Right now I'm Leroy Hill's representative on this earth. I hope soon that the solicitor's office will represent him and the state in a court of law, but we ain't got there yet.*

ঢ়   ঢ়

Frank sat in his chair in the jail apartment and slowly read the *Rome News Tribune's* account of last night's verdict by the re-convened coroner's jury. He noticed that for the first time since the investigation began, they had included a picture of Bertha. He thought it wasn't a very good picture, nor was it a true likeness. But that was the way mug shots usually turned out. The prisoner is either on the way to the cell block or, as in Bertha's case, had spent one night in jail and the picture was taken the next morning when the prisoner was in disarray. However; the written account was very explicit.

The article was titled "Hill Poison Death Slated For Grand Jury" and recounted Frank's testimony about the bag of arsenic and stated that Bertha had taken out insurance policies on Leroy totaling $5,500. It also stated that the solicitor was going to ask Alabama authorities to exhume the Hardins, and Dr. Elmore had testified that he had started the investigation due to some unexplained circumstances surrounding the death of Leroy. Later it was revealed that there were three "mysterious" deaths in the family in less than a year and all were similar in nature.

Frank was pleased with the paper's account of the investigation to this point. He didn't always agree with the way the local papers wrote their stories concerning local police matters or investigations. But then most officers didn't. He had made it a habit to elaborate on just the facts and not to include opinion or assumptions. Now he had to get ready for the grand jury this week. He didn't know the date yet, but felt sure it would be soon.

Frank walked the short block to the courthouse once again and entered the sheriff's office.

"He's waiting on you, Frank," Mrs. Jenkins said. "He told me to tell you to go on in when you got here."

"Thank you, Mrs. Jenkins," Frank said as he entered the office.

"Ain't seen you all day, Frank," Sheriff Horton said. "Sorry I haven't been around the jail in a few days. Been tied up here."

"I know the feeling. Danged jail's packed, got one deputy out sick and another was off for a few days. His wife just had a baby. I have to re-arrange the work schedule almost every day. The cook's been sick off and on for a week, plus we got two cars down."

"Sounds like everyday business, huh."

"I guess so," Frank said. "Wouldn't be too bad if we didn't have this Hill investigation hanging over our heads. Now we gotta get ready for the grand jury this week."

"Got some news about that," Mark said. "I think it will be probably a month or more before we go to the grand jury."

That got Frank's attention. He slid forward in his chair and asked the Sheriff, "Why is that? I really want to get this case to court and beyond. The longer we wait the more media attention we get. The paper today was correct, but I really don't want them to try the case. The newspaper coverage is going to grow daily. Eventually some lawyer will ask for a change of venue. And he just might get it if we try this case in the court of public opinion."

"I know just how you feel Frank. But I met with Henderson and Graham Wright this morning and we decided to wait until the disinterment and the autopsy of Mr. and Mrs. Hardin is complete. After that we'll wait and see what the results are. If they're positive like Leroy's, then we'll go to the grand jury and ask for three indictments rather than just asking for a true bill on Leroy. It shouldn't take more than a month. That will more than give you enough time to get ready to testify. And Frank, when they do the exhumation, I want you there."

"Sheriff, I had already planned on being there. Guess they'll do the autopsy at Jordan Funeral Home. I talked to Mr. Jordan about making sure we got notified of the date and time."

Frank told Mark about his entire conversation with Paul Jordan, especially his feelings about proper permits.

"Let that go," Mark said, "We want these folks to work with us, not hinder our investigation in any way."

"That's just what I was going to do," Frank said, "Unless you ordered it otherwise."

"Keep the jail running and stand by. It won't be as long as you think," Mark said. "Oh yeah, meant to ask you, what did Bertha say about the bag of arsenic under the house?"

"Said it was for her roses," Frank answered, shaking his head in disgust.

"Is she that smart, Frank?" Mark asked.

"I'm beginning to believe she is. She has an answer for everything. The trusties, visiting preachers, and Christine's little brother are enthralled by her. And she's got me lying awake at night planning my next step so I don't goof up."

"Don't let her wear you down," Mark said as Frank left the room.

Frank walked back to the jail in deep thought. *This woman is getting under my skin bad. I'm beginning to believe it ain't ever going to end.*

# Chapter 15

"Bertha you were right again," Mattie said as she folded the letter and placed it back in its envelope from.

"What was I right about this time?" Bertha asked.

"That jailer that was up here a few minutes ago brought me a note from my sister. It says that full restitution has been paid and that my attorney is trying to work out a deal with the solicitor and the bank."

"That's good, Mattie," Bertha said. "Maybe you'll be out of here shortly."

"Well, right now they're just trying to get me a bond hearing. Everybody seems to be resisting that effort. I guess they know that if I leave, I ain't never gonna talk. And they're right, I won't."

"Mattie you're in a good position. Just hang in there a little while longer and they're going to have to let you go, especially now that the bank's got their money back. I'll promise you that they're not going to be too concerned about you anymore. Whatever you get now will be OK with them."

"What about you Bertha? Where do you stand?" Mattie asked.

"Not good Mattie," Bertha said, "I think they'll try to put me in the electric chair before this case is over."

"Oh Lord, Bertha, no!" Mattie exclaimed. "They can't do that. What does your lawyer have to say about it? By the way, who *is* your lawyer? I've never heard you mention one?"

"That's just it, Mattie. They got me on an open felony warrant. I've not been officially charged, so I can't get one appointed till they do. All I can do is set here while they run around all over the county and the edge of Alabama building a case against me."

"But Bertha, eventually they'll have to get you a lawyer won't they?" Mattie asked.

"They will. I just hope it's not too late when they do," Bertha answered.

"Surely Mr. Russell will find out what really happened to Leroy. I can't believe they would try to put you in the chair with no more evidence than they got. Ain't it all circumstantial?" Mattie asked, speaking rapidly.

"It is," Bertha replied. "But yesterday Mr. Russell came up here and asked me where the bag of arsenic under my house came from and what was I doing with it?"

"What did you tell him?"

"I told him the truth. I said I bought it at the hardware and it was for my rose bushes."

"Is that when he turned around and walked away?" Mattie asked.

"You noticed that too, huh. He didn't have too much to say after that."

"I still don't believe they could ask for the death penalty on that. Surely when you get a lawyer, he'll handle all that for you."

"Unfortunately Mattie, that ain't all of it," Bertha stated. "Mr. Russell told me last Saturday that they were going to dig up Papa and Mama and do an autopsy on them."

"What for?" Mattie asked,

"They both died last year. Mr. Russell says it was very similar circumstances. He wants to see just how similar it was."

"Oh," Mattie answered. She didn't know what to say. Her brain was busy trying to sort out everything Bertha had said. She had been in jail with Bertha for the last ten days or so but she still didn't understand her. She thought that she was the nicest person she had ever met. It was hard to believe that Bertha would kill somebody, especially her own parents.

"Listen up Mattie, somebody's coming," Bertha said.

The jailer stopped in front of Bertha's cell and spoke to her through the bars.

"Bertha, since you haven't had any family visits on Sunday, the Sheriff OK'd your aunt and uncle to spend a few minutes with you. They've left a basket of personal things downstairs. I'll get them for you later."

With him were two people who Bertha recognized immediately. Her Uncle Ruben and Aunt Plemma were grinning and reached through the bars and grabbed her as close as they could. Both relatives were very glad to see her.

They spent the next fifteen minutes telling her everything that was going on in the family. Uncle Ruben said he had talked to Judge Porter about appointing Bertha a lawyer. He had told Ruben that just as soon as she was officially charged, he would do just that. While they were discussing family matters, Bertha started sobbing.

"What are you crying about, child?" Plemma McClung asked. "Didn't you hear Ruben? The judge is gonna appoint you a lawyer."

"Aunt Plemma, they're gonna take Mama and Papa up, and I don't want them to."

"I know child. I read that in the paper. That shouldn't bother you. In fact, you should be glad. That oughta clear that up once and for all."

"No aunt Plemma, it won't," Bertha sobbed. "They're gonna find them full of poison."

Plemma's motherly attitude changed immediately. Her eyes became cold and glassy. And with a frosty voice she asked, "How could you possibly know that, Bertha?"

"I saw Leroy give it to them," Bertha said, sobbing more than ever.

"You saw some man give my sister poison and you didn't stop it?" Plemma asked.

"I tried to, but it was too late. She was too far gone."

"And you didn't report it either, did you, Bertha?" Plemma asked.

"I was afraid of what Leroy might do to me," Bertha said. "I'm sorry, Aunt Plemma. I'm really sorry."

Plemma turned to say something to Ruben, but he had walked to the end of the corridor and she could hear him quietly choking back tears.

"Come on Ruben, we're leaving. Bertha we won't be staying in your house any longer. And we won't be back. Neither will any of my other sisters or brothers. The Lord's got a place for you Bertha. It's already prepared."

"I didn't do it, Aunt Plemma! It was Leroy!" Bertha yelled at her aunt and uncle as they walked down the corridor toward the exit.

Mattie lay silent in her bunk. She felt like her whole body had been submerged in ice water. She was tingling all over. She couldn't imagine anything so horrible. Finally she asked Bertha, "Was all of that true?" she asked. Her heart was pounding so hard she had trouble breathing.

Mattie could hear Bertha moving around in her cell. It sounded like she was opening a jar of preserves or fixing something to eat from this past Sunday's leftovers. She could tell by the tone of her voice that all of the tears were gone. Finally Bertha answered, "Pretty much."

שׁ  שׁ

Two weeks had passed and Frank was getting frantic. Nothing had been heard from Alabama concerning the exhumation of Mr. and Mrs. Hardin. Frank was at his desk in the jail when the phone rang.

"Yes Mrs. Jenkins, I'll be right there," he answered hanging up the phone and heading to the courthouse and to the sheriff's office. He had made himself comfortable when Mark came in.

"I called Mrs. Jenkins from the solicitor's office and asked her to call you for me," Horton said. "The report's in from Alabama concerning our request for disinterment. I thought you'd like to read it."

Mark handed Frank a copy of the report that he had received from the solicitor. Frank unfolded the paper and read:

> We received a petition to the Alabama Court. Solicitor-General of Floyd superior Court, Floyd County Georgia asked that the court grant an order to allow the exhumation of the bodies of both Mr. and Mrs. James A. Hardin for the purposes of performing an autopsy and the examination of vital organs of the deceased so that evidence may be obtained by the State of Georgia in determining the causes of their death.
>
> The petition states that Bertha Gossett Hill is being held without bond on an open felony warrant alleging murder, with the specific charge that she administered poison to her husband Leroy Hill thereby causing his death.
>
> It further states that Bertha Hill's foster parents had died under suspicious circumstances, and that both bodies had been removed from the State of Georgia where they died, without burial permits.
>
> The petition was approved by Harris G. Bailey, Solicitor of the ninth Judicial Circuit of Alabama and was submitted to Judge W.J. Haralson for final court order.
>
> Judge Haralson in approving the petition, ordered the State Toxicologist to exhume the bodies of Mr. and Mrs. Hardin and to perform an autopsy on each, with chemical analysis of the vital organs to determine whether or not either of them died from poison or other unnatural causes.
>
> The Judge also ordered that a report be filed with the Cherokee County Court where the findings would be made available to the Floyd Superior Court and to the State of Georgia in connection with charges against Bertha Hill.

"What do you think Frank?" Sheriff Horton said as he watched his chief deputy lay the paper down.

"I was about to get worried," Frank replied. "Now when are they gonna do it?"

"That I honestly don't know at this time," Mark said. "Henderson is going to give them a call sometime today or tomorrow and see if he can speed things up a bit. The toxicologist in Alabama is famous for his scientific and chemical abilities. Has some patents with various drug companies, I understand. He travels around a lot doing training with pharmaceutical company staff. We're gonna have to work on his schedule. But we'll get a first class witness."

"Sheriff, what was that about the Hardins being foster parents?" Frank asked.

"Henderson put that in the petition. I don't know where he got that. Some news source he said."

"Well you just watch, the news guys are all going to run with that now. Parents adopt poor orphan girl and she grows up and kills them. Ain't that gratitude?"

"Were they foster parents Frank?" Mark asked.

"That question hadn't come up," Frank answered. "I guess we're gonna have to find out. But you can bet Bertha's going to have a hissy fit."

₪      ₪

Frank hung the phone up and said, "Harry, get a car. Make sure that we got plenty of gas and bring it around. I'll be out front in just a few minutes."

Harry brought the Ford around to the side entrance of the jail and still had to wait for about ten minutes for Frank Russell to appear.

"Sorry Harry," Frank said, "I had to get back in touch with the sheriff. And I had to tell Christine that I might not be back for awhile."

"That's OK, boss." Harry replied. "Where to?"

"Do you remember the other day when we went to Bill May's grocery, and then doubled back to John and Pauline Black's?"

"I do," Harry said.

"Well, I understand that about half way between the store and John Black's is Howell Cemetery. That's where we're headed."

"No problem," Harry said. "I guess that means today is the day. The one we've been waiting on."

"This is it," Frank said, "It's been a little over a month since the coroner's jury bound Bertha over to the grand jury. We won't have as long to wait after this."

"Ain't this grand jury's term about over, Frank?" Harry asked.

"It sure is, and I'm afraid we'll have to wait until another one is called before we get an indictment. It took nearly two weeks before we got the results on Leroy. It will probably be the same with the Hardins."

Frank and Harry spent almost two hours finding their way to Bill May,s Grocery and then to the Cemetery. The little winding dirt road was dusty for February and there were several cars also heading the same way. The dust got so bad at times that Harry had to almost stop to let it clear up.

"Good thing it's winter time, huh?" Harry said as he squinted at the road trying to find his way. "At least we can keep the windows up. If it was summer time we'd be getting a dust bath or sweating to death with the windows rolled up."

"Just watch where you're going," Frank said. "We're not in that big of a hurry."

They reached the cemetery and were surprised to find a large crowd had already gathered. One of the first people they saw was John Black. He spotted them about the same time and came over to where they were parking their car. He shook hands and said, "This is a big day out here in the country. I don't ever recall anyone being dug up. I've seen lots of people going in the ground, but never one coming out."

"I'm glad that it's not something we have to do very often," Frank said. "I've been policing for nearly fifteen years and this is my second disinterment. Hope it's my last."

"It's my first," Harry said. "Remember Frank, you said that I didn't have to go to the actual autopsy back at the funeral home. You said that I could stay in the office or out in the front lobby or somewhere."

"What are you talking about?" John Black said. "Mr. Jordan put the word out that the autopsy would be done right here in the cemetery. That's the reason most of these folks are out here.

"I mean, I been to a traveling carnival, a bunch of barn dances and all day singings, a championship hog calling and a county wide goat roping, but I ain't never seen nothing like this. And neither has this crowd that's already here, nor the folks still coming this way."

Frank looked down the road. People were walking toward the cemetery as far as he could see. And he figured that every other road leading this way was going to have foot traffic from neighbors and friends coming for several miles.

He went over to where Paul Jordan was standing and asked, "Mr. Jordan, I just heard that the toxicologist was going to do the autopsy here in the cemetery. Is that right?"

"Mr. Russell, this is Dr. C.J. Rehlings. He is the State of Alabama's toxicologist," Paul said as he introduced the doctor to Frank. "And Dr. Rehlings, this is the Georgia police officer that's working the case, Mr. Frank

Russell."

"I'm glad to meet you, Deputy Russell," Dr. Rehlings said. "I hope I can help you with your investigation."

"So do I, Dr. Rehlings," Frank said, "But did I hear right? Are you gonna do the autopsy here in the open?"

"I told Mr. Jordan the other day on the phone that if the weather permitted I thought we'd be just as good here as we would by taking the bodies back to the funeral home and then bringing them all the way back out here and having to re-bury them. The autopsy itself shouldn't take more than an hour.

"I've got two assistants to tag and bag. We can have this thing done and be gone before we could get the bodies to the funeral home and set up. Plus, Paul won't have to scrub his place from top to bottom. He won't be out of business for a day or two. And your solicitor says he wants results as fast as we can get them.

"It's a long drive back to Auburn University where I work. The sooner I get back to the school, the faster you get a report."

"Just asking, Doctor," Frank said. "You're the toxicologist. I'm just here to observe and take notes for a possible court action. Plus Harry brought his Kodak and is going to get a snapshot or two if you don't mind. Well actually, I'll take the pictures. It's kind of a hobby of mine."

"That'll be fine, Deputy," Doctor Rehlings said. "Paul, I'm ready to go if you are."

Paul Jordan had assembled several laborers earlier in the morning to remove the caskets. They had finished digging the graves by the time the crowd had assembled and were waiting word to lift the caskets from the fresh dug earth. It seemed like no time till the first casket was sitting on two cross ties and was ready to open.

Harry Davis was already turning white. He approached Frank and said, "Are they really gonna do it here. I've never seen a body that has been buried nearly a year and then dug up. I think I'll wait in the car."

"Can't do it, Harry. You've got to take notes and log times each step of the way. I'm going to be snapping pictures with your camera, and I need one of me in the shot. You'll have to take it. That is, unless you want to get the close ups in the casket when they open them up."

"I'll take the notes Frank. You help yourself to the Kodak."

The first body that came up was Mr. Hardin. It was enclosed in a vault. Frank thought that Paul Jordan did give the Hardins a first class funeral. Most folks around this part of the country didn't opt to buy a vault with their funeral.

When the vault was opened water poured from it like it had sprung a leak. Harry was doing a little dance trying to keep the water from splashing on him and Frank could hear a man's voice from somewhere close behind him.

"I told you, Ethel, them dang vaults weren't worth a flip. Now you'll know to save your money when I'm gone."

After the casket was open, Dr. Rehlings wasted no time in removing the organs he needed for a chemical analysis. At one point he held an organ in his hand. It was black as coal. He held the organ over his head and turned and faced the throng of people that were crowding in to see what was going on.

"Folks," he said, "this is the liver. And this is what yours looks like if you drink white whiskey. I hope you get a good look and remember what I said here today."

Frank heard the crowd "ooooh" as the doctor walked a few steps with the liver of Bud Hardin in his hand so that everybody got a good look.

Dr. Rehlings repeated the organ removal on Mrs. Hardin and then they were reinterred back into the Alabama sod from whence they had come. A preacher from one of the local churches led the crowd in *Amazing Grace* and then had a prayer and asked that the Lord's will be done in everything that had transpired here today. And it was over.

Frank spoke briefly with Paul Jordan and Dr. Rehlings asking to be notified as soon as the reports of the findings were back. Rehlings said that he had to be out of town for a few days next week so he was going to try to get the analysis finished before he left. And that he would get it to the Cherokee Superior Court as soon as he could.

Frank and Harry were walking to their car when John Black stopped them at the edge of the cemetery. He had a young woman with him. Frank estimated her age somewhere in the late twenties or early thirties.

"Deputies, this is Ginny Knight," John said. "She wanted to speak with you for a minute."

Bertha's father
James A. "Bud" Hardin

The Hardins' home in the Pleasant Valley
community

Bertha's mother
Zola Dutton Hardin

# Bodies of Rome Couple in Ala. To Be Exhumed

The bodies of Mr. and Mrs. James A. Hardin, foster parents of Bertha Gossett Hill will be exhumed and autopsies will be performed in an effort to determine the cause of their deaths, according to a court order approved by Judge W. J. Haralson, of the Ninth Judicial Circuit Court of Alabama.

In the petition presented to the Alabama Court, Solicitor-General Henderson L. Lanham, of Floyd Superior Court, asked that the court grant an order to allow the exhumation of the bodies of both Mr. and Mrs. James A. Hardin, for the purposes of performing an autopsy and the examination of the vital organs of the deceased so that evidence may be obtained by the State of Georgia in determining the causes of their deaths.

Mr. Lanham said in the petition that Bertha Gossett Hill is being held without bond under a charge of murder, with the specific charge that she administered poison to her husband, Leroy Hill, thereby causing his death.

He further said that Bertha Hill's foster parents had died under suspicious circumstances, and both bodies had been removed from the State of Georgia where they died, without burial permits, and that James A. Hardin was buried without a certificate of death having been issued, also that Mrs. Hardin was interred after issuance of a certificate upon which was written "cause of death unknown."

"It being material to the State of Georgia in the prosecution of said case against Bertha Gossett Hill," the petition read, "to determine whether or not either or both of the foster parents died from poison or other unnatural causes, and since the bodies are now buried in Cherokee County Alabama, the court is asked to grant an order allowing the exhumation and autopsies to be performed."

The petition was approved by Harle G. Bailey, Solicitor of the Ninth Judicial Circuit of Alabama, and was submitted to Judge Haralson for final court order.

Judge Haralson, in approving the petition, ordered the State Toxicologist to exhume the bodies of Mr. and Mrs. Hardin and to perform an autopsy on each, with chemical analysis of the vital organs to determine whether or not either of them died from poison or other unnatural causes.

The order provided for a report to be filed with Cherokee County Court where the findings would be made available to the Floyd Superior Court and the State of Georgia in connection with the charges against Bertha Hill.

in suit on left: Paul Jordan of Jordan Funeral Home
in suit on right, with hat: Frank Russell
unknown laborers

# Chapter 16

Things were moving fast this Monday morning April 1st. Frank had just made his jail check and went over the inmate count and roster when he was notified to come to the sheriff's office as soon as he could. Before he could leave, Ben Cooper of the *Rome News Tribune* came in with another gentleman following him.

Cooper caught Russell's eye and said, "Deputy Russell, I'd like for you to meet John Henry. He's with the International News Service. At this time he's stationed out of the Atlanta office."

Frank shook hands with both men and invited them into his office and offered them a chair. After every one was seated Frank asked, "What can I do for the *Rome News* and the INS this morning?"

"John would like to go up to the second floor and interview Bertha if it's all right with you," Ben stated.

Before Frank could speak, John Henry said, "Deputy I won't be long. The INS has been following this story as it gained speed in the local paper. After last week's exhumation we figured it was time for us to run something on the wire. I don't plan for this interview to be much more than an introduction to our readers about who Bertha Hill is and where the investigation is at this time."

"Ben, do you plan on accompanying Mr. Henry up to the second floor and taking part in the interview?" Frank asked.

"I'm going to go to the second floor, but the interview is John's. We'll run his piece this afternoon or tomorrow. Just as soon as he gets it finished."

Frank thought about the request for a minute or two then said, "Ben this may be a little bit early, but I just got summoned to the sheriff's office.

I'm hopeful that the results of last week's autopsy are back. If you could just hold off for a few hours you might have a better story."

Both men were silent for a few moments. They looked at each other and then back at Frank. Finally Ben said in a very serious tone, "Frank, the report has came in. The solicitor called our office about an hour ago and they sent me right over. John arrived in town last night. I met him and took him with me to meet with Henderson. He's calling a special meeting of the grand jury as we speak. That's why we're here. This case is about to go to trial. They're going to be trying hard to get it in the April term of court. That's only about three weeks away. At least that's what we were told a few minutes ago."

"Deputy, I'll promise you that I have no interest at all of telling Mrs. Hill the results of the Alabama autopsy or the fact that the grand jury would be meeting this morning to indict her on four counts."

"Four counts?" Frank asked. "What's the other count?"

"Three for murder and one for larceny," John replied, "You know how prosecutors are. They don't worry about the mule; they just load the wagon."

Frank was livid. He should have known that as soon as this case really looked like it would be going to court, the politicians would jump for glee. He had never known a prosecutor who didn't relish 'the great white hope' type of case.

*Actually, I can also relate to that myself. I've enjoyed working this case. It's a big change from the run of the mill daily work load. I know that most solicitors get tired of trying black folks and poor whites for minor charges. Well really, for any charges. They live for the day that some well-to-do white man or woman goofs up. Maybe they'll embezzle some money from their company or get caught up in something a little juicier. Or maybe a police officer might get charged. That always livens things up.*

Frank couldn't blame Henderson for acting normally. It was apparent that he was excited, and at the same time worried about dotting all his I's and crossing all his T's. Frank felt betrayed, though, that he hadn't at least been notified before the media. But he knew, as he had told Harry a couple of weeks ago, that law enforcement was on the bottom of the criminal justice ladder.

"What larceny?" Frank asked.

"The solicitor told us this morning that Bertha had stolen a quantity of linens, sheets and towels from one of the local hospitals while her husband was a patient," Cooper stated.

*If Bertha will hold the bag, Neal will fill it up.* Frank couldn't help but remember what he had been told over in Cherokee County. This didn't surprise him, and he knew that a larceny charge wasn't going anywhere with three murder charges pending. All this did was give an indication of her personality.

"That doesn't surprise me, Ben," Frank replied. "Y'all go on up as soon as Deputy Payne comes back. Now if you will excuse me, I've got to go and meet with the sheriff."

Bill Payne escorted both reporters to the second floor about the time Frank was walking out the side door of the jail into the sunshine. When they reached Bertha's cell, Bill told her that she had visitors. She got up and walked over to where the men were standing on the other side of the bars and heard Bill say, "Bertha, this is Ben Cooper of the *Rome News Tribune* and this other fellow is John Henry from the International News Service. They want to talk to you a little bit if it's OK with you."

"Well, I don't mind, Deputy Payne, but why would two important men want to talk too little old me?" Bertha answered with a quizzical look on her face.

"I'll let them answer that, Bertha," Payne said. To the reporters he added, "Gentlemen, I'm going to leave the hall door unlocked. Whenever you're finished just come on down. Please let me know before you leave so I can mark you off of my visitor's sheet."

"Will do," Cooper said, "and thanks."

"I'll answer the question you asked the deputy about why we wanted to talk with you," John Henry said. "You're becoming quite famous around these parts, and I'm thinking that your notoriety might spread throughout the state and maybe the country."

"You mean it will, if they try me for killing my husband and parents, don't you?" Bertha asked.

"If you go to trial, it will be a big story," John said, "But even if you don't, that will also get a good bit of press."

Bertha began to sob lightly, tears trickling down her face.

"But if they put me in the electric chair, that will be a great big story, won't it?" she asked.

"It would," John answered noticing that the mere mention of electric chair seemed to shock her even when it came from her own mouth.

"Well, I want to get something cleared up right now," she said looking at Ben Cooper. "Y'all have been running stories about me being a foster child and I want the whole world to know that they were my real parents and that I'm no stepchild."

"Bertha, that's what we were told," Ben answered, "But we will certainly print what you just said, I promise."

"Well, I want you to," she said. "Even if I do die in the electric chair I want everyone to know they were my real parents. And I guess y'all know they're gonna take Papa and Mama up and autopsy them, don't you?"

"That's already been done Bertha," John answered surprised that she didn't know. And he thought she was more eloquent in establishing the fact that the Hardins were her real parents than she was in proclaiming her own innocence.

"Is it a bad report?" she asked.

"Bertha, it's not our place to talk about any report the State's preparing until they release it," Ben Cooper replied.

Still sobbing Bertha told the newsmen that her Papa had died of an ulcerated stomach and she didn't know what her Mama died from.

Looking straight at the men she said, "I didn't kill them, and I sure didn't kill my husband. I loved him too much. I worshiped him."

"Bertha, can you tell me about your early life with your first husband?" John Henry asked.

Bertha spent the next half hour telling the men about her past life with Neal Gossett.

"Where is he now?" Ben asked.

"I don't know and I don't care," she stated. "We never really got along and I have no use for him."

"Didn't you ever want children?" Ben asked.

"Of course I wanted babies," she said. "I had one but it died when it was an infant. If I were married now, I'd want to have babies—but I don't want anything more to do with men. All I want is a place to go. I have nobody—not even any brothers and sisters. If only someone would just take me in."

John Henry and Ben Cooper spent another fifteen minutes with Bertha and then John Henry said, "We're going to go now, but I want to thank you for talking to us. And I'll be back to see you again if you don't mind."

"Mr. Henry, I don't mind at all, but let me ask you a favor. They locked me up without any of my personal things. I don't have a dime. Mattie in the next cell has a sister that has been real good about getting us things from town. There are certain items that a girl has to have. If you or Mr. Cooper would make me a small loan I would promise to pay you back as soon as my insurance check comes in."

"How much do you think you'll need, Bertha?" John asked.

"I'm going to have to prepare for court and all," she said. "I think it will cost somewhere around a hundred dollars for everything I need. Any of that you could help me with would be a big help."

"I'll see what I can do," John said as he and Ben walked down the corridor and then to the first floor where they waited for a few minutes till Deputy Bill Payne marked them off the jail visitor sheet.

They had reached the door when John stopped, turned back to Bill and said, "Deputy, please see that this gets put in Bertha's belongings or take it and give it to her."

He took five twenties and gave them to the jailer and then exited the jail.

"You know you've just been snagged," Ben said. "You fell for that hook, line, and sinker."

"Sure I do," he replied, "I also know that I'm going to want to interview her some more. Wait till you read my column in about an hour. INS is going to love this gal."

₪    ₪

Johnny Jacobs knew it was going to be a big morning at the Partridge. When the newspapers were popping he always picked up not only the regulars at the morning breakfast club, but many of the guys that were classified as part-time members. Besides, that INS reporter had been here the last two mornings with Ben Cooper and he drew a crowd.

There would be a lot of new folks trying to squeeze in and pick up a word here and there. That was fine with Johnny. He knew it was good for business and he also liked to hear what some of the knowledgeable crowd had to say.

Yes, he thought, today is going to be special. I can just feel it.

"You ready for a big morning Johnny?" Dr. Elmore asked as he came in the restaurant, stopping at the coat rack to hang up his coat and hat.

"You read my mind," Johnny said. "I was just thinking the same thing, Doctor."

"Happy better have a full pad to take notes on today," he replied, "We got lots to talk about."

"Ain't that the truth?" Johnny said as he moved to the door and spoke to the morning regulars as they came in.

Johnny was busy getting everybody seated and plenty of coffee to drink. His waitresses were running this morning as the crowd kept coming.

Johnny had already spotted Geston Garner, the President of State Farm Mutual, and Sam King, the city manager, in attendance today. And the *Floyd County Herald* was represented by James Tate. All the regulars had made it today and once again Ben Cooper was accompanied by John Henry, the INS reporter. As the waitresses were finishing with the breakfast orders, Johnny saw a familiar figure come through the door.

"Y'all are going to have to behave today," Johnny said to the entire gathering. "The Preacher is back."

"How are you this morning, Johnny?" Rev. Bunyan Stephens said as he shook hands with the men gathered at the table.

"I'm fine, Preacher," Johnny said as he got the reverend a chair. "We haven't seen you in a couple of weeks. I was wondering if you were all right."

"I've just been busy, Johnny," Rev. Stephens said. "Most mornings I'm in my study for morning coffee. And then sometimes I wander down to the Busy Bee or Sam Diprima's Victory Café."

"Now you're making me jealous, Preacher," Johnny replied. "But I guess even the pastor of Rome's First Baptist Church has to make the morning rounds."

"No need to be jealous," he said. "Just doing a little visitation like you said."

"Cecil, how has the Easter season been so far?" Dr. Elmore asked.

"Better than the last few years, that's for sure," he replied. "Wouldn't you say so Hix?"

"Absolutely. Rev. Stephens just bought two suits this week," Hix replied. "They've been going like hotcakes. I think the economy is starting to shift from that of wartime to a peacetime one. And I'm certainly glad."

"They're real nice suits, Hix," Rev. Stephens said. "They're the first one's I've bought in two or three years. I know. Some of my others are getting threadbare."

"Just read something on the wire this morning about the economy," Ben Cooper said. "All the experts are predicting that by this time next year we should be booming."

"I think the housing industry will spur it along," Geston Garner said. "All these servicemen coming home wanting to get married and start families. They got to have a place to live."

"Let me ask the other Ben," Cooper said. "Mr. Rainwater, what does a housing industry boom say to the gas company?"

"Ben, don't be calling me Mr.," Ben Rainwater said. "But I'll answer that this way. I was in Atlanta just last week for a company meeting. The guys that are supposed to know are predicting a housing boom like you've never seen. They're saying that our gas lines will quadruple in the next decade. Gentlemen, I'm here to tell you that in your lifetime you'll witness the demise of coal and wood for heat and cooking and see gas and electricity rise."

"That's what INS has been saying for the last year or so," John Henry said.

"Ben were they including the folks out in the country also?" Jack Harris asked. "That doesn't sound very cost efficient."

"Well Jack. It would of course be a little further down the road than the city folks. But most of them will be using propane and we'll be setting tanks on each farm."

"Now that's what I call real progress," Johnny Jacobs said.

"I agree with the housing and baby boom both," John Powers said. "Allen's is picking up daily. And all the other 5 & 10s are too. If we have a problem, it's that the country's manufacturing plants are slower than the people's desires in changing from war goods to those of a peacetime nation. That affects jobs. That's the only reason we're in a slow climbing economy now."

"I don't think it's going to be slow for long," Bud West said. "Your friendly neighbor, the Rome Coca Cola Bottling Company has almost doubled our sales just since the War ended. And for all purposes it looks like it's going to continue."

"Did you guys hear that it's time for the annual spring meeting of the Shorter College Trustees?" Happy Quarles said.

"Yeah, Trustee's Day is always big on Shorter hill," Macon Brock said. "They got a guy named Ralph Newton speaking."

"Who's that, Macon?" John Moss asked.

"I'm not real sure," Macon replied. "I think he's from south Georgia somewhere."

"He is," Ben Cooper said. "He's from Waycross, and he is one of the trustees as you said and also Superintendent of the Waycross school system."

"Should be a great speaker for Shorter," Macon said.

"That's a fact," Reverend Stephens said. "I've heard him speak. I'm going to be there Friday. If you can make it, please do. You won't regret it."

"Hey Mr. City Manager, heard you guys were gonna make Smith Horton Assistant Chief?" Ben Cooper asked.

"That's today Ben," Sam King replied. "The Civil Service Board is meeting right after lunch to finalize that."

"Is that on the record?" he asked. "Can I print it?"

"Ain't nothing on the record till it's finished, Ben," Sam said. "You know that."

"Well, why are you doing it now, Sam?" Happy asked.

"He's been doing the job pretty much for the last year without the title,"

Sam said. "Smith came on board back about 36 or 37. He was obviously capable of moving up in the department. I sent him to that new school in Washington that J. Edgar Hoover founded in 1935."

"You talking about the National Academy?" John Henry asked.

"That's the one," Sam said. "It's the best law enforcement school in the country. In fact it might be the only law enforcement school in the country.

"Anyway, Smith graduates from the Academy and then the War breaks out. We had a lot of men in Rome and Floyd County drafted into the armed forces, but he's the only one I know of who was drafted into the F.B.I."

"I remember that," Geston Garner said. "Didn't the Bureau send him to New Orleans?"

"Yes they did," Sam answered as most of the gathering broke out in laughter.

"Y'all laugh if you want to, but Smith told me that the riverfront in New Orleans during the winter was the coldest place he'd ever been. They had him checking ships, docks, warehouses and things like that for spies and saboteurs.

"When the War started our seaports were considered vulnerable to German and Japanese agents. Anyway, during the War Chief Charlie Harris died--all y'all know that--and we promoted Wood Quarles to that position. I called the Bureau and told them I needed Smith back. It still took a year before they would release him. And like I said, he's been doing the job ever since."

"Sam, do you think that Smith will be chief some day?" James Tate asked.

"I don't know, James," Sam replied. "I think Wood has several more years. And I hope Smith gets the chance to develop while he's assistant chief. If he does then anything's possible."

"What I want to know is where have you been for the past month?" Johnny Jacobs asked.

"Well Johnny, you know that I live at the Grey Stone Hotel," Sam said. "And every morning I start walking up the street to City Hall. But your Partridge is about five blocks away and by the time I get to the Busy Bee Café, I'm about starved to death. It's only two blocks from the hotel. So I been stopping there and getting a bite so I could make it all the way to my office."

"I don't want to hear that," Johnny said throwing both hands in the air while the table roared with laughter.

"You just going to have to eat more at night," Johnny said, "so you don't run out of gas till you get here."

"Johnny, I promise to be a little more regular," Sam said. He turned and faced John Henry. "And to you sir, I've read your work all through the war and I want you to know I really enjoyed your pieces. You kept the public informed."

"Thank you Mr. King," John Henry said. "I've really enjoyed being in your city. Everyone is very polite and has gone out of their way to make me feel at home."

"We're glad you're here," Sam said. "How long are you planning on staying with us?"

"I've got to go back to Atlanta today, but I'll be back when Bertha's trial starts."

"I read your column yesterday on Bertha," John Moss said. "It was a very good piece of writing."

"Glad you enjoyed it."

"Mr. Henry, in all your travels, have you ever seen anyone who could be as cruel as they're portraying Bertha Hill to be?" John Powers asked.

"Mr. Powers, that's a loaded question," John Henry said. "I witnessed some of the Japanese atrocities. I was only in the European theatre for a short time, and that was in Casablanca early in the North African Campaign. But I was at Okinawa, Tarawa, Saipan and the Philippines as a war correspondent for INS. I witnessed a lot of misery and downright cruelty. But if you're talking about peacetime rather than War, this ranks right up there."

"I guess what I'm trying to ask is if there is a type of personality that is more apt to commit these type crimes than regular people, or is she regular ole everyday folks?"

"I'm just a reporter, not a shrink. I'd be afraid to venture a guess," John Henry said. "But during the War I saw combat and stress do all kinds of things to men's minds."

"First thing is all of y'all wait till she's tried before you find her guilty," Reverend Stephens said. "Evidence has to be presented and she gets the opportunity to question those findings. That's the way our system works."

"The preacher's right on cue," John Henry said. "I interviewed her yesterday. She's very cunning, but that doesn't mean she's a murderer."

"Well the grand jury adjourned yesterday," Happy Quarles said. "We've got two former members of that jury that heard the evidence here this morning. Surely they can elaborate on those findings for us now."

"No they can't," Hix Sims said. "At least I ain't."

"Me either," Geston Garner said in agreement. "I will tell you this.

Since the issue of insurance payments came up, and my company was one of those involved, I excused myself from voting and being foreman. I then appointed Howard Smith acting foreman. He signed the indictments. And since we're still involved, I'm being quiet."

"That was a wise thing to do," Macon Brock said.

Looking toward Reverend Stephens, Dr. Elmore asked,

"Let's assume for a minute that she is guilty. Is there anything in the book that addresses the kind of people we're talking about, like John asked our guest, or with people that think like that? I mean there are physicians starting to study personality traits in the medical profession, but nothing that I know of that's out there yet."

"B.V., the Bible doesn't list a name for those people. But they were certainly out there in the first century and before. The Apostle Paul does a pretty good job in Romans of bringing that out."

"Wait a minute. I want to hear this," Johnny Jacobs said as he grabbed up a chair. "If the preacher is about to do a little devotional then I want to hear it from the beginning."

"Actually Johnny, this isn't really a devotional, but a thought about the situation at hand," Reverend Stephens said and then continued.

"God does say in Romans Chapter One. And I'm going to start with verse 28. That's where he mentions giving up some people with reprobate minds. He actually thrice said that he gave them up. In verses 24, 26 along with verse 28 he makes that statement.

"These people did not like to retain God in their knowledge. Their understanding was blinded by their own willful aversion. They would neither know, nor do, anything but just what pleased themselves. Listen men, there are many that have God in their knowledge, but they do not retain him there.

"Because it thwarts their lusts; they do not like it. There is a difference between the knowledge and the acknowledgment of God; the pagans knew God but would not acknowledge Him. God has given these folks over to what Paul calls a blind seared conscience, past feeling."

"I've heard you preach before, Reverend," Ben Cooper said. "Can you put that into today's language for me?"

"I'll try, Ben," Reverend Stephens said. "You, like every man at this table, were raised with morals, ethics and boundaries. Your parents taught you what was right and wrong, and the difference between the two. If you took a life you would feel just awful. This would go on for days. At night you couldn't sleep. For years it would plague you, because you were raised with those ethics and morals I've just mentioned.

"Somebody in your life set boundaries and if you cross one of them you have a hard time living with what you've done. I counsel people almost daily in that position. The people Paul are talking about have no conscience, no ethics or morals, and certainly no boundaries. They can do anything to anybody and sleep like a baby. Those people never come in for counseling."

"Wow," Hix Sims said, "I got my Wednesday service over with early today. Guess I can take a night off."

"Hix."

"I'm just kidding, Reverend Stephens. I'll be there," Hix replied.

"All of you better attend services somewhere tonight," Reverend Stephens said. "There's just one thing I want you to remember. Nobody is saying that Mrs. Hill's one of those type people we've been talking about. Like I said earlier, she is entitled to a trial and is to be considered innocent until proven guilty in a court of law."

Reverend Stephens had their attention now and he knew it. He paused just a minute for effect and then continued, "The biggest problem is this. Paul gives a laundry list of things that these people do. The things on that list not only shock but break the innocence of society. That sometimes makes getting a fair trial an uncertainty in many cases."

"That's absolutely correct," Cecil Rhodes said. "I've learned a lot by just sitting here and being quiet. In fact I've enjoyed it."

"That's another sermon, Cecil," Reverend Stephens said. "And it's a quick one. Be quiet and listen and you can hear what God's saying."

"And that's another good one, Preacher," Johnny said as he was helping the men to their feet.

"Reverend Stephens," John Henry said. "I really liked the way you explained some people's thinking, or the lack of it. And these fellows usually gamble now to see who pays for breakfast. But if you will allow me in your honor, INS would like to pick up the tab for everybody this morning."

"I accept and thank you."

"If I'd have known that was gonna happen I'd of eaten a lot more," Happy said, grinning widely.

# Poison Found In Hardin Case

(AP Wirephoto).

## Jury Indicts Widow On 3 Murder Counts

Bench warrants charging Mrs. Bertha Hill, 28, with the triple poisoning of her husband and parents, were signed this morning by Judge Claude H. Porter, of Floyd Superior Court, following return of three true bills yesterday afternoon by the Floyd Grand Jury.

The bench warrants were obtained by Solicitor General Henderson L. Lanham after the Grand Jury returned indictments charging Mrs. Hill with the murder of Leroy Hill, 28, her husband, and Mr. and Mrs. James A. Hardin, her parents.

Mrs. Hill's trial is scheduled for the April term of court, opening next Monday morning. She is being held without bond in the Floyd County Jail.

Judge Porter was summoned from his home, where he has been confined by illness, to receive the true bills yesterday afternoon.

Leroy Hill died on February 14, and Mrs. Hill was arrested the next day on an open felony warrant, being held pending full investigation of the death. The probe was ordered when health authorities became suspicious of three deaths in the same family within a year. Mr. Hardin died last April and Mrs. Hardin died August 13, and they were buried near Centre, Ala. The bodies of Mr. and Mrs. Hardin were exhumed last week under court order, for autopsies.

Action by the Grand Jury followed reports by pathologists reporting discovery of arsenic in the three bodies.

Parents of Bertha Gosset Hill met death from arsenical poisoning, Alabama State Toxicologist C. J. Rallings, of Auburn, Ala., reported today as the Floyd County Grand Jury assembled to consider the charges against Mrs. Hill, who is being held in Floyd County Jail in connection with the poison death of her husband, Leroy Hill. The parents, Mr. and Mrs. James A. Hardin, were buried near Centre, Ala., and their bodies were exhumed last week.

Solicitor General Henderson L. Lanham received the toxicologist's report and prepared to present it to the Grand Jury for a thorough investigation of all three deaths. Action by the Grand Jury is not expected to be made known until adjournment expected tomorrow.

Mrs. Hill has been held without bond in Floyd County Jail on a felony warrant sworn out by Mr. Hill's mother, Mrs. Lacy Beale, of Pittsboro, N. C., while a Coroner's Jury was probing his death during February. Mr. Hill died February 14, and Mrs. Hill was arrested the following night.

An autopsy performed on Mr. Hill by pathologists at Emory University revealed that he came to his death as a result of arsenic poisoning. A relatively large amount of calcium arsenate was found in the vital organs, according to Dr. George W. Lewis, head of the Department of Biochemistry in Atlanta, and Mrs. Hill was ordered held for the Grand Jury.

Mrs. Hill, who was employed for about five years at a local ten cent store, is the former wife of Neal Gosett, to whom she was married for about 13 years, it was reported. By her first marriage, she had one child, who died shortly afterward.

She was married to Leroy Hill in July, 1945, at Rossville, Ga., according to the records in the Clerk's Office in Walker County. The divorce was issued in Centre, Ala., by mutual consent, it was revealed.

In testimony at the Coroner's inquest, it was learned that Mrs.

(Continued on Page 7, Col. 7)

## No Stepchild, Mrs. Hill Sobs To INS Writer

(Southeastern Regional Director of INS since January, John E. Henry is a former correspondent, covering five major Marine landings in the Pacific, Naval Task Force operations, and the landings at Casablanca. Previously, he wrote sports in New York, and was on the Washington INS staff. He first joined INS in Atlanta in 1936.)

**By JOHN E. HENRY**
(Distributed by International News Service)

A flash thought of her own death in the electric chair struck 28-year-old Bertha Hill today as she stood in the shadowy darkness of a Floyd County Jail cell.

It occurred to her just as a Grand Jury over in the court house learned that her parents, Mr. and Mrs. James A. Hardin, met death, like her late husband, from arsenic poison.

The sad-eyed former floor lady at a Rome dime store is held in connection with the death of Leroy Hill. He died Feb. 14. She was jailed the next day.

Floyd county's grand jury this morning received a report from Alabama State Toxicologist C. J. Rallings that Mr. and Mrs. Hardin also had succumbed to arsenic poison.

While the jury deliberated placing murder charges against her,

(Continued on Page 7, Col. 3)

# Chapter 17

Judge Claude Porter sat in his office. He thought, I'm getting too old for these type cases. I'm nearly seventy and haven't been feeling good lately. I've outlived two wives and now I'm alone again just like I started. I'm also feeling sorry for myself and that's got to stop.

As he shuffled through the stack of papers on his desk, his secretary came to his office and said, "He's here judge. You want me to send him on in?"

"Yes ma'am, I certainly do, and thank you," Judge Porter said.

The tall, lanky man entered the office and took a chair. Judge Porter thought he was probably approaching fifty, or not far away. He was lean and always well dressed, even when he wasn't in court. He asked himself what else he knew about the fellow before him. He knew he was born in Alabama, worked his way through the Berry School system and had served with the signal corps during World War I, as they were now beginning to call it. Mack had gotten his law degree from Atlanta Law School after a stint at the University of Akron. And he was now serving as the City of Rome's attorney, and was a sitting legislator in the Georgia House of Representatives.

But more importantly, Judge Porter had seen him in action in his courtroom on many occasions. He was absolutely ruthless. The judge was thinking that he wouldn't want to face him in court, and didn't really know any attorney that would relish it. He knew the solicitor was not going to like his selection, but it was his to make.

"I'm glad you dropped by, Mack," Judge Porter said to Mack G. Hicks, the man he had been scrutinizing just moments before.

"I didn't just drop by, Judge. You sent for me."

"Yes I did," he said. "I've got a little problem that I need you to help me out with."

"Depends on what it is," said Mack. "I learned a long time ago in the Army not to volunteer for anything."

"That's what I like about you Mack, you always cheer me up. Heck, I knew you wouldn't volunteer. So that's why I'm going to appoint you."

"Appoint me to what?" Mack asked. "I haven't been appointed to a case in years. There's a lot of guys out there need some State work, but thankfully I'm not one of them."

"I know that Mack," Porter said. "But I want you to hear me out first."

"Then if I don't agree, will you change your mind?" Mack asked.

"No I won't," the judge replied.

"Well, I guess I get to hear what you've got to say regardless. Just remember that I serve on the legislature and represent the City of Rome as its attorney. That takes up a lot of time."

"Mack, I used to be in the House of Representatives. And I was also solicitor. I understand about prior commitments. Someday when you're a judge you'll probably find yourself in the same predicament that I'm in now."

"I have no desire to be a judge. I'm happy with my life just like it is, or I was till today."

"Have you kept up with the Bertha Hill case in the paper?"

"How could I not?" Mack answered. "The papers are full of it every day."

"That's what I'm appointing you to. You're going to defend her."

"Slow down, Judge Porter. Let's wait a minute. That's probably going to be a death penalty case. I certainly don't have time to prepare an adequate defense with my other obligations. And just when do you think Henderson will put it on the docket?"

"I know when, Mack. It's going to be called this coming term."

"You expect somebody to get ready for trial on a case of this magnitude in two weeks? Judge, I just don't think that's possible."

"It's got to be done, Mack. Publicity is growing daily. This case is going to attract national attention. One of those shockers where the press plays up the fact that some female is charged with killing her own parents and husband for what they'll call blood money. If we don't try this woman soon, I'm afraid she'll never get a fair trial. Not even with a change of venue. Right now we can try her here before it gets much bigger."

"Well, I don't want her getting a new trial on inadequate counsel," Mack said. "And I'm telling you right now that I can't do it. I wish you'd find somebody else."

"Mack, I don't have to tell you that Henderson will probably make a better congressman than he does lawyer. He's all right but he might be in trouble on this case if it wasn't for one little thing."

"What's that?" Mack asked.

"Graham Wright," Judge Porter said. "His fingerprints are all over this case. He took it to the coroner's jury and the grand jury. He's a hell of a lawyer and Horace Clary and Chastain Parker are involved also in various ways. I've got to find somebody who can stand toe to toe with those guys or this thing is a farce."

"Well they're certainly formidable, that's for sure. But that don't change the fact that time is definitely on their side."

"I'm going to appoint you a helper, Mack. Anybody in particular you want?"

Mack sat and thought about that for a few minutes and then, looking toward the judge, he said, "Carl Griffin. He's the best legal scholar I know other than some of the ones you've already named."

"Consider it a done deal," Judge Porter said, getting out of his chair and coming around the desk to take Mack's hand.

"Judge Porter, before your clerk prepares any papers, I want you to know something."

"What is that, Mack?" Porter asked.

"I live by three principles. Give in, give up, or give it all you've got. You know what's coming don't you?"

₪   ₪

It was Friday afternoon April 5th and Mack Hicks was fit to be tied. He wanted to end this day and go and have about two or three shots of straight bourbon whiskey. He thought maybe he'd have a chaser with the last one.

But no, he had been appointed to defend this female cracker for poisoning her whole damn family. This case had the necessary ingredients to ruin his career, or at least cause it grievous harm.

He had spent the day before going over everything he could find in the newspapers and what he could get around the courthouse. And it wasn't that much. He certainly didn't expect to get much from the solicitors office. His defense partner was filing a motion for disclosure right now, but he didn't expect much from that either.

As he walked across the 5th Avenue bridge on his way to the jail he was thinking. *I've got to come up with some kind of defense that the jury will buy. But until I talk to the girl and find out what she's told them, there's no way I can get a handle on the case. Carl is going to have all of the customary motions ready to go, but that's as much for our protection as it is for the defendant.*

Mack walked into the jail and asked to see his client. The jailer led him to the small office that was used by defense attorney's for interviewing. He was shuffling through a stack of papers that he had taken out of his briefcase when the jail deputy escorted Bertha into the office.

She stood behind her chair and let her eyes settle on the man looking up at her. Their eyes locked, and neither looked away for several seconds.

Mack looked the woman over from head to toe. Not bad, he thought. I've seen a lot of good looking women in my life and this one is better than average. And she had something. Mack could spot that immediately, although he didn't know what that something was.

*She's about five foot seven and just a little heavy. But she has a good build. Not fat at all but would probably go a hundred forty pounds coming out of the bathtub.* He had always considered himself a connoisseur of fine female flesh and this gal was grade A.

"Five foot eight," she said without moving her eyes. "And I'd probably go about 135 or 138 right about now. I fill up a thirty eight C but can't handle a D. I've been here almost two months and I know I've lost some because my clothes are loose. I was a little over one forty when they locked me up. Do I pass?"

*How did she do that? She read my thoughts right down to the letter.*

"Oh yeah, I think you do," Mack said, indicating for Bertha to take a chair.

"My husband always said that a man couldn't ask for a better Saturday night date than me. I can dress to the nines and no man's embarrassed to take me out."

"I can see how he would say that," Mack said. "Mrs. Hill, I'm Mack Hicks and I've been appointed to defend you in the upcoming trial."

"I know who you are, Mr. Hicks. I've seen you come into McClellan's several times," she said as tears started to trickle down her face.

"Why are you crying?" Mack asked. "Have I said something to offend you?"

"Oh no! It's just that I'm a poor orphan and widow and I'm all alone in this world. I've got one friend and she's in the next cell and will probably be leaving any day now. The law has turned my family against me. I've been locked up without being charged for nearly two months. I begged for a lawyer and they wouldn't appoint me one until I was officially charged. And now here you are. I'm about as happy as a girl can be that's in jail. You are going to help me, aren't you Mr. Hicks?"

"Mrs. Hill, I'm going to do everything that I know how to do."

"I wish you'd call me Bertha," she said. "Mrs. Hill, or Mrs. Gossett as they call me here, is just too formal."

"All right Bertha, here's the deal. I'll call you by your first name but you have to call me Mack. Is that OK?"

"That'll be just fine, Mack," Bertha said as her grey eyes came alive and began a slow burn.

"First question," Mack said. "What have you told the deputies about your husband's and parents' deaths?"

"Why, I told them the truth," she said.

"You don't mean that you confessed to their deaths? You didn't give a statement to that effect, did you?"

"Mr. Hicks, I told you I told them the truth, and the truth is that I didn't kill either of them. I loved them too much, and I'd never hurt them."

"Bertha, you just sit back in that chair and tell me every word that has been spoken by you to anybody since the death of Leroy. I'll ask the jailer if he'll get us a cup of coffee or would you prefer a Co-Cola?"

"I get coffee ever day. It ain't much, and I'd rather have the Co-Cola, but either one would be fine.

Mack stepped out of the office for a minute and spoke to the jailer and was right back in his chair with his pen in his hand, ready to go. As Bertha began her story, the jailer brought Coca-Colas to both Bertha and Mack and closed the door after him.

Bertha talked for the next hour without interruption. She had almost total recall. Boy, was he ever wrong about calling this farm girl a cracker. She might not have much formal education, but she was certainly intelligent.

He wondered what she could have become under different circumstances. He too had struggled to get off the farm and out of a farming community. But girls in the Great Depression were not given much of an opportunity to do anything but have babies and wait on some man. At least boys had a little bit of a chance.

As she finished her recollection of the events, she looked at Mack with pleading eyes and asked, "Are they going to put me in the electric chair?"

"Bertha, I'm not gonna lie to you. They're definitely going to try," Mack said.

"Can you stop them?"

"Right now we've got a fight on our hands. They're way ahead of us. We've got all kind of doctors that will testify about all kinds of chemical testing. If you haven't confessed, and there are no witnesses to you doing anything, all they got is circumstantial evidence. Although they got is what is called a preponderance of that."

"I told you I haven't confessed. I have nothing to confess to."

"Bertha, I want you to know that this could be a long fight. Our first goal is to keep you out of the chair. I can't guarantee anything, except they'll know that we've been in court."

"What about all of them witnesses? How are you gonna discredit all those doctors and experts?"

"I've never heard a witness testify that I couldn't make a little off of on cross examination. Let me worry about that."

"I will, Mack."

"Tomorrow or Sunday afternoon my assistant, Carl Griffin, is going to come and go over this entire testimony again. Then we'll prepare it and go over it together with you and make sure that we all understand your side of the story. Is that a deal?"

"That's a deal. But I hope he makes it tomorrow 'cause Sunday afternoon is when Lemuel and Maeleigh Grace Abbott come and hold a little prayer meeting with me and Mattie. And usually some more visiting preachers join in. But if Sunday's his only day, then I'll be glad to see him."

Mack said his goodbyes and left the jail after Bertha was taken back to her cell. He left the jail with a whole different level of respect for Bertha. He knew that he was going to do his best to get her off. He had a sneaking feeling that something wasn't right about this entire investigation and that if he shook the tree just right, well, who knew what might fall out?

But right now he turned his car onto Broad Street and headed south. He crossed the bridge over the Etowah River and turned right. He was heading to the Club. The Coosa Country Club had been serving Rome's professional clientele for many years. Rome and Floyd County allowed beer and wine, but hard liquor was illegal. However, Mack kept a bottle in his locker and he didn't need a set up. Right now all he wanted was to be alone, nurse a few shots and do some deep thinking.

# Chapter 18

Frank was in his apartment on Sunday morning. The family was getting ready to go to church when the knock on the door came.

"Frank, it's me, Alec," said the voice on the other side of the door.

Frank recognized the voice of Alec Lindsey. He knew that Alec was working the jail today and wondered what he wanted. Alec was usually a road deputy but had volunteered to work for a friend this Sunday.

"What's wrong, Alec?" Frank asked as he opened the door.

"Nothing's wrong," Alec said. "There are two young women that have come to see Bertha. One of them said that you told her over in Alabama to come whenever she could and that you'd let her visit. It's fine with me, but it ain't visiting hours yet and I told them I'd have to get permission."

"Did you get a name?" Frank asked.

"Yep, sure did," Alec replied. "One of them said her name was Ginny something or other. And I didn't get the other one's name."

"Let them go up, Alec. It'll be all right. Tell them that if they're still in Rome in an hour or so church services will be over and I'd like to talk to them both."

"I'll tell them, Chief."

After Frank got back to the jail from church services at North Broad Baptist, he asked Alec if the two young ladies were still in the jail.

"Nah, they left about twenty minutes before you got back. But they said to tell you that they were going to get something to eat, and pick up a few items for Bertha. After that they would be glad to talk to you if you still wanted to."

"Let me know when they get back, will you, Alec?"

"Be glad to. Right now I gotta run, Frank. Jail's filling up with visitors."

Frank had finished his dinner and was half way through the *Tribune* when Alec once again knocked on his door and told him that the ladies were back. Frank put his paper down and went to his office where Deputy Lindsey had already escorted the young women into the office and seated both.

"I'm Deputy Frank Russell," he said as he addressed the ladies. "And I remember you Ginny, but I don't think I've had the honor of being introduced to your friend."

"This is Charlsie Patton, Mr. Russell. I guess we were Bertha's best friends growing up over in Alabama."

"We did about everything together," Charlsie said. "We were pretty much inseparable till Bertha got married to Neal."

"Well, did you ladies have a good visit with Bertha?" Frank asked.

"It was sad for a while this morning when we first got here," Ginny said. "But then she settled down and seemed to enjoy visiting with us. We volunteered to get her a few things but most all of the stores were closed, being Sunday and all, so we were unable to help her much."

"She's really depressed, Mr. Deputy," Charlsie added. "I'm worried about her a lot. She thinks y'all are going to put her in the electric chair. She asked us to keep flowers on her Mama and Papa's grave."

"I can't give you an answer to that," Frank said. "That's up to a judge and jury. The April term of Superior Court starts tomorrow, but Bertha ain't scheduled till the second week."

"Well, she told us that she had a lawyer now, and that made her feel some better," Ginny replied.

"And she got a good one too," Frank added. "Listen ladies, I asked y'all to hang around because I wanted to hear a little bit more about Bertha's early life. I just wanted to try and figure out in my own mind what brought her to the situation she's in now. Police science is so new it doesn't provide many answers. Whether she's guilty or not doesn't matter. There are things in her life that had to bring her to this point."

"I don't think so Mr. Russell," Ginny said. "Me and Charlsie were raised right alongside Bertha and we ain't in jail charged with all of that. I love her to death, but maybe you got to look at the person."

"That's the other thought I wanted to bring up," Frank said. "If it wasn't her surroundings having an impact on her, then it would be the person themselves. I see your point."

"Deputy Russell, Bertha wasn't the prettiest girl in our community. Charlsie always has been a lot prettier than Bertha, and so was I, at least that's what I've been told. But when we were young girls going to barn dances, church socials, corn shuckin's or any other get together where there were boys, they flocked to Bertha first. She has always attracted boys and men like she was made out of honey."

"And she loved them all," Charlsie said turning blood red in a deep crimson blush. "I don't mean like she was going with all of them, although I suspected she did with some. She was just a big flirt. She enjoyed it and the boys did too."

"You're not saying that she was sexually promiscuous then?" Frank asked.

"What does that promiscu thing mean?" Charlsie asked.

"It means she went to the barn with anybody that asked. Or as some of my boyhood friends used to say when we were young men, she didn't know the meaning of the word no. That kind of stuff."

"No, she certainly did not. Really she did just the opposite. She led them on and on and nearly drove them crazy. That was until she met Neal."

"What happened then?" Frank asked.

Charlsie continued, "We didn't have nothing out in the country in '32 and '33. Don't you remember? It was hard times. I can recall going to bed many a night with nothing to eat.

"Can't you remember picking blackberries, huckleberries, persimmons and plums when they were in season? And in the fall, hunting down black walnuts, hickernuts, chestnuts and then putting them on a brick and busting them open with a hammer and picking out the inside with a bobby pin or a needle.

"It was cold in the winter and hot in the summer. The only advantage we had was the river. I've eaten catfish for days on end and was glad to get it. My daddy was good at catching them ole big turtles too, and man did they make a good stew.

"Bertha was raised just like that, but the Gossetts had a store, and in it was things that we could only dream about. Every now and then one of our parents might let us have a penny or two to buy a piece of hard candy.

"Bertha's mother traded eggs for a few extra things at the store and made a few coins that way. She also made some of the most beautiful quilts you ever saw. She would sell a couple of them every now and then and hold on to her money. When a rolling store would come by, she had a few nickels and dimes to spend.

"She taught Bertha how to sew and she was almost as good as her mother. In fact, she was working on a quilt top when we got here this morning, and it's really good work. But back to my story. Most of the time my daddy used his pennies to buy rifle shells for the .22.

"I think they were two for a penny as I recall. My brothers would hunt squirrels with that rifle, and if they missed a squirrel and wasted a shell, Daddy would pitch a fit. Both of them boys got to be crack shots. Squirrel dumplings are mighty good on cold winter days when you can't go outside, and mighty filling too."

"What about Neal, though?" Frank asked again.

"I'm getting to that," Charlsie said. "Most of us were good girls. We wanted to grow up and have a family just like our Mamas, have a husband that would work and be a good provider just like our daddys.

"But Bertha didn't want to wait. She charmed Neal like she does most men and the next thing you know she has all kinds of Co-Cola's and candy from the store. Neal worked in the store some for his daddy and he would get those things for her. She couldn't see no further than that store. Neal was six years older than she was. And the next thing we knew they were married. Later they got in trouble with Neal's Papa, and he wouldn't let them work in the store no more."

"Then she had the baby?" Frank asked.

"Yes, she did," Charlsie said, "And I know what you're gonna say. I've heard all that too and I don't believe it."

"What about you, Ginny? Do you believe it?"

"To be honest, I don't know. I don't want to believe it. I've heard everybody's opinion, and they all make sense. If she did do it she needs to be in the moving pictures, cause she sure put on a good act about being tore up over it. I mean her Mama had to send her to stay with relatives in Americus, Georgia."

"Did y'all have any contact with her in the last couple of years, or after she met Leroy?" Frank asked.

"Sure, every time we came to Rome, which wasn't that often, we'd stop in McClellan's and see her. Sometimes we'd go to lunch at one of the cafés on the street. You know, just catch up on each other's lives. She told me about meeting Leroy and how much she was in love. And this time she said it was real, not like with Neal."

"Mr. Russell," Charlsie said. "I want you to know something. During the war I had a boyfriend here in Rome. And I came over here as much as I could. Bertha had a key to an apartment on Second Avenue that she used occasionally. She always let me borrow the key. I think the apartment belonged to a school teacher who worked with Bertha at the dime store during the summer and holidays. And she was at work during the school season. It saved a lot of hotel money."

"What about Bertha?" Frank said. "Did she use the apartment as a place to meet men?"

"She never said she did," Charlsie said. "But what else would she need a key for? Bertha always told us that she loved men. And when she wanted one, she wanted him right now. That was when she was married to Neal. I asked her one time about Neal. What's he supposed to do when she wanted a man? She told me he better be around."

"But you don't know any men that she went with while she was separated from Neal. Is that what you're telling me?"

"Yes sir, that's what I'm telling you," Charlsie replied. "Mr. Russell, she said that going with men gave her a feeling of power."

"Power? What kind of power?" Russell asked.

"I don't rightly know. It was just something about being able to control them. You know men are supposed to be so big and strong. She told me one day that she could make them whimper like little puppies."

"Do you think Leroy changed all of that?" Frank asked.

"Oh, I'm sure he did for awhile," Charlsie said. "Mr. Russell, you need to find out who was in charge of that marriage. If Bertha wasn't, then I can guarantee there was trouble between them."

Frank thought of everything he had been told about Leroy. There was no way Leroy was going to let a woman control him. He controlled women, or he always had till he met Bertha.

Frank asked several more questions and talked to the ladies for what seemed like an hour. Finally he said, "Ladies thank y'all for talking to me. You've been a big help. I'm just trying to understand her."

Both ladies began chuckling at Frank's comment.

"Did I say something funny? If so, I didn't get it," Frank said.

"No sir," Charlsie said, "It's just there ain't no understanding Bertha. When you think you got her figured out, she changes and goes another direction. But I will say this. Me nor Ginny think she killed her parents. Don't know about that Leroy guy. But I can promise you that if you live to be a hundred, you'll never get her to admit it, even if she did it."

۩     ۩

The Friday before court opened, Frank had been very busy. He had to add to the jail staff which meant he had to cut his road crew down to almost nothing. The jail was full and with trial week coming up he was having a hard time finding space for lawyers to interview their clients.

And then there was Bertha. She had more visitors than the rest of the jail combined. News reporters had been coming in all week and asking to interview her. Frank wondered if Mack Hicks had told Bertha to give these continuous interviews. If he did that was strange, Frank thought. Most attorneys gave their clients strict orders not to talk to the media or anybody connected with the case.

Of course, Frank knew that they weren't going to get anything from her, and he guessed Mack did, too. But she would get something from them. He knew that she would separate them from some of their greenbacks before she began answering questions.

Bertha had turned into a big celebrity. He had heard from somebody that there was a story about her in the *New York Times*, and she had certainly been on all the national wire services. Never seen anything like it he thought as he climbed the steps into the courthouse and entered the sheriff's office.

"Have a seat, Frank," Sheriff Mark Horton said leaning back in his chair and re-lighting his pipe.

Frank pulled up a chair, cut off a chew from his plug of Bloodhound, and got comfortable. He sat still and quiet waiting for Mark to get the pipe going again before he spoke. All the time he was waiting he thought to himself. Every pipe smoker I know spends half his time lighting it, packing it, cleaning it out or just holding it. If I was ever a personnel director I'd just as soon hire a one-armed man as one that smokes a pipe. You're going to get about the same amount of work.

"Frank, I sent for you to find out where we stand on next week's court calendar. Are we ready?

"I don't know, Sheriff," Frank answered. "I've never seen anything like this. There are news men coming from all over. All waiting to see if Georgia's gonna put a white woman in the chair. Have you been reading the references they make about her being a black widow? Some are calling her a poison queen, and referring to the Borgias. It's going to be a circus. I'm wondering if Mack Hicks is going to be able to get her a fair trial with all of this publicity."

"He's all ready filed a motion for a change of venue," Mark said. "But Judge Porter ain't gonna let this one out of Floyd County, I'll guarantee it. How's your jail staff? Gonna have to shuffle a lot of prisoners to the courthouse from jail and back. There's gonna be a lot of traveling here, Frank."

"We're ready for that," Frank said. "And we're used to it too. What bothers me is the size of the crowd that might show up. I believe the courthouse will be packed."

"We can only seat about three hundred packed in like sardines," Mark said. "And I've already got requests from Shorter College and Rome High

School to reserve seats for some of the classes that want to attend for classroom instruction."

"You're kidding!" Frank exclaimed. "Why does a women's college want to come and watch a murder trial. What did you tell them?"

"I told them I was sorry but we didn't make reservations for observations of trials. It was first come first served. Women seemed to be fascinated by the thought of one of their own poisoning her husband. A lady told me the other day that every woman who had ever lived thought about poisoning her husband at one time or another. 'Course, that was during a fight and they really didn't mean it. I read where a woman during the War was mad at Winston Churchill and told him that if she was married to him she'd poison him. He replied that if he was married to her he'd take it."

Frank and Mark both were laughing so hard that Mrs. Jenkins stepped into the room from her office and asked, "What's wrong with you two? You got your giggle boxes turned over."

"Mrs. Jenkins," Mark asked, "in all the time you was married, did you ever think about poisoning your husband?"

"Lord no!" she replied. "That'd take too long. When I get mad, I'm mad right now. I don't want to wait for days to get results. I just speak my peace and let it go. But I will tell you what a friend of mine did. Her husband came home one night later than he should have. He'd been to places where he shouldn't been, and doing things that he shouldn't of been doing. He went to sleep, and when he did she took a pistol and sat ride astride of him, pulled the hammer back and woke him up."

"Mrs. Jenkins, you're kidding, ain't you?" Frank asked. "What did he say?"

"Well, he opened his mouth to say something and she put that pistol barrel right in there. Wasn't no way to miss. Now he'd been doing this pretty regular, and she'd had about all she could stand. She told him to lay there and listen. And you know, he did. She preached all night. But the main thing that she got across was that the only reason she didn't kill him right there was that he had children to raise, and she meant he was going to raise them and raise them right."

"What did he do after that?" Mark asked.

"Why, he made the best husband and father in this town. He was a great deputy, too. He said for years that she preached the best sermon he ever heard. He said that he got a lot out of it. She sure does miss that man."

Mrs. Jenkins turned, walked quietly back into her office and went back to work. Mark and Frank just sat in silence and looked at each other for the longest.

"You never know do you?" Mark asked. "And she said he was a Deputy, didn't she?"

"That's what I heard," Frank said as both men reflected on Florence's story.

"Sounds like you just might get your three hundred. And I think there'll be more women than men at this trial. That's the problem I was going to bring up. I'm trying to increase my courthouse crew but I'm running thin everywhere else. I've deputized everybody in the courthouse that I could. Chief Wood Quarles of the Rome Police Department said that his guys could help catch calls close in and help with the traffic around the courthouse. We're about as ready as we're going to get."

"Frank, we've got a 134 cases scheduled on this court calendar and eight of them are murder cases. But Bertha is going to be the main attraction. I wish she was scheduled first then everybody could go home. And then it would be business as usual."

"You know Henderson ain't gonna do that. He needs the votes. He ain't no different than any other politician. He'll play this crowd for as long as he can. It's free publicity."

"I know, she ain't scheduled till the sixteenth. That's Tuesday of the second week. Frank, you going to church Sunday?" Mark Horton asked.

"You know I wouldn't miss this Sunday under any circumstances," Frank replied.

"Good, lets offer up an extra prayer for the Sheriff's Department this coming week. We're going to need it."

# Chapter 19

This is it, Frank thought as he walked down Broad Street. For two months now we've been waiting for Bertha to go to trial. And today is the day. Frank had left the jail a little early for dinner and walked all the way to the Cotton Block and had his noon meal with Joe Adams at the Quick Lunch.

He just wanted to stretch his legs and relax a little before the show began. After lunch as he was walking back to the courthouse, it looked like everybody was walking in the same direction he was. When he got to where he could see the building he was amazed at the line out on the street. Harry Davis had several deputies trying to move the crowd apart long enough to get some of the morning prisoners that had been sentenced back to the jail.

"Harry, is it that bad inside?" Frank asked.

"Chief, I ain't never seen nothing like it," Harry replied. "The place is already packed and this crowd is trying to get in."

"How many do you think you got?" Frank wanted to know.

"I don't rightly know," Harry said. "But there's more than I ever saw before, I'll tell you that."

Frank worked his way into the courthouse and down to the solicitor's table and slid into a chair. He had already been told that he was to help with the prosecution and he knew the defense would insist that he testify first.

He had about a half hour to wait till the lunch break was over. He spent that time going over his notes and answering the questions that Horace Clary, the Assistant Solicitor, had for him. Frank liked Horace a lot. He had served in the Army as a Major during the War and had only been in Rome for a short time. But it was obvious that he had a brilliant legal mind, and Frank knew that he would be a force to reckon with if he was on the other side.

Frank kept glancing back at the crowd that was filing in to the courtroom. It was already over three hundred Frank thought. Way over.

₪    ₪

Bertha sat in a small room behind the courtroom, conferring with her lawyers. She had been escorted over about two hours ago. Carl Griffin had brought her a plate lunch from one of the restaurants on Broad, and he and Mack were trying to keep her calm.

"How many people are out there, Mack?" she asked.

"I'm not gonna lie to you, Bertha. The courtroom is packed."

"Oh Lord," she said. "They've come to see me fed to the lions."

"Nobody's gonna feed you to no lions," Carl said. "You need to finish your dinner. This is going to be a long day."

"Mr. Griffin, could you eat if the state was trying to put you in the electric chair?"

"I'd try."

"Well, I am trying. It just won't go down," Bertha said angrily staring at Griffin all the while.

"Look Bertha, you got to get over this thing about the electric chair." Mack said. "Nobody's going to put you in the chair."

"How do you know that, Mack?"

"'Cause they don't put women in the electric chair, that's how."

"Oh yeah?" Bertha said as her anger became evident. "Then why don't you tell me about Lena Baker. They damn sure put her in the chair last year and she's as dead as a doornail."

"OK, Bertha, let me rephrase that. They don't put white women in the chair."

Bertha was really mad at her defense team as she stood up and glared at both of them.

"Mack, you think she didn't feel it 'cause she's colored? The woman had three kids. She was drinking with a white man that she worked for and was seeing on the side. She said they got into an argument and he pulled a gun. While they were wrestling, it went off and shot him in the head.

"Does that sound like an electric chair case to you? She faced an all-white male jury and you see what she got. Now I've got to go out there and face the same kind of jury that thinks I killed my Mama and Papa along with Leroy. And you tell me not to worry."

# Crowd Jams Court To Hear Hill Trial

Hundreds of interested spectators today crowded into the Floyd County Courtroom where the trial of Bertha Gossett Hill, 28-year-old dime store floor manager, was underway this afternoon for the triple slaying of her mother, father and husband.

Estimated at more than 1,000 men, women and children, the crowd flocked to the Floyd Court House to hear the spectacular trial of a woman who the State charges murdered three members of her family for insurance by administering arsenic poisoning.

The walls and aisles were lined and the stairs leading to the room were filled to capacity as Bertha Gossett Hill was led from Floyd County Jail to a secluded office in the rear of the court to await the selection of jurors who will hear the long line of witnesses deliver their testimony.

Witnesses will include Dr. C. J. Rehlings, Toxicologist for the State of Alabama, who performed the autopsies upon the bodies of Mr. and Mrs. James A. Hardin in the country cemetery in Cherokee County. Dr. Rehlings also conducted the pathological examinations which revealed the cause of their deaths as arsenic poisoning.

The State will also produce Dr. George T. Lewis, head of the Emory University Biochemistry Department, who led the examination of the remains of Leroy Hill, her husband, and who reported "relatively large quantities of calcium arsenic in the vital organs," which he believed was the cause of the death.

Mrs. Lacey Beale, mother of Leroy Hill, who took the warrant for Mrs. Hill's arrest on the night of February 15, the day following the death of Mr. Hill, arrived in Rome yesterday along with members of her family, including the first wife and children of the deceased.

The State will attempt to show that Bertha Hill was named beneficiary on insurance policies taken upon the lives of her father, mother and husband, and that each died "under mysterious and suspicious circumstances" within the period of a year.

Mr. Hardin, the first to go, died

The case was sounded for trial at 2:15 o'clock this afternoon. The 38 witnesses were called, and attorneys for the State and the defense began striking a jury.

on April 3, 1945, and was followed about four months later by Mrs. Hardin on August 13. During this time, it is reported, Bertha married Leroy Hill in Rossville.

She is said to have been married to Neal Gossett, with whom she lived for about 12 years. Divorced when "they couldn't get along," Bertha later married the man she is alleged to have poisoned.

Neighbors in the Pleasant Valley community on the Summerville Highway reported to County Health Authorities and to the Solicitor-General that the circumstances surrounding the deaths of the three members of her family warranted an investigation. It was then, the day following the death of Leroy Hill on February 14, that a coroner's inquest was held.

Upon learning from pathologists at Emory University the autopsy indicated the death of Leroy Hill was caused from arsenic poisoning, a thorough investigation into the deaths of Bertha Hill's parents was launched.

She has been held in Floyd County Jail without bond since the night of her arrest in February until today when she went on trial for her life.

shot of the standing-room-only crowd

# The Trial, Part One

$F$rank heard the sheriff knock loudly on the door.

BAILIFF: All rise. Superior Court of Floyd County is now in Session, the Honorable Claude H. Porter presiding.

JUDGE PORTER: Be seated please. Clerk of the Court will you call the case before us?

CLERK: The State of Georgia versus Bertha Gossett Hill

Frank sat at the State's table for the next hour and fifteen minutes while both legal teams wrangled over a jury. Mack Hicks had asked Judge Porter to purge the jury pool of all members who held insurance with any of the companys named in the indictments. And he showed utter disgust that the judge would let Graham Wright serve as a special assistant to the State from which he was hired by two of the aforementioned insurance companys.

The judge refused to purge the jury pool and allowed Attorney Wright to continue in his capacity. The trial went forward.

Frank knew that jury selection might be one of the most important aspects of a trial, but police officers found it long and boring.

After the jury was sworn and seated, Bertha was escorted into the courtroom. As packed as the room was it had gotten so quiet you could hear a pin drop. Bertha was wearing a navy blue, short sleeved dress and toeless black wedges. As she came down the aisle she would nod or smile at friends and acquaintances she recognized. She stopped briefly and spoke to John Black, asking him quietly where Pauline was.

As she reached the table, she took her seat and kept her eyes forward. Frank could see that occasionally she would sneak a glance at the crowd. Frank also noticed that she never looked at Mrs. Olivia Beale or Clara Hill who had arrived in Rome yesterday and were seated on the first row behind the State.

The lawyers were summoned to the bench for reasons that Frank could only guess. When they returned he was the first witness called to the stand. He testified for over half an hour before he returned to his seat. He had recounted everything he had done in the past two months. He had been surprised a little that Mack didn't ask him very much. Of course, he thought, I'm subject to recall.

The biggest surprise to Frank so far was that the State had decided to try her on a single count. They were trying her for the murder of Leroy Hill only. He suspected they would use the deaths of Mr. and Mrs. Hardin as similar events. He was right. The State had argued in their opening statement that the motive for the homicide was to collect insurance money. They called their first witness, Paul Jordan.

HENDERSON LANHAM for the State: State your name for the record?

WITNESS: Paul Jordan.

LANHAM: What do you do for a living Mr. Jordan?

JORDAN: I'm a merchant and funeral director in Centre, Alabama.

LANHAM: Have you had an opportunity to have contact with the defendant, Bertha Gossett, in the last year?

JORDAN: Yes sir I have, on several occasions.

LANHAM: Would you please relate to this court the events that took place that put you in contact with the defendant?

JORDAN: On December 15, 1945 I wrote a burial-insurance policy on Mr. and Mrs. Leroy Hill, dated on that day, in which Mrs. Hill paid the premium of $1.10, and which would have lapsed on February 15th 1946. She paid for only one month. We give the first one free, and the policy lacked just two days of being expired. After the death of Leroy Hill I came and took his body to Centre, Alabama, embalmed it, and returned it to Rome, Georgia.

LANHAM: Did you have an occasion in their lifetime to know Mr. and Mrs. James Hardin?

JORDAN: Yes sir I did.

LANHAM: Please tell the court in what capacity you knew them?

JORDAN: I knew them for years as friends and neighbors in Cherokee County. I had also sold a burial-insurance policy to Mr. Hardin for his family. And I had the honor to conduct their funeral and burial upon their deaths.

I later went back to the place where I had buried Mr. and Mrs. Hardin with Mr. Rehling, the Sheriff, Mr. Russell and four employees. After we got to the cemetery, we prepared to take the bodies up, and did take them up. Both bodies were taken up from the grave and contents were taken from the bodies. Dr. Rehling performed an autopsy upon those bodies at that time. He then removed some organs from the bodies of Mr. and Mrs. James Hardin and carried them with him. Those bodies were then re-interred and buried.

LANHAM: Did you retrieve Mr. and Mrs. Hardin from Floyd County upon their death?

JORDAN: Yes sir, I did.

LANHAM: Please tell the court where you picked up the bodies of Mr. and Mrs. Hardin.

JORDAN: At the home of Mrs. Hill.

"Thank you Mr. Jordan," said Henderson Lanham without looking at the defense table. "He's with you."

HICKS: Mr. Jordan my name is Mack Hicks and I'm Mrs. Hill's attorney. How are you today?

JORDAN: Well, I've been better, Mr. Hicks.

This comment caused quite a bit of laughter from the courtroom. Judge Porter pounded his gavel to quiet the crowd.

HICKS: I guess we all have. Mr. Jordan you testified that you sold a burial-insurance policy to Mrs. Hill for her and her husband. Is that correct?

JORDAN: Yes it is.

HICKS: Is that part of your business? Is that a service that you offer?

JORDAN: Yes it is.

HICKS: Have you sold burial-insurance policies to other young married couples before.

JORDAN: Of course I have. Like you said, that's one of the services that we offer.

HICKS: And when you conducted Mr. and Mrs. Hardin's funeral, was Bertha there?

JORDAN: Yes she was.

HICKS: Did she appear to be grieving?

JORDAN: Yes she was.

HICKS: Did she act any differently than any other young woman, in your experience, when you went to pick up her husband.

JORDAN: No she did not.

HICKS: Everything you did for Bertha or the Hardins was business as usual. Is that correct?

JORDAN: That would be correct. Yes sir.

HICKS: No further questions.

JUDGE PORTER: You may step down Mr. Jordan. Mr. Solicitor, please call your next witness.

The State calls Mrs. Marvin Watkins.

LANHAM: State your name for the record.

WATKINS: Ollie Watkins.

LANHAM: Were you present at the Hill household at the time Leroy Hill died?

WATKINS: Yes I was.

LANHAM: Please tell this court what you saw and heard during Leroy Hill's final illness.

WATKINS: I was present at Mrs. Hill's home during the last illness of her husband, Leroy Hill. She came for me, I believe it was on Monday before he died on Thursday.

The first day when I went there he was cramping in his stomach and his legs would be kind of paralyzed and he couldn't stand for anybody to touch his arms or legs, and he was vomiting. That first day he didn't vomit so much as that night and then it was just continuous. No one was present the first time I went there except him and Bertha. I believe I stayed about two hours that first day, and then she came back for me the next day.

While I was there the first day, Mrs. Hill did not try to get a doctor for him. I said something about a doctor, and she said that she had him in the hospital several times. She said the doctor said they couldn't do him any good. He was just as well off at home.

I suggested giving him a dose of oil. She gave him some coffee, I believe, one time and then she gave him some soda and salt water he had asked for to make him vomit. He said stuff was gathering around his heart and he wanted something to make him vomit. I was there when he died. He died in the morning about two o'clock.

Just prior to his death he'd have weak sinking spells. I believe he vomited all the time. The vomit was green except one time, the last time. It seemed yellow or reddish looking. Bertha called my attention to it and said that she thought it was blood.

I think I saw Mrs. Hill give him one capsule one time. I wouldn't say for sure, but it seemed she got that capsule from a chest of drawers or maybe from the table. I fixed some castor oil for him and gave it to him myself. My daughter, Mrs. L. E. Holloway, was also present when he died.

ת  ת

As Mrs. Watkins was leaving the stand, Frank watched her and Bertha weakly smile at each other. Ollie nodded as she walked past the defense attorney's table but kept her eyes diverted from Bertha as she left the courtroom.

The State sounded the name of Mrs. L.E. Holloway. Frank knew her as Missy and he was going over in his mind everything she had told him as she was being sworn in. Henderson Lanham had asked her the identifying questions and then to her involvement.

LANHAM: Mrs. Holloway you've testified that you were at the home of Mrs. Hill when Leroy died. Could you please describe what you did and what you saw during that time?

HOLLOWAY: I got there on Monday morning. Bertha had come for my mother and then I was notified that they needed help with Leroy. When I got there he was just vomiting. The vomit was a greenish color. He was complaining of pain, just rolling in the bed and said that if he could just get easy for one minute.

"Oh my poor baby!" came a voice from behind Frank. He spun around in his chair and saw Mrs. Beale and Clara with tears streaming down their faces. The judge had already hit the gavel and was warning the audience that he would tolerate no outbursts. The solicitor had a pleading look on his face as he stared at his team. Frank was thinking, I've got to quiet her down. He eased out of his chair and squat down right by the rail in front of her.

"Mrs. Beale, I know this testimony must be hard to hear," Frank said. "But the judge will have you escorted from the courtroom if it continues. You're gonna have to keep your comments to yourself."

"I'll try, Mr. Russell," she said in a soft quivering voice. "But I've never wanted to kill anybody like I want to kill that woman."

"Mama," Clara Hill said softly, "don't talk that way. You know you don't mean it."

"Yes I do, too. Did you hear how my baby was suffering?" she whispered.

"Mrs. Beale, do you have a weapon on you?" Frank asked quietly.

Clara Hill answered for her mother in law.

"No she doesn't, Mr. Russell. I'll keep her quiet."

The sheriff was standing off to the side of the judge's bench with a questioning look on his face. Frank summoned the nearest bailiff and told him to keep a watch on the two ladies that he had been talking to. Mr. Vincent, the bailiff, said that he would. Frank then nodded to the sheriff that everything was all right.

LANHAM: Mrs. Holloway, I apologize for the interruption. Would you please continue?

HOLLOWAY: Well on that first day that I was there Leroy never mentioned going to a hospital or wanting a doctor. Bertha told us that the doctors had told her that he'd be just as well off at home as he would in the hospital, and that they had done all they could for him.

On Tuesday we went back to the Hill house and spent the night. Leroy was mostly the same all day Tuesday. By Tuesday night he wasn't any better. Bertha was there the whole time. He just kept vomiting continuously and there was no effort to get a doctor or take him to the hospital on that day either.

I saw Bertha give him a capsule but I think he vomited that up, and then it was on Wednesday that she gave him a dose of medicine. I don't know what it was? It was a liquid medicine and Leroy asked her what it was and she said that she had forgotten, didn't know if it was for the heart or something else but that it was one of his prescriptions. Leroy said not to give him anymore because it burned him too bad.

He was complaining about stuff gathering around his heart most of the time. He'd have to have salt and soda water and stuff like that so that he would keep on vomiting. He said that when he got sick the next day, he wanted to go to Dr. McCall, I believe it was, and said that he wanted him to operate on him and see what was the matter with him, but he died that night. He didn't live till morning.

After he died I had a conversation with Mrs. Hill. We had to wait for the ambulance to get there for him. Bertha and I dressed Leroy before the undertaker got there. After we dressed him she went and got her insurance policies and brought them back in the room and was showing them to me and said it was a good thing she had the insurance, that she had spent about all the money they had for doctor's bills.

The State finished its questioning and the defense stepped up to begin their cross.

HICKS: Mrs. Holloway did you ever see Mrs. Hill do anything to harm Leroy Hill?

HOLLOWAY: No I did not.

HICKS: During your time at the Hill household you stated that there were several instances where Leroy made a comment or asked a question, is that correct?

HOLLOWAY: Yes, that's correct.

HICKS: Was Leroy able to speak and make his thoughts known? He wasn't out of his head, was he?

HOLLOWAY: No sir, he wasn't out of his head.

HICKS: And you testified that he never asked for a doctor or medical treatment of any kind until Wednesday night and then he asked Bertha to wait till the next morning. Is that correct?

HOLLOWAY: That's correct.

HICKS: Did he ever ask Bertha to do anything that she didn't do?

HOLLOWAY: No he didn't. I mean Bertha did everything he asked.

HICKS: Did you ever hear Bertha ask him if she could call a doctor?

HOLLOWAY: Yes I did. She asked him several times.

HICKS: Did he go?

HOLLOWAY: No, he wouldn't go.

HICKS: No further questions, your honor.

After a brief fifteen minute recess, the State was ready to proceed with its case. Frank had noticed that most of the audience had stood and stretched a little bit, but very few had left their seat, and the ones that had were with friends and had somebody hold their places.

Frank had wandered back and spoken to Charlsie Patton and then to John Black who told him that he wouldn't let Pauline come. John said that he knew it was going to be bad and that he was afraid that Pauline couldn't handle it. But even he had no idea it would be this bad.

Frank had explained to the sheriff what was going on earlier and he asked Mrs. Beale how she was holding up. He was thinking to himself that he had covered a lot of ground in the short recess.

The State calls Dr. Warren B. Mathews.

Before testimony could begin, the State qualified Dr. Mathews as an expert. Usually, the defense will stipulate the fact that the doctor does possess the qualities to be an expert in his field. But today Mack made them go through the motions of qualification. Maybe, Frank thought, it was because the doctor was from out of town.

LANHAM: Dr. Mathews, did you perform an autopsy on Leroy Hill?

DR. MATHEWS: Yes I did.

LANHAM: Please tell the court what you did and what you saw during this autopsy.

DR. MATHEWS: I performed an autopsy on the body of Leroy Hill in Rome, Georgia on February 15th 1946. I removed the stomach and part of the intestine and part of the liver and part of the kidneys. I found the intestines and stomach irritated and inflamed and I found what we call 'toxic changes' in the kidneys and liver.

LANHAM: Had Leroy Hill's body been embalmed when you did the autopsy.

DR. MATHEWS: Yes it had been.

LANHAM: Could the conditions, these 'toxic changes,' have been caused by the introduction of embalming fluid.

DR. MATHEWS: No sir they could not have been. The conditions that I found could not have been caused by injecting embalming fluid into the body. The conditions that I described were conditions that had to be caused before death.

LANHAM: Did these conditions cause the death of Leroy Hill?

DR. MATHEWS: My examination indicated that he died of the conditions that I described, but I could not state what was behind those conditions without further analysis.

LANHAM: Could these changes have been caused by the introduction of arsenic into the body?

DR. MATHEWS: The stomach was reddened in spots and inflamed and green with bile in other spots. The mucus membrane appeared to be bile stained and to be inflamed. There was swelling of the liver and kidneys. In the form of arsenic trioxide, which is the one I shall refer to, the lethal dose is three grains, or thereabouts. So yes, arsenic could have been the agent that caused the changes, but as I've already stated, without further chemical analysis I could not state what the exact cause was.

LANHAM: After you completed your autopsy on Leroy Hill in Rome, what did you do?

DR. MATHEWS: After I finished the autopsy on this body I took the organs to Dr. George Lewis of Emory University and delivered them to him for a toxicological examination. His specialty is that of chemistry, or particularly what we call biochemistry.

LANHAM: The State has no further questions of this witness at this time, Your Honor.

"Very well, Mr. Lanham," Judge Porter said turning toward the defense table where he simply nodded in Mack's direction.

HICKS: Dr. Mathews what do you mean by 'toxic changes?'

DR. MATHEWS: I mean changes that we see. The organ looked swollen, discolored to some extent. It looks entirely different from the normal organ; sometimes we describe it as having a cooked appearance.

HICKS: What causes that, Dr. Mathews? Please tell the court what causes these toxic changes that you've described.

DR. MATHEWS: There are many things that could cause that. From what I had, I could not determine what the cause was.

HICKS: Were you aware that Leroy Hill had syphilis and was being treated for it?

The crowd in the courtroom was stunned with the announcement that Leroy had syphilis. Frank looked around at the crowd and thought this is a moment in time to remember. He could only imagine what was going through the minds of the audience.

DR. MATHEWS: Yes I was. Deputy Davis, I believe, told me the morning that we did the autopsy that Mr. Hill was a syphilis patient.

Good old Harry, Frank thought. I got to remember to tell him how these little things really make a difference in modern day police work. Frank let his eyes glance toward Bertha. She was rigid. He could see that she appeared to be a little anxious and her breathing was a little rapid, but she kept her focus on the witness.

HICKS: Is arsenic not a treatment for syphilis?

DR. MATHEWS: Yes it is.

HICKS: And please tell the court if embalming fluid also has an arsenic compound in it.

DR. MATHEWS: Yes it does.

HICKS: Your Honor, the defense has no further questions for this witness at this time.

"Thank you Mr. Hicks," Judge Porter said. "Anything else from the State?"

LANHAM: Yes your Honor, we do have a few more questions.

LANHAM: Dr. Mathews, would you please explain to the court how arsenic is used in the treatment of syphilis?

DR. MATHEWS: Well there are several different ways. I think the most effective and the most common are injections. An arsenic compound is a standard remedy for syphilitic condition. Neoarsphenamine and arsphenamine differ, in that neoarsphenamine is a little less toxic than arsphenamine. It causes a little less reaction and it contains a different form of arsenic. There are also oral applications that can be used, but the preferred method is with injections.

LANHAM: Could an individual overdose on this medication accidentally.

DR. MATHEWS: If an individual was taking injections and became confused and took the other one. Let's say that if an individual was taking neoarsphenamine and for some reason took arsphenamine in the normal dose that he had been taking neoarsphenamine I don't think it would kill him but he would be awful sick. And if he took an additional shot pretty quick, well there would be a limit.

LANHAM: "Could that be what happened here, Dr. Mathews?"

DR. MATHEWS: No it could not. From what I saw, assuming that it was arsenic poisoning, I would say that it was definitely ingested. I say that because I've never seen so much irritation of the stomach and intestines from arsenic taken any other way. The changes that I saw were caused before death and by ingestion. A person suffering from acute arsenic poisoning lives from a few hours to perhaps a week.

LANHAM: Thank you Dr. Mathews. The State has no further questions of this witness.

"Is there anything else from the defense?" Judge Porter asked.

HICKS: Just a few, Your Honor.

HICKS: You did not do a chemical analysis, is that correct?

DR. MATHEWS: That's correct. I did not.

HICKS: You don't know what caused the toxic changes that you saw in Leroy Hill then, do you?

DR. MATHEWS: No I do not.

HICKS: You don't know what killed Leroy Hill, do you?

DR. MATHEWS: Not with medical certainty, from what I had, without further analysis, no I don't.

HICKS: That's all for the defense, Your Honor.

"Your Honor, the State asks that this witness be excused. He has a long drive back to Atlanta."

"Does the defense object?" Judge Porter asked.

"No your honor," Mack replied, "We do not."

"Then Dr. Mathews you're excused and the court thanks you for your service. Please call the next witness."

The State calls Dr. George Lewis.

This time Frank noticed that Mack did stipulate Dr. Lewis's qualifications as an expert.

LANHAM: Dr. Lewis did you perform a chemical analysis on specimens taken from Leroy Hill by Dr. Warren Mathews?

DR. LEWIS: Yes I did.

LANHAM: Would you please publish those results for the court?

DR. LEWIS: I received several specimens from Dr. Mathews. I made some examinations and chemical analyses of those things. The specimens were analyzed primarily for arsenic and secondly for lead. Large quantities of arsenic were found. No lead was found. We found twenty-five milligrams per hundred grams of stomach wall, approximately five milligrams per hundred grams of intestine, one and one-half milligrams per hundred grams of liver, and one milligram per hundred grams of kidney.

I found no lead in the contents that were delivered to me. That simply means that the contents delivered to me did not contain lead arsenate.

The greatest concentration was found in the wall of the stomach. I would certainly think that arsenic was induced through the mouth by ingestion. I say this because the distribution is such as one would anticipate following that route of administration. From the amounts that I have just previously described, I would say a lethal dose of poison was present in the body.

I found traces of that poison in the intestines and the liver and the kidneys also. I would think that the amount that I found in the liver and kidneys would be sufficient to cause death.

In my opinion arsenic poisoning caused the death of Leroy Hill. The most common symptoms of arsenic poisoning consist of vomiting, diarrhea, and a sore throat. There are pains in the limbs of the body, pains in the abdomen also.

I would characterize this analysis and the amount I found as way over the lethal amount. It is a matter of opinion as to how long a person would live normally if he had taken or was given a dose of arsenic sufficient to cause the condition I found. The length of time varies. My opinion was that it would certainly be less than twenty-four hours.

Frank slid back in his chair, transfixed on the testimony that he had just heard. He knew basically what was coming, but he had no idea of the detail in which it would be presented.

His mind retraced the steps of his own investigation and the detail in which he had prepared it. These last two witnesses were living proof to Frank that law enforcement had miles to go before it would be this efficient.

The rest of Dr. Lewis testimony was almost an exact copy of Dr. Mathews. Frank was brought back to the present by the judge's gavel and his announcement that court was over for today and would re-convene in the morning at eight o'clock.

Floyd County courthouse at the time of Bertha Hill's trial

Judge Porter with *Rome News* staffer
Dickey Barron

# Chapter 20

Frank eased out of his seat and moved through the crowded courtroom as fast as possible. He was already at the jail when Harry and his transport crew brought Bertha through the door. He told his deputies to take her to the interview room and stay with her till her attorneys got there. No one had told him that Mack and Carl were coming but experience had taught him that a case of this magnitude guaranteed that they would be here. While they were waiting he called Harry Davis into his office.

"What did you think about today, Harry? Did you have any problems? Did you get an estimate on the crowd? Are we going to be ready bright and early tomorrow morning?"

"Slow down, Chief," Harry said. "I thought today went OK. We had a few problems but it was all due to the crowd we had to go through on each transport.

"I didn't get a chance to estimate the crowd size, but I can tell you this. The courtroom was packed. The aisles and around the back was standing room only and it was full. The main steps in front going up to the second floor were packed. And the back steps were too. I heard one of those news guys say there was a thousand people here today and tomorrow will be twice that many."

"Why do you think that?" Frank asked.

"I heard Henderson being interviewed by the *Rome News* and he said that this may be the South's most spectacular court trial in the recent annals of crime, and he said it this morning so the paper has had time to get it in today's issue. The *Floyd County Herald* did a story on this Alabama doctor that's scheduled to testify tomorrow. Everybody's gonna be here to see the elephant."

"I guess you're right, Harry," Frank said. "Better have your crew here a little earlier than usual."

"I've already told them to be here at six in the morning, Chief. That ought to do it."

Mack Hicks, accompanied by Carl Griffin, stopped at Frank's door and peered in.

"Deputy Russell, is it all right if we go back and talk to Bertha?" Mack asked.

"She's waiting for you, Mack," Frank replied.

"You see Carl, efficiency is what Russell's all about. You're getting to be a little too good, Frank. You're starting to worry me. And if you're worrying me, you're scaring half the lawyers in town to death."

"I hope we are, Mack! I certainly do."

Mack Hicks walked on to the interview room followed by Carl. Both men entered the room and sat at the small table across from Bertha. Mack looked up at the deputy posted in the room and simply said, "Thanks officer. We'll take it from here."

Bertha waited till the Deputy left the room and then turned to her defense team and said sharply.

"What was that all about?"

"What was what all about Bertha?" Mack asked.

"The first thing this morning when the solicitor said they said that they were only trying me on one count. I leaned over and asked Carl what was going on and he said that he had to pay attention, and he'd tell me later. Well, it's later Carl, and I want to know."

"OK Bertha, calm down," Carl said. "The State has decided to try you for the murder of Leroy only. They think they have a better case on you in his death than they do your parents."

"Does that mean they're dropping the other cases?"

"No it don't," Carl said. "They could try you for them at any time they chose, unless we file a demand, and we ain't gonna do that."

"I still don't understand why they're doing me a favor," Bertha said.

"They're not," Carl said. "They're going to use the death of your parents to show similar events. For instance all three died at your house in very similar ways. They're going to use that against you."

Bertha turned to Mack and asked, "Mack, can they do that? Bring up their deaths without me being charged with it?"

"You're still charged with it, Bertha. And they may try you on it next year, but I doubt it."

"Why?" she asked

"If you're found guilty on Leroy and then sentenced, then they try you on your parents, it would be unlikely that you'd get a stiffer sentence. Most likely the same thing and they'd run concurrent."

"Concurrent, what does that mean?"

"If you got three life sentences you can't serve them one after the other. You serve them all at the same time."

"Oh, I get it. They can't fry my big butt but once. They're not gonna dig me up and do it again. Is that what you're trying to say Mack?"

"That's one way to put it, Bertha. Now, are you ready to get to work so that don't happen?"

ת  ת

Johnny was at the Partridge by 4:00 in the morning. He knew that this might be the biggest day in the restaurant business since he'd been open. He moved a senior waitress into the kitchen to help his Mama cook and got several young girls to wait tables during the rush that the trial was causing.

He'd been to the church and borrowed two thirty cup coffee makers and they were already going. He was told that he could expect a crowd to start arriving as soon as he was open, and he wanted to open by 5:30 if he could.

He normally didn't reserve seating for anybody, but this morning he did reserve seats for his early morning breakfast club. After all, they were regulars and were here every day. He made sure their table was ready just like they were every morning.

Some of them started arriving early. All of the newspaper and radio personalities were first to come in. They were followed by Dr. Elmore, who was to testify during today's event. Even the local businessmen got to the table a little early.

Rome was excited about all the happenings at the courthouse. The downtown area was packed yesterday and today promised an even bigger crowd. John Henry, the INS news man, was back with Ben Cooper and there were several other wire service reporters present. Johnny had to pull another table close to his regular one in order to get this crowd as close to each other as he could. Reverend Stephens was in attendance, as was City Manager Sam King.

"All right Dr. Elmore, what are we gonna hear today?" asked John Powers as he poured some of the scalding coffee from his cup into the saucer so that it would cool just a little.

"A whole lot of what you heard yesterday John, except it's going to get worse," said Elmore turning to face attorney Jack Harris. "Don't you think so, Jack?"

"Ben Rainwater and I were talking about that yesterday evening," Jack said. "The medical evidence is going to slowly get more in depth as the trial continues. At least that's the way we figure it."

"I saw Dr. Rehlings on the witness list," John Henry said. "Do you think he'll get to testify today?"

"I expect he will, Mr. Henry," Dr. Elmore said. "Unless I miss my guess, Judge Porter will get this thing to a jury today."

"What's so special about Dr. Rehlings?" Cecil Rhodes asked. "Isn't he just the Alabama State Toxicologist?"

"Well, he certainly is that," John Henry said. "But he's a lot more. Do you remember several years ago when a lot of people died across the country and no one could figure out what was causing it."

"I do," Dr. Elmore said. "It had us scared to death that we were going to have some people around here die unexpectedly. Wasn't it finally discovered that it was some kind of compound in sulfa drugs causing it?"

"Good memory, Doc," John said, "and Rehlings is the toxicologist who discovered it. He travels the country now speaking at medical conventions about all kinds of new and wonderful drugs on the market."

"And he serves on the board of directors of one of the biggest pharmaceutical companies in the country," James Tate added. "*The Herald* is doing a story on him for tomorrow's paper."

"How about you guys, Ben?" Macon Brock said. "You got any interesting tidbits?"

"Macon, we had some of our people scattered around the courthouse just for that purpose," Ben said. "Dickey Barron is sitting through the trial taking notes for us and we got a few things we're gonna mention."

"Can you tell us what some of them are?" Macon asked.

"Sure thing," Ben replied. "There was a young boy jumping up and down trying to see over the adults' heads. And an old man leaving the courthouse in disgust saying that he couldn't hear nothing and couldn't see nothing. Then there were the college students all taking notes. And best of all, there was a lady that brought a sack full of hamburgers. Women packed the building. They seemed to be especially interested in her. I mean from bobby-soxers to elderly ladies.

"Is INS gonna print any of those things along with the Rome paper, John Henry?" Hix Sims asked.

"We sure are," John Henry said as he reached for the sugar bowl.

"What are you doing with that sugar bowl, John?" Happy Quarles asked excitedly.

John Henry froze, and looked at Happy questioningly, then said, "I'm gonna put some of it and a little butter on this white stuff y'all eat."

"That white stuff is grits," Happy corrected him.

"OK, its grits," John said. "Now pass me the butter please."

"We don't put sugar on grits down here, John," Happy informed him with a real concerned look on his face.

"Excuse me," John Henry said. "Then how do y'all eat the little boogers then?"

By now everyone at the table was rolling in laughter and that was attracting attention from other tables.

"Here's what you do," Happy said. "You simply use a little pat of butter, salt and pepper--a little more pepper than salt."

"Are you guys setting me up?" he asked looking nervously from face to face. "Happy, I've only known you for a short time. And I ain't real trusting of you when it comes to something like this."

"I thought you were stationed in Atlanta," Happy said. "I know they got grits in Atlanta. I've eaten them there before."

"Yeah, with sugar and butter," John Henry said.

"Well that's the way Yankees eat them in the big city," Happy said. "But Southern boys use butter, salt and pepper."

"Reverend Stephens, I trust you," John said. "Are these guys telling me the truth, or am I being set up for a joke."

"It's the truth, John," Reverend Stephens said. "Southern folks won't waste good sugar to sweeten something up that don't need sweetening. Little salt and pepper will do it."

John Henry looked at his breakfast for a minute, then reached for the salt and pepper shakers and said, "Well, like I was told once. When in Rome."

He got a big round of applause and a few hearty cheers. That brought Johnny Jacobs on the run.

"What are y'all doing?" he asked. "Is everything all right?"

"Everything's fine, Johnny," Hix Sims said. "The boys were just training a Yankee how to eat grits."

"Mr. Henry, you be careful of this crowd."

"I am, Johnny," John Henry said. "But I appreciate you watching after me."

"That's part of my job," Johnny said. "Taking care of my customers."

John Henry bought breakfast for the table once again and the men started drifting out slowly.

"Macon, do you mind if I walk a bit with you?" Reverend Stephens said. "I've got to go to the shoe shop."

"Not at all, Preacher," Macon Brock said.

As they crossed Fifth Avenue and headed down Rome's Broad Street toward the Jewelry store, Reverend Stephens glanced over toward Macon and said, "I've been missing you in church Macon."

"I didn't figure you wanted to talk about Bertha Hill's trial," Macon answered.

"I saw Florence this past Sunday. I know Ed and Bob were with her, don't remember seeing your other boys. But we had a big crowd. I'm sure they were there also."

"They were there, I'm quite sure," Macon said. "Reverend Stephens, I've just been working seven days a week for the last six or seven months. Well ever since the War ended. The jewelry store business has been pretty tough for the past several years. I couldn't get watches to sell, much less jewelry. If it hadn't been for the repair work that I did, I don't know what we would have done.

"Now that the War is over I'm trying to re-establish my business. Like I told the guys at breakfast, I've got Swiss watches coming now and a good supply of jewelry. I guess what I'm saying is that I'm just now getting back on my feet. I don't mean I was destitute. There was a ton of repair work. Actually there was more than I could do and I was working long days. But I want to get back to the level I was before the war, and then see what we can do without a depression. Reverend Stephens, I don't know but one way to do that and that's what I'm doing. Plus, I want my boys to have an opportunity to succeed at whatever they want to do."

"Macon, the boys are just fine. They're going to all be good men. And Florence is a great woman. She's made you a fine wife and is a good mother. But my interest this morning is you."

"Reverend Stephens, I've just told you where I've been for the last six months," Macon said. "But the truth is I don't have an excuse for not going."

"Then I'll see you this coming Sunday?" Reverend Stephens asked.

"Maybe you will, Preacher, maybe you will."

Bertha with Bailiff Vincent

# The Trial, Part 2

Frank arrived at the courthouse early. He had checked with Harry and made sure he had a full crew and was ready for a big day. There was only one case on the agenda today, so there shouldn't be a lot of transport to and from the jail. However, the crowd was expected to be even bigger than yesterday.

Bertha had already come in and was seated next to Mack Hicks and Carl Griffin. The Judge entered the room and after a pre-trial conference at the bench, the announcement was made to get under way.

Frank had stopped at the sheriff's office and picked up a couple of paper cups. He stuffed one with napkins to use as a spit cup. He now cut himself a big chaw of Bloodhound and leaned back in his chair, getting comfortable. *Here we go!*

The State calls Doctor Bosworth.

LANHAM: State your name and occupation for the record.

WITNESS: Edward Bosworth. I am a practicing physician in Rome.

LANHAM: Dr. Bosworth did you have an occasion to treat Leroy Hill during his lifetime.

BOSWORTH: Yes I did, at Harbin Hospital.

LANHAM: Could you please tell the court what that treatment consisted of.

BOSWORTH: Mr. Hill was complaining about an upset stomach and a sore throat. He said that he had eaten some shrimp that disagreed with him, and he had a fever of 103. The examination revealed that he had acute tonsillitis with some ulcerations on his throat; also he had a primary lesion of syphilis in the first stage. This fact was confirmed with a Kahn test. I gave him penicillin for that, but he did not finish the complete recommended course of penicillin treatment as he was only in the hospital for five days and was discharged on January the 17th this year. He was supposed to come back but he never did.

LANHAM: Is penicillin the usual treatment for syphilis?

BOSWORTH: It's the usual treatment given, supplemented at a later date with some kind of injection of bismuth. I personally use neoarsphenamine injected in the veins at weekly intervals.

LANHAM: Your witness.

HICKS: Dr. Bosworth if an injection of neoarsphenamine was given in the tissue of the body rather than in a vein, would it be harmful?

BOSWORTH: It would certainly be irritating, but it would not become necessarily dangerous to the patient's life. But it would make an extremely sore place at the point of injection.

HICKS: Do you know what kind of treatment Leroy Hill received after he left your care?

BOSWORTH: No, I do not.

HICKS: No further questions of this witness.


The State calls Mary Rogers

As Frank was working on his chew, he once again was thinking of complimenting Harry on his interview of the medical witness's. He had done a good job. Frank took a big spit into his cup while Miss Rogers was sworn, and re-adjusted himself in his chair.

LANHAM: Miss Rogers what do you do at Floyd Hospital?

ROGERS: I'm the record librarian.

LANHAM: Are you familiar with the records of Leroy Hill?

ROGERS: Yes sir, I am.

LANHAM: Can you please tell the court when he was in Floyd Hospital? What he was treated for? And who treated him?

ROGERS: He was there twice this year. The first time he was there was from January 22nd until the 31st and he was treated first by Dr. Mull and then he was transferred to Dr. Garrard. The second time he was in the hospital from February 4th through the 8th. And this time he was treated by Dr. Garrard only.

LANHAM: Do you have a record of what medicine he was given while in the hospital?

ROGERS: Yes I do. The first time he was there he had penicillin, glucose, neoprontosil, neoarsphenamine, urotopin, morphine, milk of magnesia, cascara, citro carbonate and amphojel. The second time he was given five doses from a prescription that just said R.C.Z. All prescriptions and medicine were administered under the instructions of Dr. Garrard. He was discharged on February 8th as improved.

Mr. Hicks, you may cross.

HICKS: Miss Rogers what was the diagnosis on his visits to the hospital.

ROGERS: On his first visit he was diagnosed with tonsillitis. There is no other diagnosis listed for the second visit which would indicate it was the same diagnosis.

HICKS: Does the record indicate whether he was given any hypodermic or drugs for treatment of himself after he was discharged?

ROGERS: No sir it does not.

HICKS: No further questions, Your Honor.

"Anything else from the State?" Judge Porter asked.

"Just one more question your honor," Henderson said as he received a piece of paper from Graham Wright.

LANHAM: Miss Rogers, would you look again at your records and see if Leroy Hill was not in the hospital on February 11,12,13 and 14th.

ROGERS: No sir, my records indicate that he was not in the hospital on those dates.

LANHAM: We have nothing else from the State, Your Honor.


The State calls Doctor J.H. Mull

Frank watched once again as Henderson went through the preliminaries before questioning the witness.

LANHAM: Dr. Mull, did you treat Leroy Hill when he came to the hospital?

MULL: No sir I didn't treat him. I saw him and let them admit him. But I had previously told him that I didn't treat venereal diseases. I instructed the staff to get Dr. Garrard to treat him. The record seems to say that I ordered an injection of neoarsphenamine. This is an arsenical compound and does not have the strength to cause death.

LANHAM: No further questions from the State.

HICKS: None from the defense.


Frank was beginning to see the big picture coming together. It was apparent now that the prosecution was going to present its case on the death of Leroy Hill. He thought that they would then start bringing testimony about the death of the parents and use their deaths as similar events.

Frank knew that it was permissible in some instances but he felt sure that Mack would certainly use this forthcoming testimony as grounds for appeal.

Frank glanced at Bertha and she caught his eye. She gave him a nod and a big smile. He had noticed that when she entered the courtroom this morning she was very cheerful. All the butterflies from yesterday were gone.

She had stopped and spoken to friends and acquaintances as she came down the aisle. He thought she looked pretty good in the pale blue dress that Mack had gotten for her to wear.

Frank could only imagine the stress that she was under and he was amazed at the way she was handling it all. He settled back in his chair to listen to the next witness.

LANHAM: State your name for the record please.

WITNESS: Dr. John Garrard.

LANHAM: Dr. Garrard did you have an occasion to treat Leroy Hill while he was in Floyd Hospital earlier this year?

DR. GARRARD: Yes I did. According to my notes, Dr. Mull treated him up until or about January 22nd. And then I saw him until he was discharged on the 31st. He returned on the 4th of February and was discharged on February 8th.

LANHAM: What did you treat him for while he was hospitalized?

DR. GARRARD: "The first time he was treated for acute syphilis which was improved apparently, as no treatment was given him for the syphilitic condition when he returned the second time, in February. The chart indicates something about his stomach the last time. That was the 4th, and the chief complaint as I have it down here on the chart was nausea and vomiting. It says he started vomiting and continued to do so throughout the night and could not take medication to restrain it.

LANHAM: Could that vomiting and nausea be caused from taking arsenic orally?

DR. GARRARD: Yes it could, if it was in a large dose.

LANHAM: Did you give Mr. Hill any medication that contained arsenic while he was in the hospital the second time?

DR. GARRARD: Nothing that I know of, unless it was in the prescription and I don't believe it was.

Frank sat quietly as Mack went over the testimony again with Dr. Garrard. As he listened to Mack's line of questioning, he saw that the defense was not going to question the fact Leroy had been poisoned. Their case rested on trying to explain that Bertha didn't do it. Frank felt a punch on his shoulder and leaned over to hear what Horace Clary had to say.

"Frank, we're going to put you up again after the next witness."

"Ok," Frank said as he watched Horace and Graham Wright get back to scribbling notes and passing them to Henderson.

Ruben McClung was then called to the stand. Frank knew now why he would be next.

LANHAM: Please state you name for the record.

WITNESS: Ruben McClung.

LANHAM: Please tell the court how you came to be at Leroy Hill's house during the month of February?

McCLUNG: I was not present when Mr. Hill died. I lived in Coosa, Georgia on February 14th and Mrs. Hill came for me and my wife. She said that Leroy was dead and that she wanted us to come and stay with her at her house. That was on February 14th and we stayed about fifteen days. My wife and kids went with me.

LANHAM: What was your relationship to Mrs. Hill?

McCLUNG: My wife and Mrs. Hill's mother were sisters.

LANHAM: Mr. McClung, have you ever seen this bag I'm holding marked States exhibit #2.

McCLUNG: Yes sir I have. I found it at Bertha's house and gave it to Mr. Russell. I never told Mrs. Hill I found it.

LANHAM: Did you have an occasion to talk to Mrs. Hill after she was arrested?

McCLUNG: Yes sir, I spoke to her the day after she was arrested and tried to get her a bond and then a lawyer. But they wouldn't appoint her one at that time. Then after about two weeks had went by, me and my wife went to see her at the jail. She started crying and told us that they were going to take her mother and daddy up. She didn't want them to 'cause they would find them poisoned.

LANHAM: Nothing else from the State, Your Honor.

HICKS: Were you in the house prowling around looking for a bag such as this, Mr. McClung?

McCLUNG: No sir, I was getting a ball out from under the house that one of the young-uns had kicked under there.

HICKS: And you didn't tell Mrs. Hill about it, did you?

McCLUNG: No sir I didn't.

HICKS: Tell me about the statement at the jail. Did y'all ask her about her folks being poisoned?

McCLUNG: No sir. That statement by her was freely and voluntarily given.

HICKS: But it made you and your wife mad, didn't it?

McCLUNG: Yes sir. it did.

HICKS: And that's when you called Deputy Russell and give him the bag of arsenic, isn't that right? After you and Mrs. McClung went home mad?

McCLUNG: No sir, I had already given Deputy Russell the bag.

HICKS: Nothing else from the defense, Your Honor.

"Frank, we're going to put up his wife to and see if she can strengthen his story a little before you go up," Horace said.

Frank remembered that Graham had said they were not going to put Plemma McClung up if they could help it. He knew that it was risky business to get kinfolk on the stand no matter how they felt about each other going in. He could see that Bertha had diverted her eyes from her aunt. And Plemma was looking at her hands the entire time she testified. Her statement to the court was an exact copy of her husband's. Mack had no questions for her and she quickly left the courtroom.

LANHAM: Deputy Russell, let me remind you that you're still under oath.

RUSSELL: Yes sir, I'm aware of that.

LANHAM: In my hand I hold a bag marked State's exhibit #2. Have you ever seen this bag before?

RUSSELL: Yes sir I have. I know Ruben McClung and this bag was given to me by him on February 25th 1946, at Bertha's home. I have kept it until I brought it into court yesterday. I saw you in this court room pour some of the contents out. It looks like the same pinkish colored contents as it was when I received it from Ruben McClung.

LANHAM: No further questions, Your Honor.

HICKS: None from the defense, Your Honor.

The State calls Miss Louise Poole.

LANHAM: Please state your name for the record.

WITNESS: Louise Poole.

LANHAM: Miss Poole, are you acquainted with Mrs. Bertha Hill?

POOLE: Yes sir, I am.

LANHAM: And were you acquainted with Mrs. Hill's mother, Mrs. Zola Hardin?

POOLE: Yes sir, I was.

LANHAM: Were you present when Mrs. Hardin died?

POOLE: Yes sir, I was.

LANHAM: Please tell the court what you saw and did on July 12th and 13th 1945 in regards to the death of Mrs. Hardin.

POOLE: When I got home from work on July 12th my mother told me that Mrs. Hardin was very sick and talking about dying and all and said for me to go down there. When I got there it was just like mother said. Mrs. Hardin was laying there sick and talking of dying.

Bertha and Leroy were the only ones there when I arrived. But shortly after Dr. Williams came out and checked her and wrote some prescriptions. I stayed with Mrs. Hardin while Bertha and Leroy went to the drugstore and got the prescriptions filled. When Bertha came back, she put the prescriptions in a chest of drawers in her and Leroy's bedroom.

I didn't get to see what the medicine looked like that Dr. Williams prescribed. But Bertha said, "I guess I should give her a dose now." She brought her mother a capsule and had something in a glass. It looked like orange juice.

Mrs. Hardin kept saying that if she took that it would kill her, but Bertha insisted on her mother taking the juice. Mrs. Hardin kept saying, "If I take another drink of that it will kill me."

Mrs. Hardin was seriously sick. She was vomiting about half of the time, just every few minutes and it was a greenish-yellow kind of a mixture. She kept saying it was poison that Bertha was giving her. Over and over she said that if she took that it would kill her and that Bertha was trying to kill her.

I didn't see anybody else give her anything except those capsules that Bertha kept giving her. I'm not sure how many capsules she gave her, but I think they were coming every hour. And she kept offering her something that either was or looked like orange juice every few minutes.

LANHAM: No further questions, Your Honor.

HICKS: Miss Poole, did you say that Bertha called a doctor to come and check on her mother?

POOLE: Yes sir, she did. Dr. Williams came and saw her.

HICKS: And did you say that she went immediately and got the prescriptions filled that Dr. Williams wrote for her mother?

POOLE: Yes sir she did.

HICKS: Did she give her mother medicine after she got back?

POOLE: She gave her capsules every hour.

HICKS: Did you see her give any capsules before she went to the drug store.

POOLE: No I didn't.

HICKS: And the orange juice was to help the capsule go down wasn't it?

POOLE: I guess, I don't really know.

HICKS: No further questions for this witness, Your Honor.

Frank leaned back in his chair enjoying his chew and thought, If these witnesses don't inflame a jury, then nothing will. Nobody, including the press, has heard this before.

He could see that Bertha was locked in on what her neighbors were testifying to. She was writing little notes and leaning over and talking to Carl Griffin during the entire testimony of Louise Poole.

Frank had never heard such a large crowd be this quiet. It seemed that everybody was straining to catch every word of the witness on the stand.

LANHAM: Please state your name for the record.

WITNESS: Mrs. Carrie Poole.

LANHAM: Mrs. Poole, are you the mother of the witness that just testified?

C. POOLE: Yes I am.

LANHAM: Were you also acquainted with Mrs. J.A. Hardin during her lifetime?

C. POOLE: Yes sir, we were neighbors up in the Pleasant Valley community.

LANHAM: Did you have occasion to be at her house during the time between July 10th and the 13th of last year?

C. POOLE: Yes sir I did.

LANHAM: Would you please tell the court what you did and observed during that time in conjunction with the death of Mrs. Hardin?

C. POOLE: I was at her house on Tuesday the 10th just visiting. She didn't seem to be sick that day. The next night she seemed to be right sick. Bertha asked me if my husband would take her to the hospital, and of course the answer to that was yes. So me and my husband, along with Bertha and her mother, went to McCall Hospital.

Bertha had been giving her capsules every hour and she would throw them up. She was vomiting a right smart. After we got to the hospital Bertha went inside and the head nurse came out and spoke to Mrs. Hardin. She asked her if she wanted to stay. Mrs. Hardin told the nurse that she did not. The nurse told her it was probably just as good because they didn't have any rooms anyway.

Bertha came out and said that Dr. Mull had an emergency and couldn't see her right away. My husband said that we would wait then and Bertha told him no. She said to stop at a drugstore and that she would get her something to ease her.

We left the hospital and stopped at a drugstore and Bertha went in. I do not know what she got there. After that we went straight home and dropped Bertha and her mother off at their house.

The next day, on Thursday, I saw Dr. Williams at Mrs. Hardin's house. I didn't get back over there until later in the afternoon. Mrs. Hardin was still sick just like she had been. She didn't seem no worse or no better, just vomiting all the time. Bertha and Leroy had been to the drugstore to get a prescription filled after the Doctor left and when they got back, Bertha kept giving her Mama a capsule and orange juice about every hour.

LANHAM: Mrs. Poole, at the hospital was any attempt made to get her out of the car?

C. POOLE: No sir.

LANHAM: Why was that?

C. POOLE: I don't know why.

LANHAM: No further questions, Your Honor.

PORTER: Mr. Hicks, you may ask.

HICKS: Mrs. Poole, you testified that Bertha asked you to get your husband to carry her mother to the hospital, is that correct?

C. POOLE: Yes sir, it is.

HICKS: And Mrs. Hardin told the head nurse that she didn't want to come in, is that also correct?

C. POOLE: Yes it is.

HICKS: And you testified that Bertha stopped at a drug store to get something to ease her mother, is that correct?

C. POOLE: Yes sir that's also correct?

HICKS: From all you saw, she was trying to help her mother, is that correct?

C. POOLE: Yes.

HICKS: No further questions of this witness.

Frank thought that Mack had done a good job on the cross examination of these last two witnesses. He was starting to paint a picture of Bertha doing all she could to help her mother.

And at the same time, the prosecution kept bringing up the fact that Bertha was giving her mother some kind of capsule almost hourly and some kind of liquid that may or may not have been orange juice.

Frank did not have any idea how the jurors were reacting to the testimony. The twelve white men on the jury were not showing any kind of emotional reaction to the testimony either way. As the lawyers left the bench after a short conference with the judge, Frank got ready for the next witness.

The State calls Mrs. C.C. Lynch.

LANHAM: State your name for the record.

WITNESS: Jessie Lynch.

LANHAM: Mrs. Lynch, were you present at the home of Mrs. James Hardin when she died?

LYNCH: Yes I was.

LANHAM: Could you please tell the court how you happened to be there and what you observed?

LYNCH: I was at home when Mrs. Poole and Bertha came after me. When we got back to the house no one other than Louise Poole and Leroy were there.

I was told that another man had gone after Mrs. Hardin's father. But I don't know that for sure, although he did arrive later on.

Bertha told me she was afraid her mother was hungry and she kept trying to give her what she called orange juice. Mrs. Hardin was unconscious and couldn't swallow. She was struggling, just rattling in her throat, you know, like people do when they are dying.

I don't know where the orange juice was prepared. Bertha got it out of the kitchen. I was told that Dr. Williams had been by and had written prescriptions earlier in the day. I don't know what they were and I didn't see any medicine other than those capsules.

Bertha did make an effort to get a doctor. She and I walked back to our place and called and tried to get three different doctor's for her mother but they wouldn't or couldn't come.

My husband overheard our conversation and asked why we didn't take her to the hospital. Bertha told him she didn't want to carry her to the hospital. We went back to Bertha's house and her mother died just a little while after we got back.

LANHAM: No further questions from the State, Your Honor.

HICKS: Mrs. Lynch, did you say that Bertha and you called three different doctors to come and see about her mother?

LYNCH: That's correct, but they wouldn't or couldn't come. I don't know which.

HICKS: And Bertha was doing all she could do to help her mother, is that correct?

LYNCH: I wouldn't say that. She could have taken her to a hospital. I would have.

HICKS: No further questions from the defense.


The State calls Doctor N.L. Williams

LANHAM: State your name and occupation for the record?

WITNESS: Doctor Norton L. Williams and I am a physician here in Floyd County.

LANHAM: Doctor Williams, did you know Mrs. James Hardin during her lifetime?

WILLIAMS: Yes I knew Mrs. Zola Hardin; she was a patient of mine.

LANHAM: Did you have an opportunity to see her last July prior to her death?

WILLIAMS: Yes I did. I was called by the family one afternoon to see her at her home. When I arrived there I examined the patient and found that she was suffering from what appeared to be acute stomach upset, commonly called food poisoning. Her main symptom was vomiting. I did not see her vomit, but she was nauseated at the time.

I believe she was under the care of Mrs. Bertha Hill and some relatives at the time I was there. The patient was pale, and had somewhat of a rapid pulse. Her skin was also pale and clammy, as most people are if they have an acute illness.

I wrote her a prescription for the upset stomach and was asked by the family to stop by the next day if I could to recheck her condition. I did stop by the next day but was met in the yard by Mrs. Hill and told that Mrs. Hardin had passed during the night. I wrote out a death certificate as undetermined at that time.

LANHAM: Doctor Williams, in your experience, if a person ingested a large amount of arsenic, would they exhibit the symptoms that you saw on Mrs. Hardin?

WILLIAMS: "Yes, it would be normal symptoms under such a set of facts."

LANHAM: No further questions from the State.

HICKS: Doctor Williams, you testified that you wrote a prescription for Mrs. Hardin, is that correct?

WILLIAMS: Yes I did.

HICKS: Was it in capsule form or was it in a liquid form?

WILLIAMS: From my best recollection it was liquid. Although I can't be certain that it was. I don't believe it was in capsule form.

HICKS: It could have been in capsule form then, is that right?

WILLIAMS: It's possible, but I believe it was in liquid form.

HICKS: When a caretaker administered this prescription, if it was in liquid form, would it be something that could be mixed with, say, orange juice.

WILLIAMS: Yes, I suppose it could.

HICKS: No further questions from the defense.

"Anything further from the State?" Judge Porter asked.

"Yes your Honor," Henderson said as he retrieved a note from Graham Wright. "We've got one more."

LANHAM: Doctor Williams, what was in the prescription that you prescribed for Mrs. Hardin?

WILLIAMS: I prescribed a medicine that is commonly used for acute stomach upset. It contains an amount of paregoric and what is called kaolin. It did not contain any arsenic or arsenic compound. That would have been the wrong thing to prescribe for an upset stomach.

LANHAM: No further questions, Your Honor.

Bertha being escorted by Bailiff Vincent

# The Trial, Part 3

Judge Porter called both lawyers to the bench and after a brief conference announced that court would be in recess for lunch until one o'clock. Frank watched from his seat as Harry and the bailiffs escorted Bertha to the small office that was used as a staging room for defendants. He felt sure her lawyers would join her there and go over their plan for this afternoon one more time.

Frank left the courthouse and walked over to Broad Street and turned south. He had been in the small cramped courtroom chair for a day and a half and he felt like stretching his legs a little before getting back to the trial. The street was packed with shoppers and the traffic was also pretty heavy. As he walked down the street, he could hear the Rome police officers on each block wearing out their whistles trying to move the double parkers along. From somewhere he got a whiff of engine fumes.

He wandered down the street buried in his own thoughts. When he reached the Cotton Block, he crossed the street and went into Joe's Lunch, found an empty booth in the back and slid in where he couldn't see any customers. He ordered a Bar B Q plate sliced and a glass of sweet tea. His dinner arrived about the same time as the owner did.

Joe Adams slid into the booth opposite him and asked, "How are you doing, pard? Is everything all right?"

"It will be in a little while, Joe," Frank said. "It's about over."

"I don't want to be the bearer of bad news," Joe said, "but are you sure?"

"They got eight or ten more witnesses Joe," Frank replied. "Then they'll put Bertha up and give it to the jury. After that, she either walks or we ship her."

"I've been getting a blow-by-blow account of what's taking place," Joe said. "And I'm betting that Judge Porter has erred in a couple of rulings.

If he has, Mack will be on them faster than a hen on a June bug. Don't be surprised if he wins when it hits the state's big court. You might get to try her again."

"Lord, I hope not," Frank said. "I've about had all I can take from Mrs. Bertha Hill. A little bit of her goes a long way."

"If she does appeal, and she will," Joe said, "the state will leave her right here till it's over. If she wins the appeal, you could have her in your jail for a year or two."

"Joe, you're about to ruin my dinner," Frank said. "And this is some of the best Bar B Q I've ever ate. But I know you're right. That's all I can think about."

Joe called a waitress and told her to bring him and Frank some of that homemade coconut cake that his wife had made last night.

"That's on the house, Pard," Joe said. "Looks like you need it."

"Thanks Joe, I do," Frank replied. "There's something I was going to ask you. Haven't seen that mother and daughter team of prostitutes who were working the Depot at the end of the street and the other beer taverns here in the Cotton Block lately. We were putting them in jail pretty regular. But they seemed to have vanished. Do you reckon the city police have been picking them up?"

"Nah, they're in Gadsden, Alabama," Joe said. "They're working the returning servicemen over there for awhile. Had a customer the other day said he was in Gadsden and talked to them while he was over there."

"Did he say why they left Rome?" Frank asked. "Not that I ain't glad they did."

Joe broke out in that big ole grin of his that went from ear to ear.

"Yes he did," Joe replied. "He said that they told him they got up one morning and there was a bundle of switches and a bucket of coal on the front door steps. They were gone in less than an hour."

"Well I bet I know who did that," Frank said. "The switches are pretty easily figured out, but I don't get the bucket of coal."

"Got a little something to do with burning in hell, I think," Joe chuckled as he worked on his piece of cake. "Anyway, they ain't gonna be missed."

"Yeah and the fellows that left those little presents can expedite your trip to hell too. I imagine that was what Mama and Baby Girl were thinking."

Frank paid his tab and told Joe he'd see him real soon and was leaving the restaurant when Joe stopped him and said, "Frank, I almost forgot. We're going to be cooking chitlins this coming Saturday night down by the river. I want you and Mark to come if you can. And I've got enough to feed Harry Davis all he can eat, so bring him and anybody else you want to with you."

"You can count on me being there. After this trial I need a little socializing."

As Frank walked back to the courthouse, he was thinking about what Joe had said. He knew that if Mack lost this trial, he would appeal on everything that he could, hoping to score on just one point. He's worse than an old snapping turtle, once he bites he won't let go till it thunders. Frank was looking forward the afternoon testimony.

The State calls Harry Fleming.

LANHAM: State your name for the record.

WITNESS: Harry Fleming.

LANHAM: Were you acquainted with James A. Hardin during his lifetime?

FLEMING: Yes sir I surely was. He was a good friend of mine.

LANHAM: Were you present on the day he died?

FLEMING: I saw him on the day he died, but I was not present at the hospital when he passed away.

LANHAM: Mr. Fleming, please tell the court what you saw and observed in conjunction with Mr. Hardin on the last time you saw him alive.

FLEMING: Bud--that's what we called him--rode with me to the mill in Lindale where we both worked at night. But he hadn't ridden with me since January the 23rd. I hadn't seen him until Bertha came after me the morning that he died. I was present when they put him in the ambulance. I had been there for about thirty minutes before they loaded him up. He looked like a dying man to me at that time.

When I first got to the house he was in the bed and was so weak that he could hardly move. His wife and Bertha were there sitting beside his bed.

When he saw me, he began to try to talk and was so quiet that I had to lean over to hear what he was saying. He was somewhat out of his head. He said that he worked last night and when he came home his wife hadn't fixed him nothing to eat but it was OK 'cause he was on a diet.

He said that while he was talking to his wife, Bertha came and said that she had him some new medicine and he looked at me and said, 'I took it. But if you don't get me to a hospital or to a doctor in the next few minutes I'm going to smother.' And he just turned over.

I helped them put him in the ambulance, but I did not go to the hospital with them. As the ambulance was getting ready to leave, Bertha came running out of the house and gave one of the attendants a glass full of juice of some kind. She told the ambulance guys that it was his medicine and he needed it. When that ambulance pulled out of the yard that fellow was trying to get Bud to drink it. The next time I saw him he was a corpse.

LANHAM: No further questions, Your Honor.

HICKS: We have none from the defense.

LANHAM: State your name and occupation for the record.

WITNESS: Dr. Robert Norton and I am a physician here in Rome.

LANHAM: Dr. Norton, did you have a chance to know James Hardin or to treat him during his lifetime?

DR. NORTON: Both actually. I treated him for stomach hemorrhage back in 1943 and again in 1944 when he was hospitalized for the same ailment. I believe that was on December 4th 1944. I also saw him on the night he was brought to the hospital in January 1945. I actually recall little about that night.

He was brought into the hospital in a dying condition and did die within an hour after arriving. He was in the first aid room and was never admitted. He died before that could be accomplished. At the time of his death, it was my opinion that his death was caused by a fatal hemorrhage from an ulcerated stomach.

LANHAM: "Dr. Norton, if he had ingested arsenic would it have similar symptoms?"

DR. NORTON: "If he had ingested a large dose of arsenic in his condition it would have been fatal quickly. That alone would have been enough to have caused his death."

LANHAM: No further questions from the State Your Honor.

HICKS: Doctor Norton you testified that Mr. James Hardin was a regular patient of yours for at least three years, is that correct?

DR. NORTON: Yes, for at least that long.

HICKS: And you treated him for a bleeding ulcer for the entire time he was your patient, is that also correct?

DR. NORTON: That would be correct also.

HICKS: And you said that you believed he died from a fatal hemorrhage from that ulcer, also correct?

DR. NORTON: At the time I had nothing other than that to challenge my opinion.

HICKS: No further questions from the defense Your Honor.

Frank chomped down on his Bloodhound. *Here it comes! This is the big boy the press has been waiting for!*

The State calls Doctor C.J. Rehling.

LANHAM: Please state your name for the record.

WITNESS: Dr. C.J. Rehling and I am the toxicologist for the state of Alabama.

LANHAM: Dr. Rehling, in what capacity do you work for the state of Alabama?

DR. REHLING: We handle the scientific investigations for the state crime laboratory.

LANHAM: In that capacity did you have an opportunity to conduct an autopsy on Mr. and Mrs. James A. Hardin?

DR. REHLING: Yes, I did.

LANHAM: Please tell the court what you did and what you observed during that procedure.

DR. REHLING: In that capacity I made an autopsy on the bodies of Mr. and Mrs. James A. Hardin on March 27, 1946, at a cemetery near Centre, Alabama.

I removed the organs from each of the bodies and brought them with me to Auburn to my laboratory and made examinations and analysis there for poisons.

The examination internally of the body of James A. Hardin disclosed a remarkable state of preservation of organs. The stomach particularly was very well preserved and the examination of its contents revealed white powder therein and a graying corrosion of the walls. The white powder in the stomach was identified as lead arsenate.

The analysis of the upper end of the small intestine, of the liver, of the spleen and of the kidneys identified arsenic in each of those. The distribution of arsenic in these various organs was consistent with its distribution as occurs during life, as distinguished from post mortem. The stomach was distinctively colored and altered in a manner that arsenic itself does produce.

LANHAM: Dr. Rehling are you testifying that the arsenic entered the body of James A. Hardin while he was alive?

DR. REHLING: That's my opinion.

LANHAM: And what about Mrs. Hardin. What did your investigation reveal on her?

DR. REHLING: The body of Mrs. Hardin was in much the same condition. In my opinion, this arsenic entered the bodies of Mr. and Mrs. Hardin during life. The amount of arsenic absorbed and distributed in their bodies is sufficient to have caused death in either case. In my opinion death was caused in the case of Mr. Hardin and Mrs. Hardin by arsenic that I found.

LANHAM: No further questions.

Frank sat and listened to Mack do everything he could to make the toxicologist stumble somewhere, but it was to no avail. At one point Mack had told him his answers didn't make sense. Dr. Rehlings had shot back that his questions didn't either. Frank thought that this was at best a draw. Mack was unable to make much on this guy. The doctor had been on the stand a lot and it was evident.

The next witness was summoned and sworn in. Frank now knew that the prosecution had shifted gears. First they had established the fact and the method that he died. Then the doctors had all testified what he was treated for and died from. And now we go for motive. Frank added a little to his chew and sat back to listen.

LANHAM: State your name and occupation for the record please?

WITNESS: My name is Dick Hand, and I am employed as the office manager by the Pepperell Manufacturing Company at Lindale, Georgia.

LANHAM: Mr. Hand, please tell the court if James A. Hardin was an employee of your company and was he insured by same?

HAND: Yes he was, and our company carries a one thousand dollar group insurance policy from Metropolitan on each employee.

LANHAM: Who was the beneficiary of that policy?

HAND: Our records show that we mailed the check to Bertha Gossett, on April 20, 1945. The check was mailed to Bertha Gossett, Box 625, Rome Georgia.

LANHAM: Was that check cashed or returned? Do your records indicate that?

HAND: No sir. We do not have individual policies. We have a master policy that covers the whole company. Whenever there is a death that occurs, the certificate issued in pursuance of the master policy is sent to Metropolitan in New York, and that was done in the case of James Hardin. We wouldn't know whether or not it was ever returned. It wasn't returned to us. In other words, it was Metropolitan's check.

LANHAM: No further questions from the State.

HICKS: None from the defense, Your Honor.

The State calls Mr. Priester H. Lewis.

LANHAM: State your name and occupation for the record please sir.

WITNESS: My name is Priester H. Lewis and I am employed with

Gulf Life Insurance Company.

LANHAM: Do you know Mrs. Bertha Hill and if so in what capacity?

LEWIS: I had a chance to talk to her on the phone about the first week of July in 1945. That conversation led me to go to her home to discuss an insurance policy on her mother, Mrs. Zola Hardin. I told her that she could get up to a three thousand dollar policy on her mother.

This paper that you gave me marked State's exhibit #10 is the application that I filled out that day. Mrs. Hill wrote Mrs. Hardin's name in and I had her sign also by mark. Mrs. Hardin said she couldn't write.

I also took an application for Mrs. Hill herself. She returned the application on her mother and paid $29.00 and some cents on that application. Mrs. Hardin was examined by Dr. McCord, but she died before the policy could be put in place. Mrs. Hill came to our office after her mother died and asked if we were going to pay the claim. I told her no, that the policy was never issued and that the most we could do was to refund her down payment that she paid with the application."

LANHAM: Did Mrs. Hill also pay an application fee on her own policy and stand for a physical examination?

LEWIS: No sir she did not. That policy was never issued and Mrs. Hill never paid a premium on that policy.

Frank could see some stirring in the jury box. He thought the solicitor was starting to make points with the jury now. These country folks believed in honoring your mother and father. What they were hearing now was contrary to everything they had ever been taught. He looked at Bertha and for the first time, her face was drained of all color.

He heard Murdic L. Alford, also an employee of Gulf Life, corroborate Mr. Lewis' story.

Then the State called another insurance professional. Mrs. Pearlee H. Jenkins of State Mutual took the stand and was sworn in.

LANHAM: Mrs. Jenkins, did you have an occasion to talk to or conduct business with Mrs. Bertha Gossett Hill.

JENKINS: I did. She had taken out a twenty-five hundred dollar policy on her husband in December of 1945. A premium of $11.80 was paid on that policy for three months. She later came in the office one morning about nine or better, when we went to work. I believe it was on February 14th of this year. She said that she had the insurance policy and that her husband had died that morning and that she wanted the money. She was not paid the money then and there on that demand she made. Mr. Geston

Garner attends to filing death claims, and I took her to him and she talked to him about that.

LANHAM: Did you have any further conversation with Mrs. Hill the day she came to report Leroy Hill's death?

JENKINS: Yes I did. I asked her what he died of, and she said he died of poison from an infected throat. I then asked her where he died and she said in Floyd County Hospital this morning.

Frank sat and watched as Mack simply went over Mrs. Jenkins testimony with her. After that the manager of Liberty National Insurance testified that Bertha had also came to their office on the morning of Leroy's death and got an emergency draft for $100.00 on the policy that she had with that company.

Mr. A.A. Barrett testified that about ten days to two weeks after Mrs. Hardin died, he had been approached by Mr. and Mrs. Hill about a house that he was trying to sell. He told them he had taken it off of the market. He stated that they told him that they would soon be receiving $3,000 and that if he knew of anybody with a house for sale to tell them that they were interested in one.

After a brief conversation at the bench with Judge Porter, the state announced that they rest their case. The judge called for a recess before the defense began its case.

Frank saw his bailiffs whisk Bertha out of the courtroom to the holding room in the back of the court. Frank knew this was it for Bertha. And Mack was going to put the last minute finishes on her upcoming statement.

Frank wandered around the courtroom speaking and shaking hands with a lot of old friends he hadn't seen in years. This trial had brought more attention to Rome and Floyd County than anything Frank had witnessed in his entire life. He just hoped it was close to being over. He made his way to his seat when the judge came back into the courtroom from his chambers.

The defense opened their case by placing Bertha's grandfather, Isaac Dutton, on the stand. Mr. Dutton testified that he was present when his daughter Zola Dutton Hardin had died. He stated that he believed his granddaughter did everything she could for her mother.

Then came the moment that had kept everybody glued to their seats. Bertha was called to the stand. She was to give an unsworn statement. That meant she could say almost anything she wanted to and the solicitor could not cross examine her. The judge would tell the jury to give what weight they wanted to an unsworn statement. In other words they could believe it or not. It was up to them.

HICKS: State your name and occupation for the record please.

WITNESS: Bertha Hill.

HICKS: Mrs. Hill I want you to tell the court and the jury everything you can about the death of your parents and husband.

HILL: Yes sir. I was born and raised in Cherokee County, Alabama. I married at fifteen to a man that beat me and was always drinking. I tried to be a good wife but it just got to be unbearable. So I moved to Rome and got a job with McClellan's and worked my way up to floor manager. I moved my parents over here to live with me so I could take better care of them, and I tried to do just that.

My Papa had suffered with ulcers and a bad stomach for years. You heard his doctor say that he had been treating him for at least three years and he had other doctors that told him the same thing.

My Mama got sick and I called the doctor to the house after she wouldn't get out at the hospital. I went in and sent the nurse out. I tried to get Dr. Mull, but he was in surgery or something. Mama refused to go in when the nurse asked her. I had Mr. Poole to stop at a drug store and let me get something to ease her. Later we tried to get several doctors to come out but were unable to do so.

The same thing happened with Leroy. I begged him to go to the hospital and he wouldn't go. I loved my Mama and Papa. I'd never do anything to hurt them. I lived with them from birth until several years after I got married to Neal Gossett. And I loved Leroy; I worshipped him. I didn't hold it against him for having this awful disease.

On this emergency draft, it was my understanding through the company that in case of emergency you were supposed to use this draft. I was broke. Taxis, ambulances, hospitals and doctors had taken everything that I had.

Leroy spent every dime we had on high living and partying almost every night. He spent nearly everything he had on whiskey, leaving me to pay the bills. He took the insurance money from my father and bought a car, a motorcycle and a saddle horse. He bought a load of liquor, but they caught that and he lost the car.

Frank watched her twist the light green handkerchief she held in her hands. Her eyes welled with moisture when she told that her husband revealed to her he had syphilis and wanted to keep it a secret.

She then continued her statement, saying that he had a sinking spell right before he died. He just looked up at me and said, 'Darling, everything will be all right.' He had told me to bury him in Alabama next to my Mama and Papa so his mother up in North Carolina wouldn't find out about his disease.

So when I asked for the draft and told them it was an emergency, they were real nice. They didn't say a word. Just gave me the money. Oh, and one other thing I want to say about these capsules that they said I gave them. They were from a prescription. I don't know what's in them. I have no idea. But I do know they were from a doctor's prescription.

And I did tell my aunt and uncle that I saw Leroy give something to my Mama, cause I did. I should have tried to stop him but he said it wasn't nothing and I believed him. It was later when I figured it out. I just want everybody to know that I loved my Mama and Papa and I loved Leroy. I'd never do anything to hurt them. That is all.

Bertha left the stand and took her seat next to her lawyers. It was as quiet as a grave. There was no sound from anybody for the longest time. Frank was astonished that Bertha was able to stay cool, calm and collected during the entire twenty-three minutes she spoke. He knew that most of it was true. It was the other part that disgusted the prosecution. He could see that Lanham, Clary and Wright were totally disgusted with the Georgia law that restricted them from ripping Bertha's statement apart. *How much of this is the jury going to believe?*

Frank watched as Mack rounded out his defense. He recalled several of the experts and other witnesses in rebuttal and the arguments from both parties were started just before four o'clock. Horace Clary, assistant to the Solicitor-General opened for the state, followed by the leading member of the defense team, Mack Hicks. Carl Griffin reviewed the laws governing the case and submitted the brief to Judge Porter on the legal issues to be covered in the judge's charge to the jury.

Solicitor Henderson Lanham closed the case for the State and Judge Porter read the charge to the jury and they retired to begin deliberations at 6:15 p.m.

Frank was thinking that they covered the entire two day trial in their closing arguments in just a little over two hours. It had been a long day. No it had been a long two months. He walked downstairs to where the sheriff's office was and poured a cup of fresh coffee.

Turning to the sheriff he said, "I guess we wait. Any idea how long they'll be out?"

"Your guess is as good as mine," Sheriff Horton said. "I've seen some juries move quickly and others take days. It ain't no exact science."

"Well how long do you think the judge will let them deliberate until he sends them home?" Frank asked.

"Judge Porter will stay late and long," Mark replied. "They ain't a hurry-up bone in his body.

"Frank, I want you to know that you, Harry and any of our other guys who worked on this case in any way deserve a lot of credit regardless of how it turns out."

"Sheriff, everybody worked hard," Frank said as he poured another cup of coffee and finished up a bowl of bread pudding that had been brought to the office for the deputies and bailiffs on duty.

Frank was just getting stretched out and comfortable when Bailiff Vincent appeared at the door.

"They want you in court, Frank. The jury's reached a verdict."

Frank nearly fell out of his chair. Looking at the Sheriff he said, "I can't believe that. He must have gotten something confused. Maybe they have a question about the charge or something."

"Well, let's go and find out," Mark said as they left the office and sprinted up the stairs.

Frank noticed that not many people had left the courtroom and the solicitor's table all had big smiles.

"Horace," Frank asked the assistant Solicitor, "Does the jury really have a verdict?"

"That's what we were told Frank," Horace Clary replied. "A verdict this quick usually means we win. But it's not written in stone till they say it."

The judge came into the Courtroom and had the Bailiff bring the jury in. When they were seated, he asked if they had in fact reached a verdict. They informed the court that they had and gave it to Henderson Lanham who in turn gave it to the clerk. Bertha rose and faced the bench as the verdict was read.

We the jury, find Bertha Gossett Hill, GUILTY as charged with a recommendation of mercy.

Frank watched for any kind of reaction from Bertha. She simply closed her eyes and took a deep breath. She then turned to Carl Griffin and spoke quietly, "Does this mean no Electric Chair?"

"That's exactly what it means," he said. "The recommendation of mercy is binding on the court."

Frank knew what had just transpired. He could tell by the way Bertha changed in the blink of an eye. All at once she was cheerful and was speaking and smiling as they led her down the stairs, out of the courthouse and back across the street to her little cell that had been home for the last two months.

ℕ    ℕ

After all the deputies had gone, Bertha heard Mattie sobbing softly in the next cell.

"Mattie, what's wrong with you?" she asked.

"I've just heard Bertha. And I'm so sorry."

"Mattie, you listen to me," Bertha said. "My grandpa Dutton told me one time that when you know you're gonna lose, you cover up and lose by decision. Don't lose by knock-out. I didn't get knocked-out. It ain't over, sweetie. It ain't ever gonna be over till I walk out of here. Now you cheer up and let's have some of Maeleigh Grace's preserves. We're gonna celebrate Bertha not going to the chair."

# Bertha Hill Is Given Life Term In Poison Murder

Bertha Gossett Hill was sentenced in Floyd Superior Court this morning by Judge Claude H. Porter to a life term in the State Penitentiary for the poison murder of her husband, Leroy Hill.

The sentence, which was mandatory upon the court, resulted from the recommendation of the jury which found her guilty, asking that she be granted the mercy of the court rather than be executed in the electric chair.

Mrs. Hill stood at the bar, offering as her only answer when Judge Porter asked if she had anything to say before sentence was pronounced: "Regardless of what has happened, all I have to say is, I'm still not guilty of anything."

Her attorneys, Mack G. Hicks and Carl Griffin, planned today an attempt to set aside the verdict by appealing the case to the State Court of Appeals.

The jury received the charge from Judge Claude H. Porter at 5:15, and they retired to the jury room to make up their verdict. After deliberating for thirty minutes, they returned to the courtroom and handed the indictment to Henderson Lanham, Solicitor-General.

Bertha Hill heard the verdict which will require her to serve a life sentence in the penitentiary. She only closed her eyes quickly, took a deep breath as though she was greatly relieved of a heavy burden. Throughout the trial she had remained unemotional.

Bertha was cheerful as she was led back to her little cell in the top of Floyd County Jail to await the official sentence by Judge Porter. She had been in that cell since her arrest on February 15, when the mother of Leroy Hill, Mrs. Lacy Beale, took the felony warrant.

The spectacular trial ended at about 7 o'clock last night, climaxing one of the most sensational cases in the history of the criminal courts in this section, a trial which lasted for one and a half days, with more than two dozen witnesses testifying in connection with the mysterious and suspicious deaths of Bertha Hill's mother and father, and her second husband.

**Defendant Takes Stand**

The 28-year-old dime store floor manager, charged with the crime, took the stand in her own defense at 2:20 yesterday afternoon, and related to the courtroom, which was filled to overflowing, and to the twelve men she had helped to select as jurors, a story filled with love and affection for her parents and her husband. She proclaimed her innocence to the very last.

"I loved my parents," she de-

(Continued on Page 2, Col. 2)

## Everybody Wanted Glimpse of 'Her'

Sidelights of the Hill murder trial:

Teen-age boy hurrying into courtroom, then jumping straight up in futile effort to see over shoulders of adults and get glimpse of defendant . . . Old man giving up and turning to leave—"Can't see nothin', can't hear nothin'." The crowd was so jammed and packed that some observers estimated attendance as high as 3,000 (the City Auditorium seats only 2,200) . . . Ordinarily good acoustics of the courtroom didn't have a chance against the talking, whispering, twittering, and comings and goings of the crowd . . . Women were especially interested in the trial and a heavy percentage of the audience was female — from bobby-soxers to elderly women . . . One lady brought a sack full of hamburgers along . . . One expert witness, a toxicologist, couldn't be "buffaloed" by a lawyer. The witness told the attorney that one question relating to chemistry didn't make sense. The lawyer replied that some of the answers didn't quite make sense either, but the toxicologist shot back with "That's just a matter of opinion."

# Chapter 21

Frank was at his seat in court bright and early the following morning. The first thing on the agenda was the formal sentencing of Bertha Gossett Hill. As she stood in front of the judge's bench, she was asked if she had anything to say before sentence was passed.

"Regardless of what went on here this week, I'm still not guilty of anything," she replied.

"I sentence you to spend the rest of your natural life in the state penitentiary," Judge Porter said.

Frank watched as she was led one more time back to the jail. He made his way straight to Sheriff Horton's office and had a seat.

"I guess that's it," Frank said as he cut off his first chew of the day. "Now all we got to do is wait and see if there's gonna be an appeal."

"Mack said yesterday that he was going to appeal," Mark replied. "And you know him as well as anybody. He's not going to like losing this bad, this quick. She ain't going nowhere for awhile."

"At least the investigation is over," Frank said. "She can't cause us too much trouble locked up on the second floor."

"That's the way I see it too," Mark said.

₪     ₪

When Bertha entered the jail, the deputies took her straight to the interview room where Mack and Carl were waiting.

"I'm sorry, Bertha," Mack said. "They had us surrounded. That's the best we could do."

"Look, Mack," Bertha said with eyes so cold that they made Carl Griffin shiver all the way to his toes. "I'm not going to the chair. I will walk out of this place, sooner or later, I promise you that. Now, Carl was whispering about an appeal. So tell me what you got?"

"We're going to file all the standard appeal points," Mack said. "But we're going to lose on those. That's why we're filing them. So the big court will have a lot to rule in Judge Porter's favor."

"And it protects you two from a future appeal of inadequate council also, doesn't it?" Bertha said.

"You've been doing your homework, I see," Mack replied, grinning. "But yes, it does that too. However, I'm almost positive that the judge erred on some of his rulings and I think we will get a new trial."

"Well, don't sit here talking to me," Bertha said eyes now flashing. "Go get it started."

"We'd just lose, if we did Bertha," Mack replied. "Here's the problem as I see it. We lost today before we even got started. You were already convicted in the court of public opinion. There was way too much press. And if we got a ruling in the near future we'd suffer the same results. Plus we won't get one quick anyway.

"Judge Porter is first to rule and he ain't gonna overturn his own decisions. It might be six months--probably will--before he makes a ruling. Then we have to send it to the Georgia Supreme Court. That's where we can win. But that's another four to six months after Porter rules."

"So I'm going to have to sit here for another year and do this again?" Bertha asked. "Is that what you're telling me?"

"Well, you could just accept the decision and not appeal," Carl said. "And start building time. You should come up for review for the first time in about five years."

"Carl, you're being ridiculous," Bertha said. "If I have to stay in jail for a year, that's what I'll do, but I ain't gonna volunteer, is that clear?"

"Oh, yes ma'am," Carl said. "That's clear enough."

"There's still no guarantee that we'll win, even then," Mack said. "You do understand that, don't you?"

"Unfortunately I do," she said.

"Bertha, we need something else," Mack said. "Rack your brain and see if you've missed something. One thing in our favor is that Lanham will be gone to Congress most likely and some new solicitor will have to learn the case from scratch."

"Ok Mack, I understand what you're saying and I agree with it. But there are a couple of things you can do for me right now," Bertha said. "Make them insurance companies cough up some money. And make a call to Mattie's lawyer. She's my cell mate.

"I don't know who her lawyer is but he ain't worth a hill of beans. She's been here longer than I have and didn't do hardly anything. She stole a little money for some boyfriend that works in the bank. Restitution has been made and it's her first offense. The bank is punishing her unless I miss my guess, and her lawyer ain't fighting the powers that want her to stay in jail."

"I'll make a call today, Bertha," Mack said. "And next week I'll worry me an insurance company or two."

Carl watched as an almost eerie calmness came over Bertha, and once again he felt a cold wind on his soul. *She doesn't give a damn about going to prison. It doesn't scare her one bit. Now that she's out of the limelight she's more alive than she's ever been.*

₪  ₪

Bertha was scared awake by something banging. She sat up abruptly and stared at Deputy Bill Payne tapping on the cell bars with his keys.

"What's wrong with you, Deputy?" she asked. "Is the jail on fire or something? What time is it anyway?"

"Nah it ain't on fire, but I got a problem," Bill said. "I don't have a cook this morning. He didn't come in and I ain't got an inmate that knows anything about cooking. Willy's here but he's just the kitchen boy. He can't cook anything. And it's already four o'clock."

"Well then, Willy oughta fit right in," Bertha said, "'Cause the one that didn't show up can't cook either."

"Look Bertha, you've griped about the cooking since the day you got here. Now it's Sunday and I reckon I got a sick cook somewhere out there. So I'm asking you to help me out of a jam this morning."

"Come back in fifteen minutes. Let me at least wash my face and hands and brush my hair. Tell your kitchen boy to put on water for grits and that's all."

It had been a month since she had been sentenced. Mack hadn't been by for over a week and she hadn't heard from Mattie since she'd gotten released. Danny Garrett still came to visit her almost every afternoon when he got out of school.

Maeleigh Grace and Lemuel Abbott were still coming every Sunday. If she didn't have them in her life she thought she might go nuts. Now she had an opportunity to get out of this cell for a little while at least.

Deputy Payne was back in exactly fifteen minutes.

"You ready to go, Bertha?" he asked.

"Only if I can cook what I want," she replied.

"I can't go get nothing. But you can cook anything we got, as long as you can feed at seven o'clock," Bill said.

"One other thing," she said. "It's gonna cost you."

"I don't have no money Bertha," Bill replied. "Sorry."

"I ain't talking about money, Bill. I'll let you know what."

As Bertha entered the kitchen she saw a tall black man about fifty years old. He certainly wasn't a boy, but he did tell her his name was Willy. He had a large pot of water on the stove and it was almost to a boil. Bertha looked around the kitchen and was surprised at how clean it was.

"Willy, you're doing a good job of keeping the kitchen clean."

"Yes ma'am, Miss Bertha. I try to keep it clean," he said.

"You know who I am?" she asked.

"Yes ma'am, everybody in the jail knows who you are. They ain't never seen you but they know that you're here. You're the most famous person ever we seen in these parts."

"Well Willy, here's what I need. Flour, baking soda, buttermilk and lard oughta to do it to start with. I see you've already got the grits out. They've fed us boloney ever since I been here. Is there any fatback or bacon in the cooler?"

"Yes ma'am, a little of both," Willy said. "But Cook wouldn't fix it up. Too much trouble he said."

"You get it out and start slicing while I get these grits to simmering,"

One of the night shift deputies entered the kitchen and said to Bertha, "Bill sent me down. He said that I had to stay in the kitchen with you while you fixed breakfast."

"I figured that. So you just get over there somewhere and stay out of the way. But I do need to know how many prisoners there are in jail this morning."

"I just made the morning count. Adding you and Willy it makes forty three."

"That's what I need to know," she said as she took the rolling pin and rolled out her dough. She had Willy grease several bread pans and she started making biscuits by hand and placing them close together on the pan.

"Miss Bertha, what are you doing?" Willy asked excitedly.

"Don't tell me you ain't ever seen a woman roll out biscuits Willy. I don't think I'd believe you."

"Yes ma'am I have, but not here," he replied. "Lord you better make a lot. Some of them colored boys in the basement have been here for a long time. They gonna think the Lord done blessed them on a Sunday morning."

"Maybe he has," she replied. "But just you wait a minute before you get carried away. We ain't through yet."

Bertha slow cooked her grits, seasoned with salt and pepper, until it was almost time to carry them around the jail. She gave Willy a hot biscuit as soon as the first pan came out of the oven.

"I need you to test this for me, Willy," she said with a big smile on her face. "I ain't done this in a while and I want to see if it's fit for folks."

"Whooo Miss Bertha! I ain't had a cat head like this in months," Willy said referring to the size of her biscuits. "This is shore 'nuff some count. Man, I'm just grazing now."

Bertha finished frying the fatback and bacon and poured the grease in another pot used for transporting food around the jail. In the grease she poured a generous helping of coffee that made a dark brownish red spot right in the center of the grease. Bertha noticed that Willy was shaking all over.

"Miss Bertha, you done made red eye gravy for the boys," he said in almost a reverent whisper. "I can't remember nobody ever doing nothing like that for no prisoner in this place."

Deputy Jackson led Bertha and Willy around in the jail while they served breakfast. Bertha had insisted on going, and the deputy would simply holler "woman on the floor" as they entered each corridor. And Willy was busy telling everybody that Miss Bertha had cooked breakfast this morning because the cook was sick.

Bertha enjoyed seeing the prisoners line up next to the bars to get a biscuit, grits, and red eye gravy with a piece or two of bacon or side meat. She would never have imagined the excitement they got from a biscuit had she not been eating the same food they had for the past three months. When breakfast was over she and Willy started cleaning the kitchen up.

"What did you put in them grits that made them so different?" Willy asked.

"Not much," she said. "Let them slow cook so they won't be watery. Stir them real good and make sure they ain't lumpy. Add salt and pepper and then a little of that bacon grease to give them flavor. That's all you do. Now what have we got here to fix for dinner."

By Sunday night Bertha was spent. She had fixed the customary pinto beans, but she had mixed in a lot of white beans to change the flavor just enough to be different. Willy had found some large cans of turnip greens. Bertha had seasoned the greens with chunks of bacon. After that she stewed potatoes and made cornbread to go along with the beans. They had made enough so that they didn't have to do much for supper.

Sunday was the only day of the week that three solid meals were served. Usually the prisoners got beans, or sometimes rice and a slice of store bought bread for dinner and maybe a pickle slice with coffee or tea for dinner. Supper was always leftovers. Bertha had fed the prisoners well today. And now she was tired. She lay there in her cell looking up into the darkness.

Thinking about Willy brought a smile to her face. After dinner she had asked him what he was in jail for. He told her that he had been arrested and charged for dragging a rope. Bertha smiled a little bigger in the dark as she remembered the rest of the conversation.

"Dragging a rope?" Bertha had replied. "I never heard of nobody being charged with dragging rope."

"I'm telling you, Miss Bertha. Old Willy was on his way home from working out at the sawmill all day and it had done got dark. It was about a two or three miles to the house and while I was walking along I saw this rope laying there by the side of the road. I just picked it up and was too tired to roll it up so I just drug it along. Next day the sheriff was waking me up and put me in jail."

"For dragging that rope home?" she had asked.

"Well, yes ma'am," Willy had replied. "See I done told you it was dark, and I didn't look or nothing. And Miss Bertha, would you believe they was a cow tied to the other end of that rope. Sure did fool old Willy. But the sheriffs and the judge didn't think it was too funny. I been here ever since."

Bertha and Willy both laughed so hard at his memory of how he got arrested that Deputy Payne had to come and tell them to be a little quieter.

This day had been fun. It felt good to be tired. As she lay in her bunk and looked upward into the darkness, she drifted into a peaceful sleep and her mind took her back to 1944.

*It was the Christmas season and McClellan's was bustling. The store was packed with customers buying those last minute gifts and toys for family and friends. Peg, one of the young floor girls, suddenly appeared at Bertha's side and asked, "Mrs. Gossett, you do know that the Forrest Hotel is having a big blow-out on New Year's Eve, don't you?"*

*"Yes I do and please call me Bertha. I'm not that much older than you."*

*"Well, we were just wandering if you're planning on going to the big party. Actually it's the day before New Years Eve. We won't get to holler Happy New Year but everything else is just the same."*

*Bertha found herself answering in a faraway voice, "You know I'm separated from Neal and I don't want to go by myself. How much fun would that be?"*

"I think lots. There will be tons of guys there, all of them handsome and fun and with money to spend!

"I'll think about it," Bertha said. "But I ain't making no promises."

"Well please do," Peg said and then she bent down to remove her shoe, tipping it over to pour out a stream of quarters. "And thanks for telling me about that little trick with the shoe. That sure has come in handy."

Bertha was amazed. "Don't you mention that to no one. Most of the girls here don't know about that. It's just some folks that are kind of special that I tell about it."

Peg began to drift away, laughing and crying at the same time. And then Bertha was sitting in her bedroom in her best dress, waiting for her neighbor to drive her to the Forrest Hotel.

The dance band was booming when Bertha walked through the doors of the lobby into the ballroom. Peg appeared in front of Bertha immediately and grasped her arm, pushing her toward a table covered in shot glasses and fruit pies. Peg's boyfriend fixed Bertha a drink and she settled down to listen to the band. Some time passed and then Peg was standing before her with a tall gorgeous man with wavy hair.

Leroy.

Leroy, with a great big smile on his face said, "Come on Bertha, let's dance!" He pulled Bertha from her chair to the dance floor.

Leroy didn't seem to hear her protest. "I don't dance much, and it's been a long time," she said as he led her right in front of the band.

And then suddenly, Bertha seemed to know every dance step sweeping the nation. She spun and twirled and shimmied with Leroy right up there in front of everybody and it wasn't odd at all that after a while, Bertha realized that Peg and her friends were long gone and she and Leroy were alone on Broad Street after the dance.

"I think your friends are already gone," Leroy said. "I told them earlier that I'd take good care of you."

"Oh, then you're gonna give me a ride home," she replied, cocking her head and looking up at him.

"I will if you want me to. But I've already paid for a room here at the Forrest. It would be a shame not to use it. I was kind of hoping you'd stay here with me tonight."

Bertha turned and walked away from Leroy without saying a word. She went back into the lobby, motioning for Leroy to follow her. When she got to the elevator she stopped and asked, "What floor?"

And then it was the next morning. Leroy and Bertha were sitting in a booth at some diner and Leroy was talking about living at Chuck's Camp.

*"My Mama and Papa have been talking about taking in a boarder," Bertha replied. "Let me talk to them and I'll see what I can do. That should save you a little on living expenses."*

*And then suddenly Bertha was sleeping in her folks' room, with Leroy just down the hall in her childhood room. That was the happiest she had ever been.*

The iron door at the end of the corridor swung open and thudded against the wall. Bertha was jerked from her dream. She was groggy, wondering where she was, but then she heard Willy coming down the hall with breakfast, and she remembered.

"Sorry Miss Bertha," he said. "But we're back to the same old stuff today. The boys is shore 'nuff upset. They been telling me that you could poison them any time you wanted too."

"That's OK Willy," she said. "Maybe we'll get to do it again someday."

"Yes ma'am, I shore hope so," he said. "I saved me a couple of them cat heads from yesterday morning and a chunk of that corn pone too. I got one of them for you. The coffee ain't bad and you can make you a soaker out of the biscuit."

"Thanks Willy," she said. "I will."

# Chapter 22

The following Monday morning Frank Russell was fuming in his office. He was so mad that he thought his head might bust. *Get a grip, Frank. This ain't good for you.* He had sent for Harry Davis and was stewing while waiting for him.

Finally, Harry walked in and asked, "Do you want to see me Chief?"

"Harry, tell me what went on here yesterday," Frank said.

"You lost me boss," Harry said trying to figure out what Frank was referring to. "Start over and put it so that I can understand what you're talking about."

"Did you work the jail yesterday?" Frank asked looking disgustedly at his friend.

"Sure did," Harry replied, "Why?"

"Who did the cooking yesterday Harry?" Frank asked.

"Oh, now I see what's got you so upset," Harry replied. "I think you already know who did the cooking yesterday."

"Who approved for her to cook?" Frank asked.

"Boss, I can't answer that," Harry replied. "I didn't know we had to get approval from nobody. Never have before. When I got here breakfast was already being served. Bill said that he didn't have anybody in the whole jail to cook. He asked Bertha and she volunteered, and she did a mighty fine job too. She cooked all day, and it was some fine vittles. That old girl can cook and sew. You gotta give her that, Frank."

"I live in the jail," Frank was still red faced. "Why didn't somebody wake me up?"

"Why would they, Frank?" Harry said. "You can't cook. We've always got our cooks and kitchen boys from the population. We never had to wake you before."

"Harry, she was found guilty of poisoning her husband," Frank said staring straight at his deputy. "She was indicted on poisoning her own parents. She was sentenced to life in prison. And we have her cooking in our jail. Can you honestly tell me that you don't see anything wrong with that picture?"

"Frank, I see what you're saying," Harry replied. "But honestly, I don't. She's a dang good cook. She might be here for a year. She don't mind filling in when we need her. She ain't going nowhere, and I ate some of her beans and greens yesterday and it didn't poison me. So what's the problem?"

"How do you think I'm going to explain this to the sheriff later on today?" Frank asked. "He's bound to hear about it."

"You're not going to have to explain nothing, Frank," Harry said. "He already knows about it. He ate dinner with us here at the jail yesterday. In fact, he had seconds."

Frank was speechless. He just sat and stared at his deputy. Finally he motioned him away and just sat at his desk reflecting on what he'd just been told. I can't believe this, he thought. This just ain't happening.

ℕ    ℕ

Two hours later Frank was in the sheriff's office. Mark was busy with some citizen issuing a complaint. Frank knew from personal experience that the complaint could be about anything. He took a seat in the outer office, cut him a big chew of Bloodhound, and looked up to see Mrs. Jenkins staring at him.

"My daddy used to chew that stuff," She said. "It's a nasty habit. I wouldn't let my husband chew no tobacco. Of course he smoked and that's just as bad."

"Well, it relaxes me Mrs. Jenkins," Frank said. "And Lord knows I need relaxing these days a lot."

"I guess we all do, Frank," She said. "These last few months have been something else. My family's been in law enforcement since 1904 and I ain't never seen it like it is today."

"Ain't that the truth," Frank replied. "And I think it's just gonna get worse. I don't see it getting any better."

The citizen left the office and Frank was called back to where Mark Horton was sitting at his desk looking through some papers.

"Good morning Frank," the sheriff said. "How are you this fine, beautiful day?"

"You're awful happy, Mark," Frank said. "What's the occasion?"

"Might as well be, Frank," he replied. "Sure beats crying. What's up at the jail this morning?"

"I heard that you already knew about Bertha cooking at the jail this past weekend."

"Dang good biscuit," Mark said. "And even though those greens were canned she seasoned them with some boiling meat. It reminded me of my own mother and grandmother's cooking."

"You don't see anything wrong with a convicted murderer cooking in our jail?"

"Frank, when she goes to Reidsville, they're not going to let her sit around. She'll work on the farm or sew uniforms. Maybe they'll put her in the laundry, have her scrub floors, or even cook. But she'll have to work. Why can't she start here and help us? You know we need it. And as long as she volunteers, I don't see where it's a problem."

"It just don't seem right to have someone in jail for poisoning folks doing our cooking."

"Maybe you got a little too close to this case," Sheriff Horton said. "But if you don't like her cooking in jail, you sure ain't going to like what I'm fixing to tell you."

"I can hardly wait," Frank replied.

"The solicitor and the judge are all in agreement that Bertha ain't going nowhere for at least another year. It'll be this fall when Judge Porter rules on their appeal and request for a new trial. Mack is sure to take it to the Georgia Supreme Court and hopefully we'll get a ruling from them by next spring. I think we'll win it, but if we don't she will have to be retried."

"I understand all of that Mark," Frank said. "So where are you going with it?"

"Here's the problem. We really don't have the facilities to house women for that long of a period. I can't find a case where a woman's ever been kept in this jail for that long. You got to admit, it's pretty rough living conditions even for men. And we very seldom have them in jail for more than six months.

"Now Mr. Victor Yeargan owns the house where Bertha and Leroy were living. He wants to clean it out and get it ready for sale or rent. Mack says that he has talked to Bertha and she told him to notify the McClungs to come and get all of her furnishings. She said they could have them. But he wants to take the half bed, chest of drawers, and dresser and set it up in her cell. That would make it a little easier for her and ease up the harsh conditions. He ran that by Henderson and Judge Porter. They don't see a problem with it and I don't either.

"So I want you to get Harry and his crew to get the steel bunks from the cell and when Mack has the furniture brought in, we'll set it up for her. And make sure that no other women are put in the cell with her. And Frank, let her do some of the cooking."

Frank sat motionless and didn't say a word. He had swallowed about half of his tobacco juice. His mind was racing. *The same people who had just tried and convicted her are now going overboard to make her comfortable. Is it me, or is something wrong with this picture? My God, she's charming everybody around her, even Danny who's more like a son.*

"Mark, you're the sheriff," Frank said. "Consider it done."

"Thanks, Frank," Mark said. "Glad you understand."

"I didn't say I understand. I said it would get done."

As Frank walked out of the office he looked over to where Mrs. Jenkins was typing and said, "We're right Mrs. Jenkins. It's gonna get a lot worse."

₪    ₪

As the summer of 1946 was coming to an end, Frank was still mesmerized by Bertha's celebrity status. He was working on some budget requests one afternoon in late September when Harry Davis popped into the office.

"Haven't seen too much of you lately, Chief," Harry said as he pulled up a chair and fired up a Lucky Strike. "Me and you need to make a trip and get out of here for awhile. What do you say about going down to Joe's with me and I'll buy your dinner."

Frank looked up from his paper work and said, "You just got yourself a dinner date Mr. Davis. Give me about two minutes and I'll be right with you."

As they left the jail on foot and began the three and a half block walk to Joe's Lunch, Frank saw right quick that it was going to be awhile getting there. Frank quickly became aware of the fact that going anywhere with Harry meant stopping everybody for a quick chat. As they made it to Fourth Avenue and Broad St., they ran into an old friend from the Rome Police Department who was working that block.

"Hey Long!" Harry hollered, "You moving them double parkers along today?"

"I'm fixing to start writing some of them a ticket if they don't start listening better," Long replied.

As the two men kept walking, Harry asked Long, "Where's your rookie at today?"

"You'll see him in a minute," Long said. "He's working 2nd and Broad today, if he ain't up in the pool hall. He's a nice one, Harry. They really hired a ruby jewel when they found him."

"Who's he talking about, Harry?" Frank asked.

"Few months ago they hired this big old boy from Aragon who had just got out of the Army," Harry replied. "He didn't have a gun, so some of the fellows told him that Mr. Long had an extra one that he'd probably let him borrow for awhile. Mr. Long was working traffic out in the middle of 2nd and Broad when this young fellow pulls up.

"Howard told me he just bailed out of his car and ran up to him asking, "Are you Long?" He said he didn't cut the car off or nothing and it just kept on going across the street right through the traffic till it came to rest against the curb. Long didn't know who he was or what he wanted. Said he thought he was crazy. But then that big old boy told him he was a new officer and wanted to borrow a gun. Long said he had real problems giving this guy a gun and wanted to check his story our first. But it was true and Long's been kind of saddled with him ever since."

"Who is he?" Frank asked. "Have I ever met him?"

"I don't think so," Harry said. "His name's Bill Kinney and I'm told he is one hard worker. He's one of the happiest fellows you'll ever meet. Always laughing and joking around. Ain't scared of the devil himself and will knock you into next week if you mess with him. But you will hear about him in the future chief, just you wait and see."

They finally reached Joe's Restaurant and found the only empty booth in the place. They had ordered the special of the day and were about half way through with dinner when Joe came over and slid into the booth.

"Boys, I'm going to be cooking down on the river this Friday night," Joe said. "I hope y'all can make it."

"We'll try to," Frank said. "I don't see why we can't. Are you cooking every week Joe? It sure seems like it."

"I guess the guys just like to get away for a little bit," Joe said. "They all seem to enjoy it. And I do too."

"I'm scheduled to work Friday till about five," Harry said. "Have to run home and change clothes. I might be a little late. But I think I can make it."

"How's your star boarder, Frank?" Joe asked with a big ear to ear grin.

"Now Joe, you're not being funny." Frank replied. "That woman's running me crazy. And everybody else thinks she's the greatest thing since sliced bread."

"It's a small town, pard," Joe said. "We don't get celebrities like her very often. And I must say she sure fooled me. I never would have believed that she would do nothing like that."

"Joe, you wouldn't believe it," Frank said. "She cooks two and sometime three days a week. And she always cooks on Sunday. She sews quilt tops that I'm told are excellent quality, and makes little stuffed sock animals for kids. Danny thinks she's the greatest thing ever. She made him a quilt top and he treasures that thing like it's gold."

"Tell Joe about the writers, Frank," Harry said.

"What writers?" Joe asked.

"For the last several months these detective magazine writers have been hanging around like flies," Frank said. "Some are slick publications but most are like Police Gazette or a Grit newspaper. They interview Bertha and then make up some of the most outlandish tales you ever heard. They talk about a backwoods cult in one and the swamp people from Armuchee in another. It's plumb ridiculous."

"In one magazine, they changed the whole setting to Lindale," Harry said.

"I saw one of them," Joe said. "They've sold like hotcakes around here I'm told. And it don't surprise me a bit. People are captivated by her."

"Bertha milks'em like cows," Frank said. "If she never got another dollar she'd be fixed in prison for the next five years at least. She's still got a couple of church groups coming.

"She usually has a quilt top ready when the Abbotts show up. They take it and the ladies of the church actually quilt the thing, sell it and bring her the money to help her with necessities. They supply her with scraps, needles and thread. She don't have an investment. It's all profit. She's making a lot more in jail than she ever did at McCllelan's."

"But you got to remember," Joe said. "She's still locked up."

"Not really," Frank said. "I mean she's in jail true enough, but she has the run of the place most of the time. Half the time her cell isn't locked, at least till it gets dark.

"Mack's got the judge and Henderson to agree to all kinds of special treatment. You ought to see her apartment. It used to be a cell. It's dressed up as good as anything down town. She's got her bedroom furniture all set up, pictures on the walls and some of my deputies wives send her fresh flowers to liven the place up, they say.

"And she has visitors every day. I was told early on to let them come any day they wanted to. News folks stand and talk to her by the hour. I mean from everywhere. There are reporters from Atlanta, Augusta, Macon, and all over the state. And all the big wire services are dropping by pretty frequently.

"Joe, I stopped by the carnival last fall that set up down on Maple

Street. They had all kinds of side shows. You know what I mean. They have sword swallowers, fire eaters and all manner of entertainment that is nothing but pure carnival. But I'm telling you right now that none of them equal what we've got right here in our jail."

"And Joe, you might be the best cook in town," Harry said. "But that woman is really good. Y'all know I do like my groceries. She can make some of the best chicken and dumplings I've ever eaten. Her vegetable soup is out of this world, and she makes crackling corn bread to go with it.

"Some of our deputies have gardens at home and brought a lot of fresh vegetables during the summer for her to fix for the prisoners. Stuff like okra that got too big and hard to fry. Tomatoes by the bushel before they rot.

"Some of the deputies tried to mess with her. One deputy brought her a half bushel of squash that was too big for almost anything. I think they just wanted to see what she did with them. Well sir, she cut them squash up and stewed it with cut up onion till it was a mush. Then with a little salt, pepper, cheese and flour she made patties and fried'em up like folks fry salmon. They were the best darn things I ever did eat, and I don't like squash."

"That's what the country folks used to do to get the kids to eat squash," Joe said. "My Mama did that all the time. And you're right. They are good."

"And then there's Mattie Weaver," Frank said. "She comes almost every week, and leaves an envelope to add to Bertha's account. It's beginning to build up also. She don't always get to visit with Bertha, but she's real faithful to drop off a little cash."

"I hear she's fixing to get married," Joe said.

"You mean our Mattie. The one we had in jail with Bertha?" Harry asked.

"We are talking about the little bank embezzler, ain't we?" Joe asked. "If that's her, she's fixing to get married."

"Well, she's a looker for sure," Harry said. "Who's she marrying, anybody we know?"

"Nah, I don't think so," Joe said. "He's a cotton broker from Atlanta, I think. Good bit older than her too. I hear he's got family up here. Mack got Mattie a job and introduced her to this fellow. I guess Bertha taught her well while they were in jail together. He's loaded and she's a doll. Sounds like a match made in paradise. She don't work no more and is hanging around the Coosa Country Club with him and his friends all the time. I understand they'll be moving to Atlanta after the cotton buying season is over."

Frank and Harry finished their dinner. As they got up to leave they assured Joe that they'd see him Friday night if at all possible. As they neared the restaurant door Frank turned to their host and said, "Well Joe, it has been nice chatting with you, but we gotta get back to the jail, if we've still got one. Bertha might've sold it by now."

Joe and Harry were having a big laugh at Frank's expense.

"It ain't that bad pard," Joe said still laughing. "Show up Friday night and we'll have a good time and tell a few lies. Somebody told me that old Jim Beam might be there."

Frank cut an after dinner chew as they left the restaurant and Harry lit up another Lucky Strike. They had only walked a few steps when Frank said to his friend, "I needed that, Harry. Thanks."

₪    ₪

Mack walked into the jail and went straight to Frank Russell's office. When he got to the door Frank looked up and motioned Mack to come on in and have a seat.

"Hello there, Counselor," Frank said, "How are you today?"

"I need to talk to Bertha, Frank," Mack said with a long look on his face. "Is it OK if I go on back to the interview room and have her brought down?"

"I can do you one today better than that," Frank said. "I'm on my way to the courthouse and you can just stay right here and use my office."

"Now that's what I call being a public servant," Mack said perking up some from his sad appearance.

Mack had opened his briefcase and spread some papers on Frank's desk when Bertha came in. She was joking and flirting with the deputy who brought her down, and Mack could see that they both were enjoying themselves. Bertha adjusted her skirt, sat down in the chair across the desk from Mack. She reached into her blouse and retrieved a pack of Pall Mall cigarettes. She took a match out of the cellophane wrapper on the cigarette pack, struck it on Frank's desk top, took a deep draw, leaned forward and blew a smoke ring at her lawyer.

"I didn't know you smoked," Mack said.

"There's a lot you don't know about me honey," she replied. "I've always smoked a little. But being locked up has increased my desire. All kinds of desire."

"Well, I've sort of got bad news today," Mack said. "You ready for it?"

"Mack, I done told you and Carl, don't play games with me."

"Judge Porter turned down our appeal," Mack said.

Bertha's personality changed rapidly. She went from being a silly giggling school girl to a lioness on the prowl. Mack noticed the look on her face and it made his heart beat fast. He wandered if this was the way a deer felt just before the lion jumped. It was a strange feeling. It was somewhat terrifying and at the same time thrilling.

"Didn't you and Carl sit right here in this jail and tell me that was going to happen? Or did I just imagine it?"

"Well yes, we did," Mack said. "But you still got to believe there was a chance, even if it was a slim one. And since Judge Porter has given you every privilege that I've asked him to, I had a slim hope that we would get a ruling in our favor. I mean, the sheriff could have refused to honor those requests, but he's a nice guy."

"Well we didn't," Bertha said. "Now we appeal to the State, is that correct?"

"That's correct."

Bertha got up from her chair, crushed the cigarette butt in the ashtray, looked at Mack and said.

"Close the door Mack. This place has got a lot of eyes and ears. We've got to talk."

# Chapter 23

Bertha was leaving the kitchen and headed back up the stairs to her cell when she ran into Frank Russell in the hall.

"Deputy Russell, I need to talk to you when you get time," Bertha said.

"I need to talk to you also. Follow me to my office."

Frank went around the desk and sat down. Bertha needed no invitation and was already sitting when Frank got comfortable.

"You go first, Bertha," Frank said. "What's on your mind?"

"It's all ready the second Saturday in November. It looks like we're going to have to spend the holidays together this year. I want to cook a good Thanksgiving dinner for the prisoners and deputies on duty. I know your food budget ain't much, but I got a list of what I want. I'll get it to Deputy Davis or Payne and I'll also get it paid for. They said I had to get it approved first. So that's what I'm doing. Getting it approved."

"Give your list to Harry or Bill and tell them to bring it to me and I'll see. I ain't promising you anything, but I'll see."

"Thank you. And I also wanted to say that Danny is a darling. I think he's one of the reasons that I didn't go nuts the first few months. He told me something the other day tickled me good. I had asked him why you never wore a gun like other policemen. He said Frank has a gun that he just slides in his pocket. It's a little .32 caliber Smith & Wesson, he's let me see it a time or two. I asked him was he sure and he said yes ma'am he sure was.

"He said that he was squirming around in church the other Sunday and you just took his hand and laid it on the pistol in your pocket.

"I said, 'What did you do Danny?' He said, 'I calmed right down. I mean it wasn't like Frank was threatening me or nothing, I just got the message.' Deputy Russell he's so cute."

"He's all boy, but a good one," Frank said. "Bertha, you've got some visitors out in the lobby of the jail. I don't know what they want and I wanted to talk to you first before I told them they could see you."

"Who are they?" Bertha asked.

"I don't know their names. But they're Gypsies."

Bertha's eyes came alive and she sat straight up in her chair. Frank could see the crooked little smile that she had and she looked like a puppy trying to wag only its tale, but failing, wriggled all over.

"They were my friends. And Leroy's too, she said. "He worked for them fixing up their old trucks every year when they came through. Some of them stayed at Pleasant Valley camp right across from my house. Others would stay at Chuck's Camp, which was about a half mile from our place, or camp in that field by the river right across from Enoch Salmon's tavern.

"There were different families, but there were times when all of them were here together. They head to Florida each winter and always come and stop in Rome for several weeks."

Frank couldn't guess why the gypsies had stopped by. But now he was starting to get the picture. He had been told of their loyalty. He could now see that it was true.

"Oh Mr. Russell, did you ever go to one of their camps?" Bertha asked. "They have everything. I mean, there are cobblers for shoe repair, carpenters for furniture repair, tin smiths that can fix almost any pot or pan, or sell you a new one. There are musicians, actor and magicians. They sell some mighty good whiskey and jewelry. The men wear loose-fitting, colorful vests and poet shirts. And the women have long pleated skirts and blouses that showed a lot of bosom. And you never see anything white. That is a color of mourning and death.

"The men chop wood for folks, and the women wash clothes and clean houses. They will do anything to make a dollar, but the two biggest things are the men who trade and sell mules with the local farmers, and the fortune teller. Each family had its queen that tells fortunes. Usually the queens were accurate and right on the money."

Frank noticed a little of the excitement left her when she talked about the fortune teller. And he thought he would follow that up.

"What do you mean, they're usually accurate?" Frank asked.

"Did I say that?" Bertha replied. "Well you know, nobody can be right all of the time."

Frank left Bertha in his office and brought the two men and one woman back to visit with her. The men introduced themselves as Hugo and Pali.

The woman's name was Mala and she had a small covered bowl with her. They explained that it was a vegetable stew that had been a favorite of Bertha's and Leroy's. Frank let the trio have a lengthy visit with Bertha and as they were leaving, he asked them to hang around a minute. While the night jailer was taking Bertha back to her cell, he asked the gypsies to please sit back down in his office.

"I guess y'all know why Bertha is here," Frank said. "And I want to ask you if there's anything you can add to the investigation that we're still conducting in case we have to re-try the case."

"Nothing like that, Mr. Sheriff," Hugo said. "Leroy was our employee when we came through your beautiful town. He was a good mechanic and reasonable. Even during the war he could get parts for our trucks, and that was something we had a hard time doing anywhere else.

"We got to be friends with him and with Miss Bertha. She loved our vegetable stew. It's heavy on the garlic but she didn't seem to mind. She taught us to eat cornbread and buttermilk, a little heavy on the black pepper and with a chunk of onion."

Frank explained what Bertha had said about the fortune teller not being correct all of the time and did that mean anything to them.

"Mr. Russell, Queen Esmeralda is correct all of the time," Pali said. "She is never wrong. She is the best teller of fortunes in all the gypsy world. She is a palm reader and has insight into her glass where she is able to see many things."

"We are aware of what Miss Bertha was referring to," Hugo said. "Mala, you were there when it started. Please tell the deputy what you saw and heard."

"Leroy and Bertha came to our camp one night last year. It was right before we were to break camp and move toward Florida. Leroy had finished with the trucks and Hugo and some of the other men asked Esmeralda to read his and Bertha's fortune as a thank you for helping us.

"Lots of town folks think we're thieves. But those two had been good friends. I was in the tent with Queen Esmeralda when she read Leroy's palm. She didn't say anything, just started shaking all over and was having a hard time getting her breath. She simply put his hand down and picked up Bertha's. Her eyes lit up like fire and she screamed and ran from the tent.

"Three or four of the men went after her and finally brought her back. Bertha and Leroy had already left with a thousand apologies from our people. It was a long time before I could get Esmeralda calmed down. I was finally able to get her to talk to me. She said that she could see no future in Leroy's life, and that Bertha had a mark on her hand. I didn't see a mark, but Esmeralda said she did. That was what Bertha was referring to I'm pretty sure."

Frank thanked the trio and wished them a safe voyage South.

ℼ    ℼ

The holiday season had passed by with not much fanfare for Bertha. She had been able to cook chicken and dressing for Thanksgiving and a couple of large hams for Christmas. The jail usually released everybody they could for the Christmas holidays so there weren't that many to cook for. On New Year's Eve, she could hear all of the fireworks coming from Broad Street.

She remembered meeting Leroy two years ago on the day before New Year's Eve and what a party they had. The next New Year's Eve however; they had been at odds and Leroy had left her at home and went partying by himself. Now this year he was dead and she was in jail. Finally the firecrackers had subsided and she had gone to sleep.

ℼ    ℼ

The breakfast club was all in place this frigid morning in early February of 1947. Morning greetings had been passed around and the first cup of coffee downed in a hurry just to warm up.

As breakfast was being served and more coffee brought to the table, Johnny Jacobs asked Ben cooper, "Ben, you can hear all kind of rumors in the restaurant business. Yesterday evening there were several employees of the courthouse in here. They were talking low and whispering to each other. I heard a little. Happy's not here this morning so let me ask you what your evening headline is going to say."

Johnny had gotten the entire breakfast club's attention. They knew he had something, they just didn't know what. All eyes were now fastened on Cooper to see how he was going to answer.

"You got a good ear, Johnny," Ben Cooper said. "The announcement and results of Bertha Hill's request for a new trial are back."

"So is that what your headline is going to read?" Hix Sims asked. "Results are back."

"Afraid not, Hix," Ben said. "They're going to be more in line with Bertha Gossett Hill wins another trial."

The entire group became deathly quiet. They knew that Ben would not joke about this. Finally Macon Brock very quietly said, "Ben, can you tell us what the Supreme Court said in granting Bertha a new trial? Would that violate any newspaper code of ethic?"

"No it wouldn't, Macon. And I'm sure that it's on all the radio stations by now. The Supreme Court basically overturned Judge Porter's ruling on allowing the jurors that had policies with the companies that had insured the deceased to sit on the jury. They also found error on allowing Graham Wright to assist the prosecution, after he was hired by the same companies to help with the case. The solicitor saw no fault with either of these issues and the trial court didn't either, but the Supreme Court was unanimous in their decision to grant a new trial."

"Here we go again," Cecil Rhodes said. "Do you reckon our little town can stand round two?"

"Don't look like we got much choice," John Moss said. "The circus is coming to town again."

"Ben, let me ask a question," Dr. Elmore said. "Following up on what John just said, do you think this will be as big a deal as it was last time?"

"Doc, I don't think there's any way to predict that. We're going to have a brand new solicitor. Sandy Clower is one heck of a lawyer. I think he has a photographic mind. He seems to have all the law books memorized. But he's starting all over. That might be a problem. However, his evidence is strong. Then on the other hand, Mack's going to be more than ready this time. I'm sure he didn't like losing the last time and the jury only taking thirty minutes to convict. We may have the crowds back to watch the lawyers go at it again. I would suspect that we would."

"Well Johnny, looks like your business will be booming again," John Powers said.

"I'll be looking forward to it, but we're doing pretty good anyway," Johnny said. "In fact I think we all are. And If I remember correctly, the streets were full on the trial days last year. Maybe they will be again."

"You've been mighty quiet this morning, Preacher," Ben Rainwater said. "Do you have any thoughts on the upcoming new trial of Bertha Hill?"

"I've just been sitting here listening." Reverend Stephens said, "and I believe you will have just as big a crowd this time as you did for the last one. It may be even bigger."

"You got my attention, Reverend," Ben Cooper said. "Why do you believe that?"

"We've just gone through a great depression and a horrific war. These are things that can't be predicted, but they can be explained, and overcome. At least they can be to a certain extent. Now that brings us to Bertha Gossett Hill.

"What she is accused of is unexplainable in the mind of our citizens. We have a certain shroud of moral and ethical justice that covers us completely.

It is a certain type of unwritten rules for behavior. Bertha ripped that shroud."

Reverend Stephens stopped for a moment, slowly sipped his coffee, put his hand over his cup to indicate to the waitress that he didn't need a refill, then continued, "People will be coming, trying to understand what happened and why. This one act has frozen this entire community for over a year. Did you see how it stunned all of y'all when it was announced? The same feeling that you had is going to permeate throughout the county."

Reverend Stephens paused for a second or two, just to let his words have a little more effect. "I would just like to caution you on one thing. With the granting of a new trial, last year's conviction is set aside. She must be proven guilty by a jury, not tried in the court of public opinion. I'm not saying that she isn't guilty. Or for that matter that she is.

"It's just been a little longer than it was last time and people have had time to digest the whole concept of the crimes that she's accused of committing. Not that it's going to taste any better than it did last year. They're just not going to gobble it all down as quickly as they did before. And like one of you said, her attorneys have had a lot longer to prepare this time."

"Ben, I'd like to know what Sandy had to say?" Cecil Rhodes asked.

"We tried to get in touch with all affected parties, Cecil," Ben Cooper said. "Sandy was in Summerville when we reached him by phone. He said that he was going to Atlanta on Monday and wanted to study the Supreme Court decision. And if he felt like there was any possibility of success he would ask for a re-hearing before the court. If not he would bring it to trial at the earliest possible time."

"Were you able to get in touch with Mack or Carl Griffin?" Hix asked.

"Actually we were," Ben said. "Mack is in Atlanta. The legislature is still in session and will be for awhile. He stated that he couldn't make a comment at this time because he has not seen the decision.

"Carl stated that he was extremely happy for Bertha. He felt that it was his duty to stay with this case until the Georgia Supreme Court made a decision, but since his election to the position of Ordinary and now that the case has merited a decision, he was now off the case."

"Who do you think Mack will get to help him?" Macon asked.

"Carl told us that Mack had already asked W.T. Maddox to assist if the ruling was favorable," Cooper added. "And boys, he's a good one."

The breakfast club was quiet. All the members were slowly letting the news and the new players sink in. Dr. Elmore looked at the faces of his friends and thought they resembled the anticipation of an audience awaiting the curtain to be drawn back and the show to begin.

Ben Cooper bought breakfast this morning without a flip and the club members filed out quietly and headed to their respective offices.

# Chapter 24

Frank poured himself a cup of coffee from the pot in the sheriff's office. Mrs. Jenkins had made a fresh pot before she left for the day. Frank returned to his chair in the inner office, looked toward his friend and said. "Well, Sheriff, we've been in this position before. How long do you reckon we'll be here this time? Remember, last year we didn't even get to finish our first cup of coffee."

"Yeah, I think thirty or forty minutes was all it took. But I think it'll take a little longer tonight."

Frank sank back into the most comfortable chair in the office. While the sheriff was busy talking to several other deputies, Frank let his mind reflect over the past two days.

The second trial of Bertha Gossett Hill had started just about like the first one. One of the main exceptions this year was that Mack challenged every witness, and Frank thought he was able to score a lot of points by doing so.

Sandy Clower, the Solicitor, was absolutely brilliant and so was Mack. It was a battle that should go down in the Georgia annals of criminal justice. Frank thought it was more like a duel without pistols than a trial, and Mack had W.T. Maddox in his corner. Frank thought he had performed brilliantly.

But in all actuality there were only several small differences between the two trials. However, they could be significant.

This time the court had gone through a panel of seventy nine jurors before they got a jury. There was not going to be a chance of another reversal on an incorrect jury selection. The jury that was finally selected consisted of H. Dwight Avery, John W. Clements, Smiley Johnson, Hoyt Barron,

F.C. Perry, Paul Craven, C.H. Hester, O.H. Kilpatrick, J.M. Simmons, J.J. Lumpkin, S.W. McKinney, V.G. Smith.

Frank knew most of the panel and thought they were excellent jurors. And he had to admit, Bertha once again did a fantastic job on her unsworn statement.

The only thing she did different this year was that she remembered there was a man named Sam Mercer who was running around with Leroy during the last three months of his life. She did not know who or where this man came from or where he might be. She did not know what business that he and Leroy were involved in, or even if they had any business ventures together.

Mack testified that he had tried in vain to find Sam Mercer, but was unable to. Frank felt that the whole Sam Mercer escapade was to give the jury another suspect besides Bertha. And it seemed to have worked beautifully. He could see the quizzical look coming from several jurors.

The courtroom had once again been packed. And no one had gone home, anticipating another quick verdict. So here it was at six in the afternoon and the jury had just been charged and started with their deliberations.

"Frank, the judge wants us to get six rooms in the Forrest Hotel if the jury is unable to reach a verdict by midnight. He intends to sequester this jury. He is adamant about them reaching a verdict."

"Will do, Sheriff," Frank replied as he rose to go and find Harry and send him to the Forrest. "If we sequester them, we'll have to have a deputy or two in the hallway all night. But surely they aren't going to take that long."

"Use one deputy and a bailiff," Horton said. "And I believe you're right. I don't think it will come to that. But just in case, we've got to be ready."

Bertha with her legal team of Mack Hicks and
W.T. Maddox

Five days later Frank was still sitting in the sheriff's office when the word came down that the jury had a verdict. Frank looked at the sheriff and said, "Sixty five hours of deliberations. Just a little longer than last time, huh."

"Let's go find out which way it went. We know they've been split since the first day. I can't believe that Judge Porter didn't miss-try this thing."

Bertha was found guilty again. And Judge Porter sentenced her to life in prison one more time. And just like last time, Bertha said that she was not guilty no matter what went on here, or what the jury said.

"Mack, I gotta tell you, you guys did a super job," Frank said. "It could have gone either way."

"Thank you Russell, I appreciate that. But I can't believe the judge let this trial go on like he did. I'm telling you, something ain't right with this jury. Someone or some of them held out for a long time, and then for some reason caved. I've never seen a jury hold out for anywhere near that long and then come together on a verdict. I don't guess we'll ever know what happened. But I'm going to appeal, just the same."

Several days later, Deputy Bill Payne came to Frank's office and said, "Hey Chief, Bertha wants to come down and talk. What do you want me to tell her? Her girlfriend Mattie has just left and now she wants to talk to you."

"She's due to be shipped almost any day, so let's see what she wants."

Bertha came into the office with a big smile on her face and was as cheerful as she could be. "How are you today, Deputy Russell? I haven't seen much of you since the trial."

"Been kind of busy Bertha. What can I do for you?"

"Well, I've got a couple of problems that I need you to help me with," she said.

"I will if I can, as long as they're part of my official duty. I guess you know that you'll be gone in a couple of weeks at the latest."

"I do. Mack said we lost on the appeal by a vote of four to three with the big court. Was kind of close though, wasn't it? I told him just accept the decision and let's move on till next time."

"What next time? It's over Bertha," Frank said.

"Oh no, Mr. Russell, it ain't ever going to be over till I walk out of here."

"No use in arguing now Bertha. What can I do for you?"

"I want to get married," she said.

Frank was speechless. He didn't know if she was serious or was this some other trick on her part. He studied exactly what she had said for a considerable length of time and when he couldn't figure out any ulterior motive, he finally replied, "Bertha you've been in jail for almost fifteen months. Just who do you plan to marry?"

"Wiley Gravett," She replied.

Frank knew that Wiley Gravett was one of the trusties and had been one for a month or so. He also knew that Wiley was several years younger than Bertha and as far as Frank knew, he'd never been married before.

"Just how do you plan on doing that?" Frank asked.

"It's all set. We're to be married right here in the jail on May 3rd by the ordinary. You remember my old lawyer from the first trial don't you, Frank? Mr. Griffin is now the ordinary and he says there's no problem in us marrying."

"I don't understand what you have in mind. Why in the world Wiley would want to marry some woman that had a life sentence hanging around her neck is beyond me. But far be it from me to interfere with true love. Go ahead."

"Thank you, Mr. Russell. I knew you'd understand," she said.

"But I don't, Bertha. I don't understand at all."

"Well, let me see if I can explain it in a way so you will understand. Without going into a lot of detail let me just say, I'm going to have a baby."

ﬡ    ﬡ

"Frank, the judge is livid about Bertha," Sheriff Horton said as they finished their dinner at the Busy Bee Café. "He wants her gone now. Yesterday would have been better. But he'll settle for now."

"Well Sheriff, no disrespect to anyone, but what could he expect? She almost had free run of the jail and at certain times she did have free run. She had unlimited visitation, and has a pretty good bankroll from folks wanting to help her out financially.

Frank had paid his check and was waiting for his change. Without looking toward his boss he continued, "and she came danged close to walking out of here a free woman. Lots of folks are saying that the judge let the jury deliberations go on way too long. They think that a mistrial should have been called after about twenty or thirty hours. Obviously there were members of the jury who didn't believe she was guilty."

"I understand that, Frank," Mark said. "But I have to think that the judge's and solicitor's intentions were good. They were simply trying to make her accommodations a little bit better."

"And you see what it got them," Frank said. "Or really, what their actions got us. Most people think we're to blame for letting her get pregnant. Wiley's already saying how much he loves her, but that it ain't his baby. And although Bertha's been asked by everybody who it belongs to, she just smiles and walks off."

"Well, rumors are flying," Mark said. "I've heard that it could be almost anybody. She's been visited daily for fifteen months. And most of the time she was left by herself."

As the two men walked out onto Broad Street and headed back toward the courthouse, Mark again spoke to his Chief Deputy. "I called down to Reidsville today and told them of the problem we had. They were very understanding and said to bring her on. So tomorrow morning, bright and early, get her out of our jail."

"That is one order that I'm going to enjoy carrying out," Frank said. "You just don't know how much."

The next morning right after breakfast, Bertha Gossett Hill was loaded into a sheriff's car and spent the day traveling the highways of Georgia until she reached her new home. This was the place where she had been sentenced to remain for the rest of her life, the women's penitentiary at Reidsville.

₪    ₪

Bertha sat in her bunk and read the letter from the Parole Board. When finished, she angrily wadded the letter up and threw it as far as she could. Then after a minute, she retrieved it and straightened it out. She got her writing materials and dashed off a letter to Mattie. It was short and sweet. She said that she wanted to talk to Mack and had enclosed the board's answer to her request for parole.

It had been four years since Bertha had arrived at Reidsville. She had lost the baby she'd been carrying when she got here. She had become a model prisoner and was well thought of by the prison staff and guards. They thought it was hilarious for a woman tried and convicted of poisoning her husband to be cooking most of the food. It was certainly a fact that none of the other prisoners wanted to make Bertha mad at them.

Bertha and Mattie had written back and forth since her arrival. At times letters from Mattie were sporadic. Then there were times that she might write several times a month. Mattie kept her up with the news from Rome. That's how Bertha had learned that Mark Horton had been defeated by Gilmore Johnson for Sheriff in 1949. And that Mark was now a security officer for the Health Department. Harry Davis had taken a job with the Lindale Police Department. She was informed also that Frank Russell was now the Personnel Director for the Anchor Rome Cotton Mill.

And on a sadder note, Bertha learned that her attorney, Carl Griffin, was found shot and critically wounded in his home and had died shortly after. This had been in early 1951, and Bertha was genuinely sorry for Mr. Griffin. He had been very nice to her and she thought he did his best in trying to help her win her case. He had also married her and Wiley, whom she hadn't heard from in a couple of years. Carl just seemed like a good man. Mattie hadn't given her any details. She just sent her the newspaper story. The gun was found by his side and it didn't indicate any investigation was ongoing. Bertha thought how sad that was.

צ    צ

Several weeks after the Parole Board letter, Bertha was summoned to the warden's office and informed that her attorney was here and wanted to speak to her. She was led into a small interview room and took a seat. A few minutes later Mack was escorted into the room and the door was closed, leaving her and her lawyer alone.

"I got your summons, Bertha," Mack said. "Mattie said that you wanted to see me. So here I am."

"That was nearly a month ago, Mack," Bertha said. "It took you long enough. Did you get the letter I sent you from the parole board?"

"Yes, I did," Mack said. "What about it? We told you that you wouldn't get paroled on the first try."

"You didn't read the letter did you, Mack?" Bertha asked.

"I glanced at it," Mack said. "It's just a form letter. I've seen dozens like that. What's your point, Bertha? I'm not hurrying you, but I've got other clients over at the men's prison. I'm trying to see everybody today."

Bertha's breathing slowed down, her eyes narrowed and Mack swore they turned a fiery shade of yellow. Her face was like a stone mask and Mack felt once again that he was in the presence of something dangerous, although he didn't know what.

Bertha spoke very slowly and softly, but her enunciation was crystal clear. "I don't care who else you've come to see. You're going to hear me out. I copied the letter word for word. I was afraid that you wouldn't read it or it would get lost in the shuffle somewhere. The bottom line, Mack, is that the Board says that I will never be eligible for parole because I have two indictments for murder that are still open and hanging over my head. I want you to get rid of them, do you understand that?"

Mack took the letter and read exactly what the board had written. He gave it just a minute to sink in and said to Bertha, "There's only one way to do that. And it's a little risky."

"Mack, risks don't mean a thing to me. I'd take a chance on swimming the Atlantic if it meant that I had a chance to be free again. What do we have to do?"

"You don't have to do anything. I will have to go back and file a demand for trial on the open indictments. That should get us some results."

"What kind of results can we expect?" Bertha asked.

"Well, it's a gamble. You could go to trial and be found guilty of murder two more times."

"And either add more time to my life sentences, or go to the chair," Bertha said sarcastically. "Is that it?"

"That's part of it," Mack replied. "But I don't think that's what will happen."

"Then what do you think will happen?" Bertha asked.

"It took sixty five hours to get a verdict the second time, and then we lost the appeal by a vote of four to three. In legal work that's about as close as you can get without winning. I don't think they would want to try you again. We'd have a better case than we did last time by saying that Leroy did it. I'm sure we could put a little doubt in some juror's mind. And even if they won, what are they gonna accomplish? They got you in here for life. You're not going to get the chair. And a new life sentence would just run concurrent. I think they'll *nolle prose* both cases."

"What does that mean?" she asked.

"They'll drop them. Elect not to try them. Do away with them and forget about them," Mack said. "Take your pick."

"I'll pick them all," she said. "Then we'll never hear from them again, is that right?"

"That's right," he replied.

"Well, you said it was my decision and I want you to file your motion and get started," she said. "I want to be at least eligible for parole."

"It'll take a few months to get everything ready. You'll know when we're getting close, because they'll come and get you and take you back to Floyd County."

"I can hardly wait," Bertha said. "Mack, now that we've got that took care of, tell me, how did Mattie look."

"She's gorgeous," Mack said. "She got a divorce, and I guess a big settlement with it. I understand that she's living out west some of the time and in Florida the rest. She has made some good investments I'm told, and seems to be loaded. I mean really loaded."

"Yeah, she wrote and told me all that. I just wanted to know what she looked like after the last five years. I kept hoping she'd pop in one day. But I guess I'm doing good just to get a letter now and then."

"All right Bertha," Mack said as he rose to leave. "I'll see you in Rome in a few months."

# Chapter 25

Bertha was transported to Floyd County in July of 1951. Once again, the papers were full of her story. It was rehashed all over again for a couple of weeks. The solicitor had exclaimed how he was ready and looking forward to justice being served.

Then, on the morning of July 20th 1951, Mack Hicks came to the jail to talk to his client.

"Bertha, have you got your bags packed?" Mack asked.

"Where am I going now, Mack?"

"Back to Reidsville, my dear. The Solicitor just *nolle prossed* both murder indictments. They're over. We've finally won one, Bertha."

"No, we've won two. I'm finally cleared of something I didn't do to start with. There's one more to go Mack, one more to go."

Frank Russell sat in his office in the Anchor Rome mill reading the *Rome News Tribune.* He had figured it out after Bertha had been shipped. She had talked Wiley into marrying her so that when she was eligible for parole she could claim a home and support. The Parole Board refused to grant parole to women prisoners without visible means of a job and home. And Bertha had no family that would stand for that support. She had however, fixed that before she left. It was uncanny that she could see things and plan that far ahead.

The baby, he figured, was just an insurance policy. He had come to know Bertha like a book. There was no way she was going to be that isolated and not have somebody back home able to supply her needs and send them to her when she needed it. *Yep,* Frank thought, *she's got somebody over a barrel.*

*You're a tiger, Miss Bertha. I gotta give you a tip of my hat. There ain't no quit in you.*

## Hearing Delayed For Bertha Hill

A court hearing on Bertha Gossett Hill's demand for trial on indictments charging the murder of her mother and father over five years ago have been delayed to next Friday.

Floyd Superior Court officials disclosed the hearing, originally scheduled today, will be held at 10 a. m. next Friday.

Mrs. Hill demanded trial on the old indictments last week. Now serving a life sentence for the arsenic poisoning of her husband, Leroy Hill, in 1945, she requested trial on the two standing indictments because she cannot qualify for parole until they have been cleared.

She was accused of poisoning Mr. and Mrs. James R. Hardin after an autopsy allegedly showed traces of arsenic in their bodies.

₪    ₪

Bertha sat in her bunk and read the letter again from the Parole board. After the second reading, she lay back and stared at the ceiling. *This is the third time I've been turned down. I've been under lock and key for over twelve years. I'll be forty in a couple of months. It looks like I'm actually going to have to stay here for the rest of my life.*

She put her thoughts on hold and wrote two letters. One she wrote to Mack Hicks, the other to Mattie. Both letters expressed a mild form of resignation. Bertha was thinking as she wrote, this looks like it, I don't know when I'll get another chance at parole and there's no guarantee it would be successful anyway. She wanted both to know how much she appreciated their friendship over the years and the efforts that they had made to help her with her case.

She knew there was not much Mack could do anymore. He had been appointed Judge of Floyd County Superior Court back in 1954 to fill the rest of Judge Nichols term, who had been appointed to the court of appeals. Mattie was all over the country. Bertha could always get in touch with her eventually by writing directly to her sister and that is what she did today.

All in all Bertha didn't have a bad life in prison. She had been through a couple of wardens and was in the good graces of the guards. That had been something she had accomplished soon after her arrival. She was now in charge of the kitchen and really had a supervisory role. But she just wasn't free, and she yearned for that more and more each passing year. She placed the letter from the Board in a cigar box that held her letters and writing material and headed for the kitchen. It was time to get started with supper.

ℼ      ℼ

"Mr. Addleton, your one-thirty appointment is here," Mrs. Smith, the receptionist, said as she directed the party to the chair opposite the giant desk of Bob Addleton.

"I understand that you wanted to talk to me about an old Floyd county case," he asked. "Is that correct?"

"That would be correct," the party answered.

"I've read through all the court records that you sent me and I have your retainer, but I still need to know why me? This is Griffin, Georgia. We're a pretty good piece from Rome."

"Mr. Addleton, I'm looking for the best lawyer in the state of Georgia. I don't care what part he comes from. If you aren't the best, you're in the top ten. At least that's what I've been told."

"There are very good lawyers in Rome. You didn't need to waste your money coming down here," Bob Addleton said.

"I don't feel it was a waste. Yes, there are some great lawyers in Rome. But in my opinion they're too close. I want someone who is removed from the case. Someone that can give an unbiased opinion, and won't be afraid to stick his neck out a little bit. I'm told that's you."

Bob Addleton stared at his prospective client for what seemed to be a long minute and then said, "Here's what I'm willing to do. I'll do my best to get her a new trial. But if I'm successful I will not try the case. Is that understood?"

"That's fine with me. How do you propose to get her a new trial?"

"In looking over the '47 case, I see that the jury deliberated for over 65 hours before a verdict was reached. That's an awful lot of time. I can't imagine the deliberation going on that long without something going on in the jury room. And I'm going to find out what it was. Then we'll have a better idea on which way to travel. Does that suit you?"

"You're the lawyer. If you need any more money let me know."

Bob shook hands with his client and spoke to his secretary as he showed them the door, "I need a reservation at the Forrest Hotel in Rome for next week and get in touch with Judge Hicks and see if he is available for dinner one evening."

l to r: Leroy Byars, Hoot Gibson, unknown child, Cap Hicks, Lloyd Summer, Rachael, Frank Barron, Kathleen Hight (Smithson), Gordon Lee Hight, Porter Grant, unidentified female, Slaton Clemmons, Hillis Hollingsworth, Billy Maddox (back to camera), C.W. Orr (this photo was taken years after the Hill trials, but most of the 1960 members are shown)

It won't be long till Christmas, Johnny Jacobs thought as he hurriedly helped set the table for the morning breakfast club. It's already the first day of October and the year has flown away.

The clubbers began filing in a few at a time and Johnny was amazed at how long this club had lasted. Most of the members had changed over the years. But it seemed that the more they changed, the more they stayed the same. He looked at the table and silently called the roll. Leroy Byars, Hoot

Gibson, Cap Hicks, Lloyd Summer, Frank Barron, Gordon Lee Hight, Porter Grant, Slaton Clemmons, Hillis Hollingsworth, Billy Maddox and C.W. Orr all were in attendance this morning.

Bankers, lawyers, newsmen and local business leaders Johnny thought, and they still flip to see who buys breakfast. As the last order was served, "Cap" Hicks one of Rome's foremost newscasters looked over to Hillis Hollingsworth and asked, "Hillis, did you read the report in the paper yesterday that Bertha Hill was seeking a new trial after some eleven years in Reidsville?"

"Good gracious alive Cap, I certainly did!" Hillis replied. "And I'm really interested in how this is going to turn out. I don't think the Georgia Supreme Court has ever ruled on an extra-ordinary motion before."

"Hillis, you're the club's resident lawyer," Hoot Gibson said. "How about put in layman's terms what that motion is all about."

"It's pretty simple, Hoot," Hillis said. "It's simply a motion that's presented to the supreme court that new evidence has surfaced. Evidence that the defense council and defendant were unaware of. In this case it was the testimony of three jurors. They have stated that they never voted or believed that Bertha Hill was guilty. In fact they stated in the motion that they actually thought she was not guilty."

"Looks to me like some pretty fancy legal work," Hoot said. "Is all this on the up and up?"

"Absolutely," Hillis replied. "Bob Addleton is a super lawyer. He was the assistant Attorney General for the State for several years. I think you would categorize him as a legal scholar."

"And he and Judge Mack Hicks served in the legislature together back in the late forties is what I was told," Cap said.

"Cap, are you and the judge related?" Johnny Jacobs asked as he was walking by the table.

"The judge is from over in Alabama, Johnny," Cap replied. "As far as I know we're not."

"Hillis, don't they usually poll the jury in these cases?" asked Leroy Byars.

Yes they do," Hillis said. "And it's my understanding that they polled this jury. But the motion also states that there was turmoil and confusion in the courtroom when the jury came in with its verdict. And that prevented the defendant and her council from obtaining the information that's in the motion going before the court."

"Listen guys," Hillis said, "like I said a few minutes ago, an extraordinary motion for a new trial must show that new evidence is available which could have affected the original verdict but which could not have been known to the defendant or his council."

"Do you think this thing has a chance to fly?" Porter Grant asked.

"Porter, if it was just one juror, I'd say no," Hillis answered. "But Addleton says there are three. And the *Rome News* is doing an excellent job of explaining what was actually stated in the motion by the three jurors. One juror says that he became ill and was actually treated by the county physician. He says that due to age, pressure, and illness he did not at all times know what was going on. He just wanted to go home. He says, according to the *Rome News*, that a verdict of guilty was not his verdict, but that his verdict was a verdict of not guilty."

"I read where another juror stated that during the polling he made no statement or gesture," Hoot said. "And the other one said that after 65 hours of deliberation and pressure from other jurors, he just went along with the group."

"Well, they're still going to need an affidavit from Bertha Hill, Mack Hicks and W.T. Maddox to go with their motion," Hillis stated.

"They've already got that, I think," Cap replied. "This is going to be interesting. Can you imagine if she did get a third trial after eleven years in prison? I'm fixed for news for a while."

"Here we go again," Johnny Jacobs said shrugging his shoulders and letting out a deep sigh.

כ   כ

The morning jailer led Bertha down from the second floor to the interview room. After Bertha was seated, the jailer asked her if she would like a cup of coffee or a Co-Cola.

"Why, yes I would," she replied. "Either will be fine."

"I got a call from the sheriff at the courthouse that said your lawyer was on the way and wanted to speak with you," the deputy said. "I thought we'd just beat him to the punch."

"Sheriff Adams has been real nice since I've been back," Bertha said. "When I worked on Broad Street I used to eat in his restaurant a lot. How long has he been Sheriff?"

"He was elected in '52. He defeated Gilmore Johnson after his first term. Joe's pretty popular. I expect he'll be sheriff as long as he wants to."

"Well, what happened to Deputy Frank Russell?" Bertha asked. "He was the deputy that investigated my case. I'd sure like to talk to him."

"Frank runs his own photography studio, "the deputy replied. " He was personnel director at Anchor Rome mills for about ten years before he opened his studio. He's doing real good I hear."

Bob Addleton walked into the office and took a seat.

"Mrs. Hill, do you remember me?" Addleton asked. "We didn't get much time to chat the last time I was here. I was in a hurry to file your motion and I needed to get the affidavit signed."

"Yes, I remember you," she said. "And I want to thank you for all you've done."

"That's partly why I'm here," Addleton said. "I want to update you on where I think we are."

"Well, I'm not going anywhere," Bertha said. "I can assure you of that."

"We have a court date on November 26th before Judge J.L. Davis of the Cherokee Circuit. Judge Hicks had to excuse himself due to the fact that he was your lawyer for the '46 and '47 trials. Today's the 5th day of October so for the next six weeks you will have to wait."

"Do you think I will get a new trial?" Bertha asked almost timid-like and then added, "I've gotten awful good at waiting."

"I'm not sure," Her lawyer said. "We've got one major problem that I can't predict."

"What's that?" She asked.

"In 1952 the State of Georgia, in a Supreme Court ruling held that the judge of a superior Court has no legal power to receive or hear affidavits of jurors to impeach their verdicts. My thoughts are that we should be grandfathered before that ruling was established. However, in talking to members of the local bar there is some thought that since the three did sign the verdict, it indicated that they did in fact vote guilty. Others think that they did not vote you guilty and are not impeaching their verdict. This is for Judge Davis to decide."

"Well, whatever happens, I still appreciate what you've done," she said.

"Bertha, part of the deal I made in taking your case was that I'd do everything I could to get you a new trial. I think there are better qualified trial lawyers than me at this point in my life. And I live quite a distance from here and don't believe I could put in the time it is going to take to try the case. I'll be here on the 26th of November, but after that I'm finished. I certainly hope you get your trial. And the reason I've told you this is for you to begin shopping for the right lawyer to help you with your case."

"I'm sorry that you aren't able to continue," she said. "And I'm afraid I'll have to let the court appoint me somebody if I win. I certainly don't have the money to hire anybody and after all these years I wouldn't know where to shop."

"I certainly hope you get a break then on an appointment," Addleton said. "I'll see you on the twenty sixth."

# Bertha Hill Seeks New Trial in Murder Case

## Three Jurors Sign Statements They Did Not Vote Rome Woman 'Guilty'

Bertha Gossett Hill, twice convicted for the arsenic poison death of her husband in 1946, today filed an extraordinary motion for a new trial.

Her motion is based on affidavits from three members of the jury which convicted her, each stating that he did not vote for a guilty verdict. All three said they did not cast a vote of "guilty" even when the jury was polled individually after it had returned the verdict.

The 40-year old former dime store floor manager, has served 11 years of a life sentence. Most of her sentence has been served in Reidsville State Prison but Mrs. Hill has been held in the Floyd County Jail for the past several weeks as preparations were made for today's motion.

The motion was filed on her behalf in Floyd Superior Court by attorney R. L. Addleton, of Griffin, a former assistant state attorney general.

**Three Jurors**

The three jurors who signed af-

ed as Mrs. Hill's defense counsel in her second trial. They stated the information contained in the affidavits of the three jurors has never been known to them.

The motion also stated that "turmoil and confusion" in the courtroom when the jury returned its verdict prevented the defendant and counsel from learning from a jury poll the information contained in the jurors' affidavits filed today.

An extraordinary motion for a new trial must show that new evidence is available which could

# Chapter 26

November 26th finally came. Bertha had gotten permission to have the deputies take her to Lu Hannon's beauty shop on Fifth Avenue. She wanted to look her best for her court date. Sheriff Adams also let her assist with the cooking when Sam Atkins, the cook, was out due to sickness. She had talked her way into getting a sewing machine put in her cell and she made a lot of stuffed animals and toys which she gave to visitors and to the children of the deputies.

She sat silently in court and listened to the lawyers argue their motions before Judge Davis. This trial was not at all like the previous two trials. She really didn't know everything that was going on, but listened attentively and tried to catch a phrase now and then. It was over quickly. She was escorted back to her cell on the second floor.

On December 17th 1958, Bertha received word that Judge Davis had ruled in her favor. She was to get her third trial.

₪   ₪

"Bertha, your lawyer is in the interview room and he'd like to speak with you," said Deputy Jack Smith. "Do you want me to give you a minute? Most of the ladies like to freshen up when their lawyers or visitors come to visit."

"Deputy Smith, if you'd be so kind, I would surely appreciate it," she replied.

Half an hour later Deputy Smith led Bertha into the interview room and had her seated across the desk from the forty year old attorney shuffling through a mountain of papers.

"Mrs. Hill, my name is John Frazier. I'm your attorney and I'd like to speak to you for a few minutes, if that's alright with you."

"Mr. Frazier, I don't get a lot of company anymore and I appreciate any and all opportunity to get out of that cell for a few minutes. You just talk to me all you want."

"That sounds good. First, let's go over where we're at right now. If my information is correct, Mr. Addleton told you that he would do everything that he knew to do in order to bring your case to trial again. Is that correct?

"Yes it is," she said. "He then indicated that he would not be able to handle the actual trial of the case. He told me that I would have to hire my own lawyer."

"OK, we're together so far," John Frazier said.

"I told Mr. Addleton that I had no money and could not afford to hire an attorney. I'd have to depend on the state to appoint me one," Bertha said. "And I guess that's you."

"Not exactly Mrs. Hill," John stated. "Actually, I've been retained to represent you, if you want me to. I thought you may have another attorney picked out, but after what you just said, I doubt it. So I figured that we'd just have a little chat today and come to a couple of conclusions. The first would be to see if I wanted to represent you, and the second would be to see if you wanted me to."

"Mr. Frazier, you're pretty blunt, aren't you?" Bertha asked.

"That's just my personality, Mrs. Hill," John said. "I'm going to tell you exactly where you stand. That's the only way I know to practice law."

"Well, I like that, Mr. Frazier," she said. "I've had some pretty good lawyers in the past. Mack Hicks, Carl Griffin and Mr. W.T. Maddox were great lawyers. Although I did think it was sad about Mr. Griffin back in the early fifties. Are you a good lawyer, Mr. Frazier?

"Mrs. Hill, you've had excellent lawyers in the past. And you've had excellent lawyers prosecuting you. It was sad about Carl Griffin. And don't forget about Congressman Henderson Lanham, killed by a train on the way to make a speech last year. However Chastain Parker is now the Solicitor General. He will be handling the prosecution in the upcoming trial, if we get a trial. But yes, I like to think I'm a pretty fair old country lawyer."

"What does that mean, if we get a new trial? I was told last week and it was in the papers that Judge Davis ruled in my favor."

"That's correct. He did rule in your favor. But earlier this morning I was in the courthouse trying to get somebody to tell me when they thought the trial would be put on the calendar. At that time I was told that the State was going to file a Bill of Exceptions that will ask Judge Davis' to set the ruling aside."

"Oh Mr. Frazier, this is ruining my day. I thought we were all set to go to trial once again."

"And we may be," John said. "I'm going to prepare for a trial and be ready regardless of what the State does."

"What do you think they'll do?" she asked.

"I really don't know," John said. "Every attorney in the state is watching this case. This is the first time that anyone can find where the Supreme Court of Georgia granted a new trial on an extraordinary motion. And if the State does file a bill of exception, it would be unprecedented. In other words, the situation is unpredictable at this time."

"My Lord," Bertha replied. "They don't ever just give up, do they?"

"No they don't, Mrs. Hill," John said. "And you can't either. You have to keep fighting."

"Mr. Frazier, you said you'd been retained. Who retained you?"

"I was given a retainer, but actually you'll have to decide if you want to hire me or not."

"Can you tell me how that came about?" she asked.

"I sure can," he replied. "I got a phone call that asked me if I was familiar with your case, and if I would defend you in the upcoming trial if one were granted. That phone call was before the ruling, so we had to wait and see. After briefing the previous two cases, I decided it all depended on how you and I are able to work together and if you even wanted me to represent you."

"That was all that the caller said?"

"No it isn't," John replied. "That was kind of funny. The caller first asked if I was John Frazier. I was then asked if I was the John Frazier who was in the Army during the War and served as Secretary to the Court Martial Board."

"I don't understand," Bertha said. "What did that have to do with anything?"

"Well, next they asked if it was true if I really got upset when enlisted men were punished a lot harder for disciplinary infractions than officers."

"I'm beginning to see," Bertha said. "You kind of favor the underdog, don't you, John Frazier? Would that be correct?"

"It's like this, Mrs. Hill," John said. "I believe in an individual getting everything that the law allows them to have. It's obvious to me that you didn't get that. In the first trial Mack was able to get a new one on appeal. The second one is also tainted by the admission of three jurors in the motion filed by Addleton. I agree with Judge Davis that you're entitled to your day in court, even if it has been nearly thirteen years since the first one."

"Mr. Addleton told me that when he was retained, the person that retained him wanted an out-of-town lawyer with no ties to the community," Bertha stated. "Why do you reckon they changed their mind and came to you?"

"That was one of the things we discussed," John said. "And I'm going to tell you what I told them, and that was that I'd rather be right than fit in. You see Mrs. Hill, I'm somewhat of a maverick around here. And to be honest, I like it that way."

"I like your attitude, Mr. Frazier," Bertha said. "I'd be honored to have you represent me in the next trial, if there is one."

"Let me finish Mrs. Hill before you make any statement," John said. "I said that I believe that all rights should be applied. But if that's done, and the person is found guilty after all avenues have been exhausted, then I'm pretty big on long, hard, serious punishment."

"Sounds like you ought to be the solicitor or the judge, Mr. Frazier," Bertha said. "But I agree with everything you said, and I can only see one problem. If you're willing to represent me, you're gonna have to call me Bertha."

"OK Bertha, I'll meet that stipulation gladly," John Frazier said. "We've most likely got a long battle ahead of us. One other thing the caller asked me was if I ever worked on the railroad. I couldn't figure that one out."

"My Papa was a track layer for a while on the railroad," Bertha said. "It makes perfect sense to me. Somebody wanted to know if you were afraid of hard work. Now they know."

ת     ת

On January 23rd 1959, the Assistant Solicitor General of Floyd County, Horace Clary, filed a bill of exception with the Supreme Court of Georgia asking that Judge Davis' ruling be set aside. Although Bertha had been told that this bill was going to be filed, it still upset her. For several days she was not herself. She kept busy by making little stuffed animals and toys and working on any kind of needlework she could find.

After several days, the visitors from the media began once again to trickle in. Since August, *Rome News* reporter Charles Graves was about the only media attention Bertha drew. She thought that he was a very good reporter. Although he was only twenty-one he was a rising star with the paper. He didn't try to sway or sensationalize the news in any way. So many other journalists had taken that route with Bertha's story that if not for Graves and a few others, her case would be unbelievable by now.

Graves was relentless when it came to a story. The jail deputies had all told Bertha that Charlie would go to any length and talk to whoever was necessary to get his story. They had also said that they liked Graves because he was straight with the law enforcement community. He sometimes ran them crazy for a story, but would honor and keep his word when they told him something was off the record. This was what he had done to gain the respect of not only of law enforcement but the courthouse gang also.

Charles Graves was in the jail every day. He always stopped by her cell and asked her how things were going and if she had heard anything concerning her case. It was on one of these mornings that she told Charles that the State was trying to set her new trial aside. She told him that she was worried that she would have to go back to prison for ever. That was when she found out that John Frazier had also filed a brief asking the Supreme Court to deny the Bill of Exception from the State. That perked Bertha right up.

"Charles, you could have told me that earlier," Bertha said. "I feel better already."

"I got that from Frazier himself this morning," He said. "I'm sure he'll be headed this way later on to let you know. I guess now we wait on a ruling."

"I'm pretty good at that. They locked me up on February 15th 1946 and I've been confined ever since. In three more weeks it will be thirteen years. At least right now I have something to look forward to."

Every day Charles Graves would check with the Clerk of Court to see if the ruling had returned. They had nicknamed him Scoop because of his relentless pursuit of a story. He felt like he had a story with Bertha and he wasn't about to let anyone beat him to it. On March 20th he wrote a story in the *Rome News* which stated the ruling was not expected until at least April 9th.

The closer it got to that date, the more the courthouse gang would tempt him. They would do things like take a large, official looking envelope with Bertha Gossett Hill written on it and leave the envelope on the desk Everybody would then get busy and leave it unattended. It was hoped that Charlie might sneak a peek, but he never did.

On April 10th the ruling was received at the courthouse. Bertha Hill was approved by the Georgia Supreme Court for a new trial. Seven months of anxious waiting were over.

"Bertha, I just came from the courthouse," Graves said. "You win! The Supreme Court has approved your third trial. They denied the State's bill of exception."

"Are you kidding me?" she exclaimed.

"Here, read it yourself," Graves said, handing her an account from a news service.

"Boy! I did it, didn't I!"

"Are you happy Bertha?" Charles asked.

"Of course, you know I just can't say how happy I am, but I won't be really satisfied until it's all over and I'm proven innocent. It's been a long, hard fight and I'm still fighting."

"Bertha, congratulations on your new trial," Charles said. "But I got to go and see if I can catch John Frazier for a statement in tomorrow's paper. I'll be back later this week."

"Charles, thank you for letting me know about the ruling," she said.

Charles did find John Frazier and his story that afternoon reported the conversation that he had had with Bertha earlier that morning and the statement of her lawyer which read. "Of course I'm very happy that the Supreme Court affirmed the granting of a new trial. We of course hope to be able to prove to the satisfaction of everyone concerned that Mrs. Hill is not guilty."

Graves also got a statement from Horace Clary who stated he felt that the Supreme Court followed the law to the letter in this case. But since they had never ruled on an extraordinary motion and considering the expense a new trial would incur, Clary felt his duty as the prosecuting attorney to have the Supreme Court rule on the matter. He added that the new trial would possibly be set for May 18th.

₪   ₪

On May 12th the Solicitor General, Chastain Parker, announced in court that the state was having a hard time putting its witnesses together and would not be able to try the case during this term. John Frazier immediately petitioned the court for bond and it was granted without opposition. Judge Foster of the Tallapoosa circuit, who had been scheduled to hear the case, set Bertha's bond at $5,000 and it was signed by Davis Bonding on East Main Street.

At a few minutes after noon on the 12th of May 1959, Bertha Hill, accompanied by her attorney John Frazier, walked into the sunlight from the Floyd County jail a free woman still awaiting trial at a later date.

After her release, Bertha was given a job at the Maple Street 5 & 10 owned by her former attorney and now sitting Superior Court Judge Mack Hicks. She also did domestic work for Hicks and his wife at their home. Her attorney had told her that she had to stay local until they went to trial.

After the September term of court ended without her case being called,

Bertha goes free. Shown here with John Frazier

John Frazier, filed a demand for immediate trial on October the 6ᵗʰ. The November term of court came and went without her case being called.

ﬡ    ﬡ

"Johnny it's cold outside," Hoot Gibson said as he peeled his heavy coat off and hung it on the rack at the front of the restaurant. "Did you order all of this cold weather?"

"Not me," Johnny said, "I like it just a little warmer than this."

One by one the breakfast bunch came into the Partridge all complaining about the cold weather that Rome was experiencing. And they were anxious to get that first cup of hot coffee this morning. As breakfast was being served, the talk turned to the state of the local economy.

"Lloyd, did you ever think that the economy would take off like it has for the last several years?" Billy Maddox asked.

"No I didn't," Lloyd Summer said. "I just saw a Chamber report that said the third quarter of last year turned over twenty-one million and they expect it to be higher this year."

"What about the fourth quarter?" Leroy Byars asked. "It had to be higher. The stores were packed every day during the Christmas rush."

"No doubt about that," Lloyd said. "It'll just be a month or two until we know how well we did. But I can guarantee it was good."

"Let me change the subject a minute," Slaton Clemmons said. "We got a Presidential Election coming up this year. How do you guys think Lyndon Johnson will do against Nixon?"

"You sure Johnson's going to get the nomination?" Porter Grant asked. "I hear that young Senator from Massachusetts is starting to make waves."

"Surely he won't get the nomination," Cap Hicks said. "I would go with Johnson myself. But I do like the way that Kennedy fellow talks. Maybe after Johnson serves a couple of terms, he'll be ready. He's still pretty young. No need to hurry him."

"How about you guys, Frank?" C.W. Orr asked. "Was Santa good to the Coca Cola Company this Christmas?"

"Man, we're booming," Frank Barron answered. "We're doing well both locally and nationally. We've had a big year. And Coke is ready to expand into all kinds of markets. Coke is going into countries that we never would have dreamed of a few years ago."

"Look guys, I've been reading that young reporter Charles Graves' stuff on Bertha Hill," Hoot Gibson said. "Have y'all been following that?"

"Absolutely," Gordon Lee Hight said. "Why do you ask?"

"Well, she's on the calendar for this month," Hoot replied. "I wanted to get Hillis' opinion of what's going to happen."

"It's pretty simple, Hoot," Hillis replied. "John Frazier's going to announce ready. He filed a demand way back last October. If the State fails to answer, then she'll walk."

"You mean she'll be acquitted?" Gordon Lee asked.

"That's exactly what I mean," Hillis Hollingsworth said.

"Do you think Frazier will do that?" Clemmons said. "I mean announce like that, put the State in that position."

"All y'all know John," Hillis said chuckling slightly. "Of course he'll do it, and I would too."

"Well, I saw Frank Russell the other day," Hoot said. "And he still can't believe this case keeps resurfacing every so often. But he says you got to know Bertha. There's no quit in her. He was telling me that she charmed everybody she came in contact with. He thinks she'll walk."

"Well, she didn't charm Frank," Slaton Clemmons said. "What becomes of her if she gets out?"

"I asked Frank that," Hoot said. "He said if she's true to her nature, she'll just disappear."

"What did he mean by that?" Hoot asked.

"You got me," Slaton said. "You boys ready to flip?"

ℕ   ℕ

It was now the 18th day of January 1960 and Bertha Hill was once again in court. She sat quietly by herself and reflected on the huge crowds that she had drawn in the first two trials. Now it appeared that no one was interested anymore, and that was all right with her. It was strange to look up on the bench and see Judge Porter. He was now Judge Emeritus and was handling her proceedings.

It had not started that way this morning. Judge Hicks was the presiding judge who John Frazier had approached in open court and announced ready. Hicks once again stated that he had disqualified himself from hearing any of the action and called upon Judge Porter to handle today's findings.

Bertha thought Judge Porter was obviously not a happy man as he asked the State if they were ready to proceed. Upon hearing that they were not, and telling them that they had failed to call the case during the September and November term, he would now sign an acquittal. As soon as he signed the order, he stated that the official record clearly shows that the jury was polled, that the verdict was guilty and each member concurred.

He added that the worst violation of the law he could conceive of would be for a juror to judge a person guilty of a crime and then change his verdict. "Such a person has no business in the jury box, and if he knows what he is doing, he should be indicted," he said.

Assistant Solicitor Clary replied that his office was considering such action and that the case would be given to the grand jury now in session.

Bertha now watched her own lawyer approach Judge Porter, but he did not ask for a private conference. Frazier seemed to be somewhat perturbed at the judge's previous statements.

"Judge Porter," Frazier said. "Since you made your remarks in open court, I want to state that I had nothing to do with Mrs. Hill getting a new trial, but that I was retained after the ruling for a new trial was granted. It was my responsibility to defend her as best I knew how since that time. And that's what I've done."

"Mr. Frazier, I know that you had nothing to do with the granting of a new trial, and it is a pleasure for me to say that you did not."

₪     ₪

With the last statements by all parties, the saga of Bertha Hill was over. She hurried from the courthouse with her lawyer and they stopped outside on the steps.

"It's over, Bertha," John Frazier said. "Is there anything else I can do for you?"

"My divorce is final now, isn't it?" she asked. She had asked John to file for a divorce from Wiley Gravett in December and had petitioned to have her maiden name restored.

"You're single, and are now Bertha LaNelle Hardin once again," John said. "Although I think we made a mistake. We petitioned to have your maiden name restored, and I saw on some papers this week in the office that it was Bertha Mae Hardin."

"No mistake," She said. "I like LaNelle just fine."

"I'm glad," said John, " 'Cause from now on that's who you are."

# Bertha Hill Acquitted In 14-Year-Old Death

## Accused Poison Slayer Wins Freedom; Perjury Charges Hinted Against Jurors

Claude H. Porter, judge emeritus of Floyd Superior Court, today signed an order of acquittal for Bertha Gossett Hill, twice convicted murderess, and in the same official action suggested the possibility of bringing perjury charges against three members of her second trial jury who signed affidavits that they did not render a guilty verdict.

For the 41-year-old former five store floor manager, the order climaxed two sensational murder trials, 13 years of imprisonment on a life sentence and more than a year of legal finagling over a third trial.

She first was convicted of the arsenic poison murder of her husband, Leroy Hill, in 1946, won a new trial and was again found guilty and given a life sentence in 1947. She was also indicted for murder in the poison deaths of her mother and father, but was never brought to trial and the cases were dropped.

Mrs. Hill was returned to Rome in August, last year, and Griffin attorney R. L. Addleton filed an extraordinary motion for a new trial on September 30.

### Affidavits from Jurors

Basis for the motion was sworn affidavits of three of the second trial jurors who swore they had not voted the woman guilty. These

Judge Mack G. Hicks, who was Mrs. Hill's defense attorney had disqualified himself at the beginning of the proceedings and named Cherokee Superior Circuit Judge J. L. Davis, of Cartersville, to rule in the case.

On Dec. 17, 1958, Judge Davis granted Mrs. Hill a third trial.

In an effort to block the trial Asst. Sol. Horace T. Clary filed a bill of exceptions with the State

Supreme Court. The high court ruled, however, that the state could not appeal from a verdict in a criminal case and said it had no jurisdiction to review the case.

The state announced in May that it was not ready to re-try the case and Mrs. Hill was freed on a $5,000 bond.

The next step came in October when Rome Attorney John A. Frazier Jr., who was not hired until after Mrs. Hill was granted the new trial, filed a demand for immediate trial.

The order of acquittal which was signed today by Judge Porter stated that Mrs. Hill was being freed because the state had not called the case for trial during the September or November terms of Floyd Superior Court.

Solicitor Clary told the court today the state "would not be ready to try Mrs. Hill because it could not locate witnesses in the case, which is now some 14 years old.

Today's acquittal came swiftly as trials of criminal cases were about to get underway. Attorney Frazier approached the bench and stated to presiding Judge Hicks that he would like to announce "ready" in the Hill case.

Judge Hicks, again stating that he had disqualified himself from hearing any of the action, called (Continued on Page 2, Column 7)

# Epilogue

Bertha shook hands with her lawyer and turned to start down the courthouse steps when John stopped her once again.

"I almost forgot," he said. "This envelope came in the mail. I was told to give it to you if you were acquitted."

"What is it?" Bertha asked.

"I didn't open it," John said. "I don't have the foggiest idea."

"Well Mr. Frazier, you're one hell of a lawyer, that's all I got to say."

Bertha walked down Rome's Broad Street and stopped in front of McClellan's ten cent store. *I promised myself that I wouldn't go back in there until I was free.* As she walked into the store, the same smell of wood floor wax and hot peanuts rekindled something that she thought was dead.

"May I help you, ma'am?" a young clerk asked.

"No thank you, I was just looking," Bertha replied.

She spent more than a few minutes in the store. She still loved this place. The happiest years of her life were spent right here during World War 2. She knew every inch of this building, from the basement to the second floor. But things had changed since February of 1946. She recognized no one working there. And after all these years she didn't expect to know anyone.

Two weeks later she boarded a Greyhound Bus on Fourth Avenue. As she climbed aboard the driver asked, "Where are you headed lady?"

She noticed the driver was maybe a few years older than she was and was wearing sharp-pointed Western boots.

"West," she replied.

"Just west? That's a big place, anywhere in particular?" he asked. "I guessed that you probably had family out there that you were going to visit."

"Actually, I'm a widow and an orphan. I have no brothers and sisters and am all alone in this great big world. I'd thought about Texas but I really don't know."

"Hey, that's where I live," he said. "This old bus gets lonely and confining, and it's a long way to Texas. Just have a seat right behind me and keep me company for a while. I mean if you don't mind."

"Oh I don't mind at all," Bertha said. "What's your name, honey?"

"Jimmy," he replied. "Jimmy Callahan."

"Well I'm glad to meet you Jimmy Callahan. My name's LaNelle Hardin. And don't worry about this bus being confining. To me it's as big as the great outdoors."

꒐   ꒐

Bertha re-read the letter and placed it in her purse. There had been a cashier's check and an address. And there was a note. *We once celebrated Bertha not going to the chair. My sister found the Abbotts and sent me a jar of Maeleigh Grace's preserves. They haven't been opened yet. You've got the address.*

"Hey Jimmy," Bertha said. "What do cowboys like you do for fun in Texas?"

# About The Author

Mike Ragland was born and raised in Lindale, GA where he attended Pepperell Elementary and High Schools. After losing his mother on Mother's day 1961, he went to work at Pepperell Manufacturing in Lindale, GA. From there he went to work at JC Penny's in Rome and then on to Dalton, GA's Crown Cotton Mill in the summer of 1962. After graduating from Pepperell High in 1963, he joined the Navy and was assigned to the submarine, *The USS Choppper* (SS-342) and served from '63 to '67. During that time he served in the north Atlantic, Mediterranean, South America and throughout the east coast and Gulf of Mexico. When Mike rejoined civilian life, he worked briefly laying carpet and was fired the day he planned to resign to join the Rome Police Department, where he served 40 years and retired as a Major. As a member of the force, he served as a motorcycle officer, patrol Sgt., Shift Commander, and Captain in charge of the Detective Bureau. He also served as Juvenile Officer and as a liaison officer to Juvenile court. Later, Mike also served as Training Officer where he was charged with the task of converting a city-owned building to what was to become the new Cleveland Training Center. He secured a grant during this time to build one of the nicest outdoor firing ranges in north Georgia. He served as Training Officer until 1999 when he was promoted to Major. As Major he rotated serving the three major bureaus of the police department: Operations, Administration and Support Services. During that time he was also the principal grant writer for the police department, bringing in many Federal and State grants to secure police officer jobs, positions, and equipment, including the Call to Duty monument that stands in front of the Rome Police Department today.

Mike was married to Martha Highfield on August 23rd, 1968, and they have one daughter, Bekki Ragland Fox, and two grandchildren, Caleb and Mattie Parris. He is an avid Crimson Tide and NASCAR fan. A much loved speaker and writer in Northwest Georgia, Mike is devoted to writing full time since his retirement from the Police Department in April, 2007. He and his wife currently live in Cave Spring, GA. Mike can be reached at mike@mikeragland.com

CPSIA information can be obtained
at www.ICGtesting.com
Printed in the USA
FSOW01n0505130916
24897FS